SOCIAL POLICY FOR NURSES AND THE HELPING PROFESSIONS

Second edition

Stephen Peckham and
Liz Meerabeau

Open University Press
Maidenhead ● New York

CONTENTS

ABBREVIATIONS

A&E	accident and emergency
ADL	activity of daily living
AHA	area health authority: countywide NHS organizations established in England in 1974 to coordinate community health and hospital services and social services but abolished in 1982, middle tier, between DHA and region
AHP	allied health profession/al (previously termed professions allied to medicine)
BMA	British Medical Association
BME	black and minority ethnic
CAM	complementary and alternative medicine
CDM	chronic disease management (now termed long-term conditions)
CEO	chief executive officer: the chief officer of an organization
CHC	Community Health Council
CHS	community health services
CJD	Creutzfeld Jacob Disease: a transmissible neurological disease with a poor prognosis, thought to be related to similar diseases in animals such as bovine spongiform encephalopathy
CMO	Chief Medical Officer
COS	Charity Organization Society
CPN	community psychiatric nurse
DHA	district health authority: established in 1974 to govern the delivery of NHS services in England
DHSS	Department of Health and Social Security: responsible for benefit payments and health and social care services prior to 1988, when it split into the Department of Health (DoH) and the DSS
DoH	Department of Health: directly responsible for government strategy and health services in England.
DSS	Department of Social Security
FHS	family health services: general practice, opthalmology, opticians and pharmacy services
FHSA	Family Health Services Authority: commissioning and planning agency for these services prior to 2001
FPC	Family Practitioner Committee
GMC	General Medical Council: the regulatory body for medicine
GMS	general medical services
GNC	General Nursing Council: the first regulatory body for nursing, superseded by the UKCC
GDP	gross domestic product
GP	general practitioner

GPFH	GP fundholder/fundholding
HA	health authority
HCHS	Hospital and Community Health Services
HMC	Hospital Management Committee
HPC	Health Professions Council: the regulatory body for a wide range of health professions, including physiotherapy and occupational therapy
LA	local authority
LTC	long-term condition
LHB	local health board (Wales)
MPC	Medical Practices Committee
NCSC	National Care Standards Commission
NGO	non-governmental organization
NHI	national health insurance
NHS	National Health Service
NICE	National Institute for Clinical Excellence
NMC	Nursing and Midwifery Council: the current regulatory body for nursing and midwifery
NPM	new public management
NSF	national service framework
NSSEC	National Statistics Socio-Economic Classification
ODPM	Office of the Deputy Prime Minister
Ofsted	Office for Standards in Education
PBC	practice-based commissioning
PbR	payment by results
PCG	primary care group
PCO	primary care organization
PCT	primary care trust
PFI	Private Finance Initiative
PHCT	primary health care team
PI	performance indicator
PMS	primary medical services
PPIF	Patient and Public Involvement Forum
QALY	quality-adjusted life year
RCGP	Royal College of General Practitioners
RGSC	Registrar General's Social Class
RHB	regional hospital board
RSL	registered social landlord
SEG	socio-economic group
SEN	special educational needs
SEU	Social Exclusion Unit
SHA	strategic health authority
SSD	social services department
SMR	standard mortality ratio: number of deaths expressed as a rate per 1000 population
TPP	total purchasing pilot
UKCC	United Kingdom Central Council for Nursing, Midwifery and Health Visiting, the regulatory body superseded by the NMC
WHO	World Health Organization

WHAT IS SOCIAL POLICY?

Introduction

Walk through any shopping centre and you immediately see that people are different – different ages, race, ethnicity and sex. These are obvious ways that people are different. But there will be other factors that are not so obvious such as income, type of job or where they live. You may think that this is an obvious observation and what has this to do with health and social care professionals and delivering care services? The answer lies in how these differences appear, the impact they have on people's lives and how society responds to them. Essentially these are social divisions and such divisions have real consequences for people in terms of how they live, their health, life expectancy and relationships with other people. In particular they are closely related to social inequalities and, for social policy analysts, examining how such inequalities arise and how they can be addressed are key concerns.

This chapter outlines the scope of social policy as an area of study and introduces the reader to major themes and issues within the discipline of social policy concerning the role of the state in the provision of welfare, the key actors in the provision of social welfare, the complex interactions between these providers and the influence of ideology on social policy. In particular, it explores the recent shifts in how social policy is conceptualized and highlights why an understanding of social policy is important for understanding health policy and the delivery of health care services. Central to the current study of social policy is the recognition that society is divided by differences such as age, gender, income, ethnicity and so forth. Traditionally the focus has been on divisions of class (as discussed in the next section), but increasingly other key differences and divisions in society are being seen as important and relevant to social policy. It is recognized that these differences are the result of social processes and the acceptability of such differences varies within societies. In relation to health care, what is particularly important is the way these differences affect people's health and experience of care. They are of central concern to the study of health.

The discipline of social policy

The discipline of social policy is relatively new, at least in comparison with other social sciences. The study of social policy began at the London School of Economics (LSE) in 1950 and was mainly concerned with the training of welfare professionals during a period of expansion in the welfare state. This led to a focus, within the discipline, on the statutory sector – on what the welfare state itself provided. Close links, between the then Labour government and Fabian socialists such as Richard Titmuss (head of the social policy department at the LSE), led to a demand for information to guide the future expansion of the post-war welfare state. The scope of the discipline in these early years was, therefore, strongly influenced by the institutional structures of the welfare state. Housing policy was primarily concerned with the development of public housing and health policy with the setting up of the National Health Service (NHS). Optimism about the prospects of the post-war welfare state's ability to solve the social problems of the day and bring about greater social justice thus led to a very narrow disciplinary focus.

It was around this time that T.H. Marshall developed his work on welfare and social citizenship. Marshall argued that, prior to the welfare state, a person's access to social resources (such as food, education and health) and their personal welfare depended primarily on their income from paid employment. Those with higher income (and/or wealth) could thus command greater social resources while those with low or no incomes went without (or were dependent on the parish for Poor Law support). The development of a system of social entitlement which derived from citizenship (or membership of a given society), irrespective of ability to pay, was, according to Marshall, the litmus test of a civilized society. The welfare state then, with its universal health service, pensions and state education, was to modify existing patterns of inequality, based on social class, and ensure that certain kcy social goods were available to all. The relationship between income from paid work and individual welfare was mediated by the introduction of collective social policies provided by the state. Academic concern then focused on the role of the state as the primary provider of welfare.

The changing nature of social policy

The discipline has since broadened considerably in response to a number of pressures. First, there has been increasing recognition of the role of other actors which contribute in important ways to individual welfare; it is not only the state which provides welfare and not all welfare professionals are employed by the state. Second, the role of the state in relation to social policy has changed considerably. Housing departments are now seen as enablers and facilitators of housing, working in partnership with the voluntary sector (housing associations and cooperatives), tenants and the private sector in the provision of new housing. Health policy, similarly, has become less concerned with the institutional operation of the NHS (although this remains an important area of policy) and has become more involved in performance management and commissioning to develop a more patient-responsive service with multiple providers in the public, private and voluntary sectors. Health policy has also increasingly been focused on public health issues, tackling inequalities and key health problems such as cancer, circulatory disorders, obesity, smoking, mental health and sexual health.

The discipline of social policy is thus no longer concerned solely with what the state itself provides in terms of welfare, but more broadly with the whole structure of social entitlement and social responsibility in society, which forms the basis of citizenship. Early concerns, regarding the narrow focus of the discipline, led Richard Titmuss to write an essay on the 'Social Division of Welfare' in 1955 (reprinted in Abel-Smith and Titmuss 1987). Titmuss drew attention to the contribution of two areas of welfare provision (in addition to that provided directly by the state), hitherto neglected in academic study: *fiscal welfare* (that provided for individuals via taxation policy), such as mortgage tax relief, and *occupational welfare* (welfare resources provided via employers to their employees), including various forms of occupational perks such as low-interest mortgages, crèches, company cars, tied housing etc. Titmuss argued that it was necessary to consider the contribution of all three sectors in order to understand the redistributive impact of welfare. While some aspects of state provision may indeed modify the relationship between income and access to welfare (e.g. universal free health care), the contribution of the other sectors may in practice compound existing inequalities as welfare entitlement increases with status. Occupational welfare, for example, typically benefits those in white-collar jobs and is often regressive; that is, the more you earn the greater the value of the 'perk'. It was for this reason that Titmuss referred to occupational welfare as the 'concealed multiplier of occupational success'. Referring specifically to the development of occupational pension schemes, Titmuss noted that the cost to the Exchequer (in 1955) of such schemes was *'substantially in excess of the cost of national insurance pensions ... contrary to the intentions of the 1920 Royal Commission, which considered tax relief for such schemes appropriate for poorer taxpayers, the benefits have increasingly favoured the wealthier'* (Abel-Smith and Titmuss 1987: 50). Recent changes to the pensions system, such as stakeholder pensions and the inclusion of property portfolios also, provided tax relief benefiting the more wealthy rather than the poorest in society. The impact of modern welfare systems on social inequality is thus quite complex and requires an understanding not only of direct provision of welfare goods by the state, but also of the role of the state in other areas as a financier and regulator of policy.

Since the 1950s, it has become increasingly recognized that even this categorization is inadequate if we are to understand fully the redistributive implications of social policy. In addition to these areas of provision, we might add a further three: the contribution of the *voluntary or not-for-profit sector* (through agencies such as Age Concern, the National Society for the Prevention of Cruelty to Children and the Red Cross), the role of the *commercial sector* (through the purchase of welfare directly from commercial agencies) and, finally, the enormous contribution of *informal care* provided by families, neighbours and friends. Despite their importance historically in meeting welfare needs, these systems have been largely ignored or treated as marginal, as the focus of attention has been on the state provision of welfare services rather than on the influence of public policy more generally. It is important to remember that we are not talking simply about three parallel systems of resource distribution operating independently of the state, but of a complex relationship between the state and these sectors, which has profound implications for citizenship and the distributional implications of social policy. We are not simply concerned, then, with what the state itself provides, but how it uses the power and resources vested in it, to control and determine the whole basis of social provision through the regulation and financing of private and voluntary support. Clearly the broader aspects of public policy are important here (such as economic policy and taxation), but so too are areas of non-decision-making or *policy vacuums*. In many cases, the lack of provision is just as significant as policy intervention. Nowhere is this more evident than the way in which state welfare providers have, until recently, ignored and thereby failed to acknowledge the important and essential role of informal welfare – especially that which is provided by wives, mothers and daughters.

The mixed economy of welfare

It is important to recognize that the model of the UK government, as welfare monopolist or the main provider of welfare, is not and *has never been* a correct one. Not only does it ignore or marginalize the role of the private, commercial and voluntary sectors, but it also 'naturalizes' informal provision by families and carers – particularly women. Feminists in particular have pointed to the major contribution made by women to the provision of informal, unpaid welfare (Abbott *et al.* 2005).

Recognition of the complex and changing nature of the state, in contemporary welfare systems, has been reflected in the introduction of the concept of *welfare pluralism* or the '*mixed economy of welfare*' in place of the term 'welfare state'. This concept emphasizes the need to consider the contribution of a plurality of providers to individual welfare. Figure 1.1

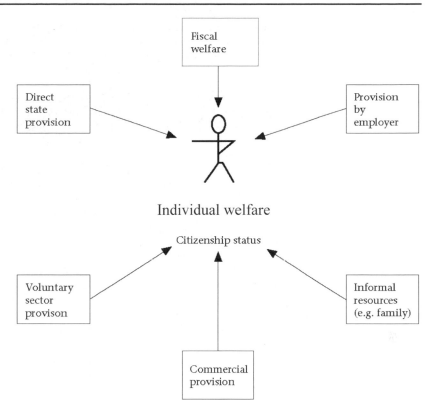

Figure 1.1 Public policy and individual welfare.

illustrates the broader impact of public policy on individual access to welfare, and Box 1.1 illustrates how the mixed economy works in practice in the context of health care.

We can see from the above examples how a person's health status – or their access to health resources – is dependent on a range of providers, all of whom are influenced, to a greater or lesser extent, by public policy. Moreover, our health status depends not only on what is construed as 'health' policy specifically (as in the example above), but also on many other aspects of social policy. There is a range of policies that have important implications for personal health status, including policy on the environment, on housing, employment and education. Indeed, the main cause of childhood mortality is accidental death, often as a result of proximity to road traffic, lack of adequate play areas and poor environmental planning. Employment status also has an important impact on personal health (see Chapter 5).

Box 1.1   Provision of health care by the six welfare systems

The service provided by the NHS is *statutory welfare*, as is, for example, the provision of sports and recreational facilities/services – they are provided directly by central or local government. Examples of *fiscal welfare* (welfare promoted through the taxation system) include tax incentives for older people to subscribe to commercial health schemes. *Voluntary provision* includes the contribution of organizations such as the Macmillan Foundation, which provides nurses for cancer patients, or the hospice movement for the care of people who are terminally ill. (Charities such as these also benefit from certain forms of tax relief; that is, they benefit from fiscal policy as well.) *Occupational schemes* include the provision of private health insurance, health education classes and sports facilities by employers for their employees. Some employers, for example, provide their own antenatal classes for pregnant employees. The *informal sector* is responsible for many areas of health care, including the care of people at home (by family and friends), the provision of transport to hospital and educating children about health care. *Commercial health care* includes the buying in of private nursing care at home as well as purchasing in- or out-patient hospital treatment, or paying for homeopathy, physiotherapy or acupuncture as a supplement to, or a substitute for, NHS provision.

Health is not something separate from the rest of the social context: it is inextricably bound up with income, housing, education and every other facet of public policy. There can be no lasting good health without income adequate to provide the required diet and clothing or without adequate housing and the means to heat it. Health is improved and health inequalities diminished not just, or even primarily, by attention to health – housing, income and all the other aspects of welfare, are just as likely to be in need of attention and to be capable of making a contribution to the health of the populace. A situation that has increasingly been realized by successive governments in relation to public health policy (Baggott 2000). A similar point could be made about any branch of welfare provision.

Thus, while it is important for health professionals to understand the history and philosophy of their own service, in order to locate current practice in its context and to understand current trends, they also need to understand the contribution of other aspects of policy and the role of other caring professions. Provision for children with special educational needs (SEN) provides a useful example of the need for welfare professionals to be aware of their respective roles and services, in order to plan effectively to meet the complex physical, psychological and educational needs of this group of children.

So far, we have seen how the scope of social policy extends to all aspects of the mixed economy of welfare, of which the welfare state is only one component. We have emphasized the fact that welfare pluralism is nothing new. In Britain after the Second World War, there was already a mixed economy of welfare with the state as the main provider. The state provided welfare (e.g. hospitals), subsidized private provision (e.g. through income tax relief on private pensions) and supplied surveillance and regulation (e.g. the regulation of the private rental sector in housing). The government also made a commitment to maintain full employment. However, employers, the voluntary sector, the commercial sector and informal provision were all expected to continue to make a contribution to meeting people's welfare needs. Indeed, Beveridge, who is often seen as the architect of the welfare state in Britain, preferred the term 'welfare society', a society in which people's welfare needs were met by a partnership between statutory and voluntary services. The specific *balance of responsibilities* within this welfare mix has, however, been subject to change and reflects the shift from certainty and stability in the post-war period to a situation where society seems more uncertain and unstable (George and Wilding 1999).

Perspectives on welfare: the influence of ideology

The modern welfare state has been seen as a benchmark of a civilized society, altering the basis of social entitlement from one simply of ability to pay, to one based on some notion of citizenship (Marshall 1975). However, neither Marshall nor Beveridge expected to eliminate social inequality in this process, but they did want to reduce the effect of such disparities on people's access to basic social goods. Thus the introduction of comprehensive, free health care would result in a broad equality of health status, and a universal education system would produce a broad equality of life chances or equality of opportunity if not of outcome. Under such conditions, the persistence of other aspects of inequality in society would be both tolerable and legitimate – on the grounds that those with greater income and wealth had achieved it via greater effort or ability.

Marshall's vision of the welfare state was one of a redistributive system promoting social justice and consensus, but in practice this has not necessarily occurred (Powell 1999). Also, the notion of a welfare state as redistributive, fulfilling broader moral objectives, is not universally accepted. It is important to be aware of the extent to which policy-making and implementation are part of a wider political process, which is affected by both political expediency (often, electoral considerations) and ideology (a set of more or less coherent ideas about the way in which social welfare should be organized). Ideas about the role and function of the state in social policy (and particularly about the nature of the welfare state itself) are conditioned by and reflect specific moral, political and ideological positions about the causes of social problems and the apportionment of responsibilities. Where social problems, such as unemployment, ill health or poor housing are interpreted as the fault of individuals (a reflection of personal failure), there may be some question about the responsibility of the state to rectify the problem. Indeed, it could be argued that, state intervention in such circumstances may be counterproductive, providing incentives for people not to work or to provide adequately for their families, or to apply themselves to their studies. On the other hand, if social problems are interpreted as a reflection of the failure of the state itself, perhaps of its economic policy resulting in inadequate wages and lack of employment prospects, then it could be argued that the state has a responsibility to those in need as a result (subjects we return to in Chapter 2).

Much of the debate in social policy is concerned with ideas about moral responsibility and the meaning of citizenship, about when and how the state should assume responsibility and when it should be left to individuals and their families. The shifting nature of this debate and the dominance of particular perspectives over time has resulted in a reordering of the balance of responsibilities between the sectors involved in the welfare mix.

Models of welfare states

One of the first attempts to illustrate the impact of ideology on social policy, was Richard Titmuss' classical distinction between 'residual' and 'institutional' welfare states. These 'models' of social policy reflect very different theoretical perspectives on the causes of social inequality and the appropriate response of the state. The *residual welfare state model* is based on individualistic explanations of social problems and places responsibility firmly in the hands of individuals (and their families). The state only assumes responsibility when the family or the market fails; it thus limits its commitment to those marginal and 'deserving' groups who lack sufficient resources either to purchase welfare support from the commercial sector or draw on family support. Supporters of this type of system argue that collective provision stifles initiative because it demands high levels of taxation and encourages dependency – that is, reliance on welfare benefits and services undermining individual responsibility, initiative and self-help. The welfare state exists to provide a residual safety net to prevent people falling into abject poverty. State benefits, under such a scheme, are 'targeted' at the poorest sections of society, providing a low level of benefit (in order not to deter people from taking low-paid work). Services are provided on a selective, as opposed to universal, basis requiring extensive means testing of claimants.

The *institutional/redistributive model*, on the other hand, was the one favoured by Titmuss and Marshall. It provided a platform of universal services for the whole population, reflecting an institutionalized commitment to collectively financed and provided welfare. The objectives of this model were not restricted to preventing people falling below a certain basic modicum of welfare, but sought instead to promote social justice, modify patterns of social inequality and create solidarity.

Titmuss' approach has been developed in recent years, in comparative social policy research, as the basis for classifying and categorizing contemporary welfare states. The work of Esping-Anderson (1990) has been influential in this regard and has sought to develop a typology of 'welfare regimes' according to the ways in which different societies allocate social goods. He identified three 'regime-types' outlined in Table 1.1.

Table 1.1 Esping-Anderson's three models of welfare regimes

Regime type	Type of provision	Impact	Country
Liberal	Social rights do not reflect work performance or citizenship but demonstrable need – providing generally meagre and means tested (selective) benefits	The welfare system reinforces existing inequalities through work-enforcing, stigmatizing benefits reserved for those unable to compete in the market	USA
Conservative	The state assumes responsibility over individual welfare by requiring employers and employees to provide compulsory social insurance cover with fairly generous entitlements	The distribution of social resources rewards occupational achievement via the welfare state	Germany
Social democratic	Generous systems of high-quality universal benefits for all citizens irrespective of prior earnings, contributions or performance	Achieves social citizenship (as defined by Marshall) by providing a broad equality of status for all citizens	Sweden

As with any system of classification, a level of generalization is required to illustrate key points and it would be unrealistic to expect any given country to fit exactly within Esping-Anderson's typology. Britain provides a good example of a welfare system which contains elements of all three models (including a core of universal services alongside occupational and means tested benefits). This combined approach is clearly central to New Labour's view of the welfare state and they advocate a concept of *progressive universalism* (Kemp 2005). This increasingly means moving from universal benefits to selective benefits and a safety net provision for those unable to provide for themselves and their families. Welfare has also become closely linked to work but also includes some universal provision – a good example being Child and Working Tax Credits that are paid to people earning under £58,175 (2006/7) a year but which provide more support to lower-income families. The approach of the New Labour government (elected in 1997) is discussed in more detail in the next chapter. There have also been criticisms of the three welfare regimes model, given the western democratic context in which it was developed, and suggestions that there should be a broader typology (Powell and Barrientos 2004). In addition, it has also been argued that the model overlooks key aspects of welfare such as the role of the voluntary sector, is gender blind and in fact may simply be illusory and of little relevance (Rodger 2003; Bambra 2004; Dahlberg 2005).

Criticisms of state welfare

While the institutional model claims moral support for collective social provision, on the grounds that this promotes social justice and equality, supporters of the residual model would contend that an 'institutional model' welfare system requires unacceptable levels of state intervention in the personal lives of citizens – reducing individual choice and requiring high levels of taxation. Although the existence of, for example, universal health care increases the quality of life of those without adequate means to purchase private care, the burden of taxation may restrict the ability of others who, if they were taxed less, could have exercised their right to purchase from the commercial sector – either by buying private health insurance or by paying for it directly – thus limiting choice and freedom.

Concerns about the impact of interventionist, universal welfare systems have also been raised in other quarters, by feminist and black academics and by the disabled persons movement. While the type of welfare system envisaged by Marshall would doubtless improve the quality of life of many people, the unquestioned benevolence of welfare and the association of welfare with the 'good society' fail to deal with important questions about institutional power and social control. Clearly, such large bureaucratic welfare organizations wield enormous power and may become the mechanism for controlling the lives of citizens as much as helping them. Education policy, for example, may be as much about reinforcing traditional class boundaries – by selecting, sorting and inculcating norms into the prospective workforce – as it is about the promotion of equal opportunity and merit. The caring professions are centrally concerned with welfare, providing care and helping individuals and groups to meet their needs. However, they are part of the 'welfare system' and are often in an ambiguous situation: they act on behalf of the state and tend to have a control function over individuals in terms of their structural position, at the same time as the conscious motivation of individual workers may be to help, support and work on behalf of their clients/patients. This ambiguity has been thoroughly explored in the case of social workers, and to some extent, with regard to health visitors and psychiatric nurses (Hugman 1991; Williamson 1992; Abbott and Meerabeau 1998), but it is equally true of all who work within the welfare system, in whatever capacity.

The role of the state as an instrument of social control, responsible for reinforcing existing patterns of social inequality, has been highlighted in the work of feminist social policy academics (Williams 1989; Pascall 1996; Lister 2003). Gillian Pascall (1996: 13) notes that: *'Marshall asserts the rights of citizenship, but nowhere does he analyse the problematic relationship between citizenship and dependency in the family as he does between citizenship and social class'*. In a similar vein, Lewis (1992: 161) argued that comparative work *'misses one of the central issues in the structuring of welfare regimes: the problem of valuing the unpaid work that is done primarily by women in providing welfare, mainly within the family, and in securing those providers social entitlements'*. On the basis of this analysis, she developed an alternative framework that stressed the broad commonality of women's experience and the dominance of the male breadwinner family model, which cuts across established typologies of welfare regimes. Although the strength of this model, varies depending upon the extent and nature of social entitlement, Lewis (1992) emphasizes its persistence and universal impact:

> *Modern welfare regimes have all subscribed to some degree to the idea of a male breadwinner model – the strength or weakness of that model serves as an indicator of the way in which women have been treated in social security systems; of the level of social service provision particularly in regard to childcare; and of the nature of married women's position in the labour market.*
>
> (Lewis 1992: 162)

Issues of welfare provision have been bound up with ideologically-motivated notions about gender relations which restrict women's involvement in paid work (and their financial autonomy), effectively creating a vast army of unpaid workers upon whom the welfare state depends. As a result, many married women in the past, as now, had no independent social entitlement but instead gained access to social resources (such as income support and pensions) via their male bread-winning partners. The impact on women's autonomy has been well documented (Lewis 1992, 2002; Ackers 1994) and continues to impact on the position of women today, particularly in relation to pension provision. In addition, inequalities between men and women, between those with and without disabilities and between different ethnic groups, have become institu-tionalized within state welfare systems in terms of income and the distribution of paid work, with much part-time, informal and non-professionalized care being undertaken by women and people from ethnic minorities (Carter 2003). The following section looks in a little more detail at the evolution of British social policy and the changing balance of social responsibility.

The development of the welfare mix in Britain

In Britain, the welfare state is seen as having moved from a residual (safety net) position to a more collectivist one, although in the last 25 years there has been some movement back towards a more pluralist position – with critiques developing on both the political Left and Right. The history of the post-war British welfare state is generally presented as the progressive development of social policies designed to stamp out want, poverty, ignorance and ill health – a move towards the gradual and progressive assumption, by the state, of responsibility for the welfare of all citizens. A civilized society is seen as one that cares and provides for all its members, especially the weak and vulnerable. Indeed, Titmuss (1968) argued that the collective provision of welfare encourages *collective altruism* – that is, a concern for the welfare of others. He used blood donation as an example, pointing out that in Britain, people are prepared to donate their blood without charge, thus ensuring a supply of good quality. The NHS has been presented as the pinnacle of the idea of state welfare – a free health service, provided equally to all, based on need and not the ability to pay.

Until the 1970s, there was a general consensus in Britain that the state should be the main provider of welfare services. The major concern then was about providing *more* services, about funding the growth of state welfare services. The concern now is whether the state *should be* the main provider or even the main funder of welfare services, and the extent to which the welfare state actually meets people's welfare needs.

It became clear from the 1970s onwards that all sides in Britain were dissatisfied with aspects of the old system of welfare. The New Right (a term used to describe political ideology in the 1980s that espoused libertarian and conservative approaches to the role of the state – Baggott *et al.* 2005) denounced the profligacy of public services and the traditional Left questioned their paternalistic and bureaucratic character. Furthermore, it had become evident that welfare policies did not meet the needs of the British black and southern Asian populations and were often racist. Feminists have pointed out not only the patriarchal assumptions that informed much social policy, but also the ways in which state policies assumed the nuclear family with dependent wife as natural and inevitable. Changes in the social composition of the UK, demographic changes (such as an increasing older population), changes in family composition (such as the increasing number of single-parent families) and in employment patterns (particularly increasing women's employment); created debates about the causes of the social problems to which welfare was directed and the proper role of the state in its provision.

One response has been to argue for '*welfare provision which is universal in that it meets all people's needs, but also diverse and not uniform [reflecting] people's own changing definitions of difference and not simply the structural differentiation of the society at large*' (Williams 1989: 209). Initial responses from the Conservative governments of the 1980s and 1990s, were to argue for a reduction in the provision of state welfare, the more effective targeting of benefits and services and the reorganization and reduction of public services. In doing so, they reinforced the idea of the primary responsibility of individuals and their families – especially in caring for children and dependent relatives, whose care was seen primarily as a matter of private concern rather than as a collective responsibility.

Central to Conservative reforms in the 1980s and 1990s was the opening up of the supply of welfare services and making them subject to market-type forces. Three strategies were pursued, involving the introduction of internal or quasi-markets into public services such as health, education and social care; the use of private investment and provision in welfare (such as housing and pensions); and the development of public-private partnerships drawing private sector management into public sector provision directly and indirectly (Powell 1998). The role of the commercial and voluntary sectors was emphasized, especially in terms of competitive tendering for the provision of meals and laundry services in the NHS and in providing community care, as well as in the privatization of public utilities and other previously state-owned services. In reality, the Conservatives did not 'roll back' the welfare state, and indeed the percentage of gross domestic product (GNP) spent on state welfare remained remarkably constant. However, there were significant changes in the way in which the welfare state itself was organized and administered, which provided the basis for a mixed approach to welfare provision, shifting the relationships between and roles of the public, private and voluntary sectors (Powell 1998).

When the New Labour government came to power in 1997, there was a further shift in approach which saw the retention of many features of previous government policy, including an emphasis on privatization and individual responsibility, combined with a commitment to tackling poverty and inequalities. A central theme was the link between welfare and work, with an emphasis on opportunity with responsibility (Deacon 2002; Lewis 2004). The Labour government promoted a new philosophy of the Third Way, treading a line between paternalistic, bureaucratic state control and the uncertainties of the market (Powell 2000). We can see how this approach dominates debates about welfare services today, with the emphasis on paid work, rights and responsibilities and the individual's relationship with welfare services encompassed in debates about how pensions should be provided and proposals to increase choice in health care services. An important element of this new approach was to see welfare not as a burden but in terms of social investment: '*In place of the welfare state we should put the social investment state, operating in the context of a positive welfare society*' (Giddens 1998: 117). A further, and an increasingly important element of New Labour's approach to welfare is the idea of choice, which has cast the welfare user as consumer, choosing between different welfare services (Clarke 2004). Choice currently dominates the public services agenda and this, together with welfare pluralism and increasing privatization, impacts on the type of welfare state that exists in the UK. In health and social care, choice has become a dominant paradigm. In England, *Our Health, Our Care, Our Say* (DoH 2006) explicitly focuses on the role of the consumer as being responsible for managing their own health and choosing between different locations for treatment.

Social policy and social goods

This chapter has so far looked at the scope of social policy as a discipline. It has emphasized the need to consider the whole breadth of welfare provision within a mixed economy approach and the complex and changing nature of the state. A central aspect of this involves consideration of the welfare state in the provision and regulation of welfare. The concept of the welfare state itself has been shown to be highly sensitive, not only to economic expedients but also to ideological, moral and politically motivated pressures. The final point to be made here concerns the concept of a social resource itself. We have noted the concern of social policy with systems of social distribution, or how social goods are distributed in society and needs are met. But we have not yet defined which 'goods' or resources are 'social' as opposed to economic, political or simply luxury. Traditionally, concern has focused on resources such as health care, domiciliary care, social work, education, income support, housing, employment and education. Michael Cahill (1994), however, has suggested five additional 'social goods' that should be included within the study of social policy:

1 *Communicating:* telephone, fax, letters and e-mail.
2 *Viewing:* radio and television.
3 *Travelling:* rail, road and air transport.
4 *Shopping:* location and planning of shopping centres.
5 *Playing:* provision of leisure facilities, swimming pools, youth clubs etc.

Cahill goes on to point out that studying these areas is important, not only for understanding old and new inequalities, but also because policies are interdependent. This is illustrated in Chapter 5, with the prevention of obesity as an example. We cannot, he suggests, understand or evaluate policies in isolation:

> we can only provide good social policies if we are sensitive to the context in which government policy programmes operate ... Adopting this perspective does mean that we must see social policy as part of a wider public policy. Health care is a good example, where governments now acknowledge that many other public policies have a health dimension. But the process should work the other way as well: transport policies are dependent on housing and retailing policies, retailing policies have health dimensions, and so on. One could produce a long list of these policy inter-dependencies.
>
> (Cahill 1994: 2)

We might add to this list the issue of environmental policy, which is increasingly seen to fall within the parameters of social policy and which has important implications for health status (George and Wilding 1994). In fact, social policy now covers a very broad range of social programmes, with its increasing concern with social need and social inequalities, and divisions and areas of policy include criminal justice, equal opportunities, race and ethnicity, immigration and a concern with international dimensions, including European social policy, development issues and the role of international trade and finance together with its impact on welfare in the UK and other countries. For example, labour migration, as illustrated in Chapter 10, is highly relevant to the study of health in the UK, in terms of movements of skilled health care professionals in the European Union (EU) but also from developing countries, where inward migration to the UK has severe implications for staffing health care services in countries such as Ghana and South Africa. Increasingly, the language of social policy is developing around concepts such as inclusion and exclusion, social capital and inequality (Baldock *et al.* 2003). More importantly, much analysis of social policy examines the interrelationship of these concepts and what the role of the state is in addressing these, and what needs to be done to alleviate social exclusion and inequalities.

Social policy: a contemporary analysis

The discussion in this chapter has identified different ways that social policy can be examined. Writing in the early 1980s, Alan Walker (1983) suggested social policy could be defined as:

> The rationale underlying the development and use of social institutions and groups which affect the distribution of resources, status and power between different individuals and groups in society. Thus social policy is concerned both with the values and principles which govern the distribution as well as their outcome. The task of the social policy analyst is to evaluate the distributional impact of existing policies on social welfare, their implicit and explicit rationales, their impact on social relations and the implications of policy proposals.
>
> (Walker 1983: 141)

Baldock *et al.* (2003: 7) suggest that social policy can be categorized into three broad areas:

1 The intentions and objectives that lie behind policies.
2 The administrative and financial arrangements that are used to deliver policies.
3 The outcomes of policies, particularly in terms of who gains and loses.

While the intentions or aims of policies are often clear, in many areas of social policy it is more difficult to identify what the intentions of a policy are. This is particularly true when the benefits or services have been accumulating over a number of years. In addition, intentions may be contradictory or not stated explicitly. Generally, the intentions of social policy can be grouped into three headings: redistribution, risk management and reducing social exclusion (see Box 1.2). Redistribution has always been a concern of social policy, but while addressing risk and tackling social exclusion may seem more recent concerns, in reality the development of public health services, universal education, pensions and social security have always been focused on supporting those at risk and promoting inclusion. In fact, a prime concern of many of those in favour of the post-war welfare state was the need to promote social solidarity. This goal has not been abandoned, but the language and how people think about society has changed, so that terms such as social inclusion and social capital are now used rather than solidarity. Thus, key social questions today include how different communities can be integrated – especially recent immigrants and asylum-seekers – concerns about access to employment, public services etc. and in particular, what the proper role of government is in ensuring these things happen *vis-à-vis* the responsibility of the individual.

As can be seen from the preceding discussion in this chapter, the study of the administrative and financial arrangements of social policy formed much of the first development of the subject. While initially focusing on the delivery of the welfare state, analysis became more complex with the understanding of the six forms of welfare referred to in Box 1.1. More recently social policy analysis has begun to focus on the processes of poli-cy-making and implementation (Bochel and Bochel 2004; Lowe and Hudson 2004), the importance of understanding how policies are made and delivered and the role of government, the private sector and the enormous range of not-for-profit agencies and interest groups. This has also involved a renewed interest in the role of professionals and managers in service delivery and what relationship the individual, especially as recipient of services and benefits, has with the policy process (Taylor 2003).

Box 1.2   Intentions of social policy

Redistribution
Two forms of redistributive policy are generally pursued. Vertical redistribution moves from richer people to poorer people to address what may be considered unacceptable levels of income inequality. Horizontal (or lifetime) redistribution is where the state taxes people to provide services they might otherwise not pay for, such as education or pensions.

Risk management
While social policies have always been about addressing social need, it is argued that there are a much wider range of risks in society, such as pollution and the negative consequences of new technology. We now live in a risk society (Beck 1992) where individuals have little power to protect themselves, so this is the responsibility of the state.

Reducing social exclusion
There is some ambiguity about what social exclusion means – it is a contested concept. It has been argued that it is just another word for poverty but its meaning is broader than this and originates in France, where its use relates to the way some people are excluded from society by virtue of a lack of skills, education, poverty or disability. Therefore, policies are needed to re-include them in society. Social exclusion occurs when there are substantial inequalities and thus relates to issues of redistribution and risk.

An interest in policy outcomes has become increasingly important and the New Labour government has invested substantially in approaches to ensure that policies succeed. The debates of the 1970s and 1980s identified what was seen by many as the failure of the welfare state in terms of the continuing problems of poverty, homelessness and ill health (Townsend 1979). While this relates to both the content and process of policy, in terms of identifying why it fails, it is also clear that analysing the effect of policy is an important element of social policy analysis. We need to know whether particular policies have achieved their desired results. However, this still places a relatively narrow focus on specific policies and their implementation. More recently, social policy has included broader analyses of the relationship between the state and society, to include areas such as governance, leading Levin (1997: 26) to argue that social policy is primarily about '*the coming into being of policies and measures, which is part of a wider phenomenon, the interaction of government and society. From this standpoint, the definitions and boundaries which academics seek to assign to "social policy" are irrelevant as well as arbitrary*'.

Conclusion

The scope of social policy is thus very broad. While it is true that health policy forms one area of social policy, it is also clear that an understanding of the wider aspects of social policy is important to understand its development and to provide a clearer understanding of how people's lives are shaped by social problems. An understanding of health inequalities requires a broader understanding of wider social inequalities in society and a recognition of the way that health impacts on wider social issues is necessary to understand the full impacts of ill health. Similarly, the impact of social contexts on people's health is also a key component of understanding health and disease. Health and social care practitioners need to recognize that individual patients must be seen within their social context (family situation, socio-economic status, ethnicity, whether homeless etc.). The NHS itself is the construct of social policy and the way health care practitioners or social workers practice is the result of social processes.

The remainder of the book explores many of the issues raised here in more depth, mainly adopting a 'case study' approach. Chapter 2 examines the evolution of the welfare state, using health as an example, as it is only through an understanding of how the welfare state evolved that we can come to understand where it is today. Chapter 3 examines in more detail the changing context of health policy in the post-war period, demonstrating how health care has responded to changes in society and advances in health services. Chapter 4 examines the extent to which welfare services have met one of the major objectives of the founders of the welfare state: a reduction in poverty and inequalities. It also examines the nature of inequalities in relation to social division and how inequality and poverty relate to social exclusion. Chapter 5 builds on this discussion and examines the nature of health inequalities in the UK, and how the government has responded to them. In Chapter 6, we consider the pluralization of welfare services. In particular we explore the way in which private sector management practises and market forces have been introduced into the public sector, and the privatization of welfare, using health services and pensions as examples. Chapter 7 develops the discussion in Chapter 6, focusing on the increasing fragmentation and diversification of the delivery of public services. In Chapter 8, we focus on the increasingly important role of the voluntary sector in the provision of community and health care services. Chapter 9 then explores the development of lay involvement in health through the growth of the user movement. It also examines the role of carers and the importance of informal care in health and social care. Chapter 10 examines the occupational histories of different health professions, in particular nursing, medicine and social work. It discusses professional regulation and professional education and development. Each of these latter chapters considers how the boundaries between sectors, professionals and lay people, have been progressively blurred in recent years as a result of welfare retrenchment, more pluralistic provision and having to address more complex problems. The final chapter draws out themes arising from the previous chapters to highlight the growing importance and impact of globalization, workforce issues, public health, changing patterns of service use and provision and new technologies. The chapter also examines how current issues such as health inequalities, the role of the state and social policy will remain central to future debates about health and health care. It asks whether the new balance of responsibility, within the mixed economy of welfare, has met the criticisms of the post-war welfare state and considers the implications of the new forms of partnership for social equality and citizenship.

Summary

- The study of social policy has evolved from a narrow concern, with the development and evaluation of state welfare, to a broader concern with the whole basis of social entitlement and social responsibility.
- The concept of welfare pluralism is used to describe welfare systems in which social needs are met through a wide range of sources including the voluntary, commercial, informal and state sectors.
- These sectors do not operate independently of each other but rather interact in a complex manner with other welfare providers and with other aspects of public policy (e.g. on the economy and environment).
- While a mixed economy of provision characterizes the whole history of social policy in the UK, political ideology has an important impact on the balance between the main providers of welfare.
- The influence of ideology is illustrated through the concept of welfare models (the residual and institutional models) and subsequent welfare regimes.
- Central concerns of social policy now address the problems of diversity and difference, and how these interact with inequalities.

Further reading

Baldock, J., Manning, N. and Vickerstaff, S. (eds) (2003) *Social Policy*. Oxford: Oxford University Press.

Lowe, R. and Hudson, J. (2004) *Understanding the Policy Process: Analysing Welfare Policy and Process*. Bristol: Policy Press.

Timmins, N. (1995) *The Five Giants*. Harmondsworth: Penguin.

THE DEVELOPMENT OF THE WELFARE STATE

Introduction

In this chapter we consider the development of state welfare provision in Britain. We pay particular attention to the development of health care provision but also briefly consider other state provision. The chapter will examine the debates concerning the extent to which the state should intervene in family life and civil society, and the ways in which it does so; although much of the focus is on health, we use this as the basis for exploring debates about the provision of welfare which apply more broadly.

During the course of the nineteenth and twentieth centuries, the state gradually became involved in the supervision and direct organization of welfare – of formal welfare services – most notably health, income maintenance, housing, education, employment and personal social services. Nevertheless, the commercial sector, employers, the voluntary sector and most notably the informal sector, have all continued to play an important role in the provision of welfare. Indeed, the informal sector – the welfare we provide for ourselves and others – has always been and continues to be the main provider of welfare. The development of state-provided welfare has resulted in increased surveillance (especially with the spread of computer technology and the development of state information systems), increased regulation of the population and increased power for welfare professionals, including doctors, teachers and social workers (Wilding 1982; Abbott and Wallace 1990; Exworthy and Halford 1999).

It was only in the twentieth century that the British state came to play a major role in organizing welfare services and meeting the welfare needs of the population. Indeed, all western societies developed welfare states in the twentieth century, although the extent of state provision and the range of services provided varies considerably. At one end of the spectrum are countries, such as Sweden and the UK, that provide comprehensive welfare services for all citizens, primarily funded out of general taxation, while at the other end are countries like the USA where universal provision is limited and the role of the state is seen as providing a safety net for those who are unable to make provision for themselves out of their own resources (Ginsberg 1992).

There is considerable variation as to the extent to which it is thought desirable for government to make provision for citizens and the extent to which it is thought to be individuals' responsibility to meet their own needs, with the state intervening only when individuals are unable to provide for themselves and their families. The role that the state plays in the provision of welfare and the ways in which this role changes and develops is to a considerable extent the outcome of these competing ideas – between the state playing a major and a residual role. Those who take the former position tend to argue that most needs are the result of factors outside the individual's control, such as old age, unemployment, sickness and low wages, and therefore that costs should be socialized (i.e. paid for collectively). Those who take the latter view tend to argue that most needs are the result of individual inadequacies and failings and that state provision tends to create welfare dependency. While debates about welfare have moved beyond such binary positions, contemporary government social policy is still characterized by a tension between targeting benefits and services and providing universal care and benefits. The development of consumer choice in welfare services brings these issues to the fore in relation to what types of choices should be offered and to whom, and the extent to which people should take responsibility for their own health and social care (Clarke *et al.* 2005).

State welfare and state intervention

In the early part of the nineteenth century, the dominant view was that the state should *not* provide for the welfare of the population and indeed that it should deter the able-bodied from becoming unemployed. This view was underpinned by the idea of *laissez-faire* (which literally means 'to leave to do'), that the state should not interfere in the private sphere of the family, nor in the economy. Individuals, it was argued, should be responsible for providing all their own and their family's needs and market forces should determine the price of goods and services, including the price of labour. If income support was provided for the unemployed it was thought that this would influence the price of labour and the labour market. People would be unwilling, it was suggested, to take employment that paid a lower wage than that provided by state support, and if state support provided an adequate standard of living, then people may not be prepared to take available jobs, preferring to live on state benefit or wait until more attractive employment became available. The Victorians also believed that most poverty was the result of personal inadequacy, an unwillingness to work, spending money inappropriately and failing to save for sickness and old age. It was thought that if the state provided for the unemployed, not only would there be no incentive for them to take employment, but others could be encouraged not to continue in employment. The Victorians argued that the respectable poor would be contaminated by the residuum – the non-respectable poor. Current moves towards personal responsibility and the promotion of consumerism reflect a *laissez-faire* approach in some ways, as the government is shifting its role in relation to how it provides services to individuals. Choice by consumers in terms of lifestyle and service use, it is now thought, should be less directed by government, with decisions based on personal criteria rather than public service discretion.

During the course of the nineteenth century, the state did come increasingly to intervene in the private sphere of the family and in the economy and to take on more responsibility for providing for the welfare needs of the population. *Laissez-faire* remained the dominant influence, however, and it was not until the early twentieth century, following the publication of surveys challenging the view that poverty was mainly caused by individual failure, that the state began to provide for individual welfare. Reforms in the nineteenth century were targeted at whole populations (e.g. sanitary reform), at protecting what were seen as vulnerable groups (e.g. factory legislation), or at developing a resource (e.g. the Education Acts). Charitable endeavour developed alongside increasing state intervention in the private sphere of the family and in the market.

Schooling, for instance, was provided by voluntary organizations, albeit with some government support after 1832, until the late nineteenth century. It was not until the Forster Education Act of 1870 that local School Boards were set up with the powers to provide schools, and not until 1880 that schooling was made compulsory from the ages of 5 to 10. Charitable organizations made considerable efforts to help the poor, weak and vulnerable, where notable individuals spearheaded campaigns for reform in a number of areas. The 'visiting movement' of Victorian times – charities whose primary purpose was the visitation of the poor – were mostly concerned with inculcating habits of thrift, cleanliness and middle-class morality in working-class families. Mutual aid organizations (e.g. Friendly Societies) that enabled working-class men to provide for unemployment, sickness and old age collectively, also developed and grew in the nine-teenth century (Green 1993).

The challenge to individualistic explanation

By the beginning of the twentieth century, however, ideas about the causes of poverty and the 'social problem group' (the undeserving poor) were beginning to change, influenced by research which demonstrated that a significant proportion of the poor were not responsible for their plight. Poverty, it was suggested, was not generally the result of personal inad-equacies but of low wages, the scarcity of employment, old age or sickness; it also became recognized that most working-class people did not earn sufficient, when in employment, to make adequate provision for periods of unemployment or sickness, or for their old age. The other influence was the concern that the health and fitness of the British population was in decline and that this threatened Britain's position as a leading industrial nation. This concern was fuelled by the condition of working-class men who volunteered to fight in the Boer War: three out of five were rejected as unfit due, it was said, to chronic sickness, the result of degenerate and shiftless lifestyles, such as early marriage and, the ignorance of mothers (Abbott 1982). One consequence of this was the establishment of the school health service (Baggott 2000).

In the ensuing debates, the view developed that health, hygiene and the fitness of the population were keys to progress (Baggott 2000). However, although the interdepartmental committee set up to investigate the lives of the poor, which reported in 1904, made 53 recommendations mainly concerning the importance of physical conditions, housing, poverty, diet etc., the ones that were taken up, and developed, focused on the role of motherhood as the key to a healthy population. The emphasis on the mother, and women more generally, as having a 'duty of care' has con-tinued to the present day, so that women are now seen as natural carers and those who 'fail' to fulfil this duty are seen as inadequate, in an almost biological as well as a social sense (Abbott et al. 2005). This ideology also underpins the assumption that informal care is to be preferred to formal care and is the 'natural' duty of women. This debate is still important today, given that most of the 6 million informal carers are women (see Chapter 9), and that following the development of a new caring economy in the welfare state, many caring roles are undertaken by women doing low-paid and often part-time work (see Chapters 6, 7 and 9).

While the emphasis on the prevention of ill health changed from the collectivist one of the nineteenth century – sanitary reforms aimed at the whole population – to an individualistic one in the twentieth century. There was also an increasing recognition that state intervention was necessary to alleviate ill health and poverty. Nevertheless, the tension between ideologies that stress a need for collective measures to overcome social problems such as poverty, ill health and inadequate diet on the one hand, and those that stress individual responsibility and personal inad-equacy on the other, continued to underpin the changing provision made by the British state and are reflected in debates about the nature of social provision today. The welfare state legislation of the 1940s was concerned with providing for the welfare needs of the population and included the NHS, the social security system, the education system and the personal social services. However, the extent to which these measures were intended to result in a more equal society (or have resulted in one) or were merely to provide a safety net, has been a matter of considerable debate (see Chapter 4).

The public provision of welfare

The public provision of welfare, including public health provision, can be traced through the nineteenth century, back to the voluntary hospitals of the eighteenth century and earlier, such as the Westminster, St Thomas's and St Bartholomew's, and the Elizabethan Poor Law of 1603. But it is the period from the 1830s to just before the First World War which saw an increasing trend of state intervention in matters of health, sanitation and welfare generally, areas which had once been regarded as private (see Boxes 2.1 and 2.3).

Box 2.1 Key developments in nineteenth-century Britain

1833 Factory Act – limited the number of hours children could work
1834 The New Poor Law
1844 Health of Towns Movement founded
1847 The 10 Hour Act – limited the working day of women and children
1848 Public Health Act
1853 Infant vaccination against smallpox made compulsory
1857 Foundation of the Ladies' National Association for the Reform of Sanitary Conditions
1860 Adulteration of food made illegal
      First district nurse began work in Liverpool
      Nightingale Nursing School started at St Thomas' Hospital, London
1861 Foundation of Manchester Ladies' Sanitary Reform Society
1864 Poor Law Board argues that Poor Law Unions could pay for basic medicines
1866 Sanitary Act
1867 Poor Law Unions allowed to build infirmaries away from workhouses and to open separate fever hospitals
1868 Artisans' Dwelling Act
1869 Formation of **Charity Organization Society**
1870 Forster's Education Act – Local School Boards permitted to provide elementary schools
1875 Public Health Act

	Food and Drugs Act
	Artisans' and Labourers' Building Improvement Act
1878	Formation of the Salvation Army
1879	Artisans and Labourers Building Improvement Act
1880	Education Act – compulsory schooling for children aged 5–10 years
1890	Poor sick no longer had to go to the Relieving Officer before they could be treated at the public infirmary
1890	Housing Act
1891	State education made free
1891	Publication of Charles Booth's *The Life and Labour of the People of London*, Volume 1

Poverty and health

In the early nineteenth century, the conditions brought about by indus-trialization became a cause for considerable concern, leading to the Poor Law Amendment Act 1834, which aimed to 'persuade' the poor to work and deter the able-bodied from seeking poor relief from the parish. They were to be offered only 'indoor' relief, in the workhouse, and the condi-tions of the workhouse were to be less desirable than those of the poorest outside. The aim was to reduce public expenditure and to encourage the able-bodied to take any available work. By distinguishing between the able-bodied and those deemed unable to work, the Act created *paupers*, an underclass of those assumed to be lazy, indigent and unwilling to work.

In this period a new way of defining what came to be known as 'the social question' gradually developed and was used as a technique for characterizing and regulating the population. The conditions in which the poor lived, were seen as a potential source of contagious disease and also of social and moral corruption. To counteract this, reformers suggested a programme of social hygiene reforms, improving welfare and at the same time obtaining detailed information about the lives of the poor. This programme was aimed not only at disease but at the chain of conditions which were seen as linking susceptibility to contagion with criminality, moral depravity and political sedition. The family was seen as the prime target for intervention. Jacques Donzelot (1980) refers to this strategy of surveillance as 'the policing of the family'; that is, the use of political power to investigate the details of the population's everyday lives and to secure its well-being and happiness, its fitness for work, morality and dis-cipline, the quality of its health and so on.

The early Victorians thought that poverty was inextricably linked with health, and this led to a concern with the health of the poor. Edwin Chadwick, the architect of the 1834 Poor Law, began by 1838, to recognize that much poverty was caused by sickness and that much sickness could be prevented. It was evident that cholera, typhus, tuberculosis and other diseases spread among the population in the poor areas of crowded towns. The growth in the urban population in early nineteenth-century Britain resulted in endemic and epidemic contagious diseases. Cholera broke out in Britain in 1831–2 (having been brought into Britain from the Middle East as a result of trade links), and recurred in 1848–9, 1854 and 1867. Although it started in the poor districts of towns it eventually spread to middle-class areas. Typhus and typhoid fever were mainly diseases of the poor, and there were epidemic outbreaks in 1826–7, 1831–2, 1837 and 1846–7, coinciding with periods of economic recession and high unemployment. Both of these diseases were endemic; that is, there were high incidence rates even in the periods between epidemics.

Sanitary conditions and health

The Inquiry into the Sanitary Conditions of the Poor, headed by Chadwick which reported in 1842, demonstrated a close relationship between insanitary living conditions, overcrowding, lack of sewers etc. and the death rate. One of the responses to the report was the formation of the Health of Towns Association in 1844, which carried out a propaganda campaign for the implementation of sanitary legislation. The (male) membership comprised leading citizens, including doctors and lawyers. Local sanitary associations were also founded in a number of cities.

In Victorian England, the course of reform was set by the clashes and debates between factory owners and philanthropically inclined reformers whose wealth came from land: between those who saw a need for the state to regulate the conditions under which diseases, like cholera, flourished and the shopkeepers and other middle-class groups who would pay for proposed reforms through local rates; between those who feared political centralization and those who saw it as necessary if greater evils were to be avoided. Most public health reforms of the early period challenged the principle of *laissez-faire* directly, though in a limited way. The Factory Acts limited the hours that could be worked by labourers, particularly women and children, and laid down basic minimum conditions. The Royal Commission on the Health of Towns (1842) led to the Public Health Act of 1848, which set up a general Board of Health. Municipalities were permitted to set up their own boards of health to consolidate and extend public health networks and to appoint staff, including a medical officer of health. They were, in addition, given powers to deal with sewage and drainage, street-sweeping and cleaning. They had powers to register slaughterhouses and common lodging houses, to regulate offensive trades and dangerous chemical wastes, and to clean and purify 'unwholesome homes'. While the Act laid provisions for every new house built to have a toilet, a cesspit and drains, the legislation was enabling rather than mandatory for precisely the reason that the costs fell on local ratepayers: local authorities were *empowered* to carry out these works but were never *required* to do so. However, the General Board of Health could enforce action if it received a petition signed by one-tenth of the ratepayers in an area or if the death rate exceeded 23 in every thousand.

What is usually referred to as 'the sanitary movement' continued throughout the Victorian period and into Edwardian England. Its aims rested on a discourse which changed and evolved, but certain elements remained constant throughout the period:

1 The connection between dirt and disease, which has been part of our taken-for-granted common sense for many years, but which was vehemently denied by many in early- and mid-Victorian Britain. A germ theory of disease was not fully accepted until the 1860s (following Pasteur's discoveries).
2 The recognition that public health was indivisible – that the illness of one class was a problem for all classes. The ideological implications of this recognition were important because it meant that the state could, and should, intervene in private lives and in independent local government. *Laissez-faire* could not be allowed to run as far as imperilling ratepayers' lives.

There was considerable opposition to the reforms, not only from ratepayers and municipal authorities, but also from the medical profession, who were concerned that treatment for epidemics was being prescribed by sanitary engineers as opposed to medical professionals, However, in 1866 the Sanitary Act made the provisions of the 1848 Act mandatory, though without central control, and the 1875 Public Health Act consolidated all the sanitary legislation and required all municipalities to appoint a medical officer of health. Municipalities were prepared to accept the legislation because there was no central control, and by the time of the 1866 Act the medical profession, whose status had been enhanced by the Medical Qualifications Act 1858, came to recognize the value of preventive medicine (and, indeed, turned it into a medical specialism).

The concern about public health also resulted in reforms to improve housing and clear slums. The Artisans' and Labourers' Building Improvement Acts of 1875 and 1879, gave local authorities the power to purchase land in slum areas and redevelop it. The Housing Act 1890 gave them the power to clear whole areas, repair and improve houses and build new ones of better quality. The 'public good' aspect of health – the view that the state should intervene, on behalf of society, to ensure the availability of services for which the commercial market would not pay – led to public provision of clean water, sewage, cemeteries, factory inspection, compulsory vaccination against smallpox, controls on house building and regulation of overcrowding. All these reforms raised public expenditure and were resisted for this reason by the minority who paid local rates, despite the arguments of people like Chadwick, who had calculated that getting rid of avoidable disease would actually save money, principally by lessening demands on the Poor Law, which was paid for and spent locally. The public good cannot be seen simply as providing services to the poor which they could not afford to buy. Public health and sanitation measures also meant regulation and control of the poor. Controls on overcrowding, for example, raised rents and were resisted by the poor. We are now so used to seeing the great Victorian reforms as bringing in desirable improvements, that it is easy to lose sight of the fact that many of them were regarded at the time as profligate with the public purse, an invasion of privacy, and an erosion of the rights of families and individuals to keep their living and health arrangements private.

The Victorian reforms greatly expanded the power of the state – that is, both central and local government – to intervene in the personal and private matters of health and health-related issues. The intervention was not neutral in ideological terms, but embodied values and social constructions which continued into later schemes for the public provision of health care: into the Liberal government's reforms of the National Insurance Act (1911) and into the National Health Service Act (1946).

Public health and personal health

Richard Titmuss (1968) has identified two features of publicly-funded health care: it is collectivist and it is preventive. It cannot be supplied on an individual basis: clean water supplies and efficient sewage disposal (which between them eradicated epidemic diseases such as cholera) cannot be supplied to some people, and not to others, without the attendant risk that those who do not receive them will infect those who do. Everyone, according to collectivists, has an interest in seeing that minimum standards of water purity and sewage disposal are enjoyed by all and, if necessary, imposing (through the state) the requirement that all conform to the regulations in this area. They argue that public goods, like clean water, cannot be provided on a pay-as-you-consume basis because of the danger that some will not pay for them. That is why there is strong pressure to finance such public services from taxation; everyone pays for them, to varying extents, and everyone enjoys the benefits. This argument for limited state intervention was accepted in Britain by the 1870s, when Disraeli's government passed a number of Acts regulating public health and sanitation which extended, or strengthened, the reforms of the early Victorian period.

Individual health

Personal health is individual health, the complaints which now take us to our general practitioner (GP) or result in us being admitted to hospital. Clearly, the public and personal merge into one another because diseases caught due to a lack of public facilities (e.g. clean water) will lead to personal illness. The distinction can be maintained in diseases which appear to be accidental, of unknown origin or appear to arise due to personal neglect. The patterning of individual health problems is not random, as we shall see in Chapter 5, but follows divisions of social class, gender, ethnicity and region. This patterning makes it increasingly difficult to maintain a clear distinction between personal and public health but, we are concerned, at the moment, with how the Victorians and Edwardians saw the connection and how the 'health debate' evolved then.

The connection between poverty and disease was graphically illustrated by a number of research reports in the early- and mid-Victorian periods. The consequences of poverty in the rapidly expanding cities of industrializing Britain were seen as overcrowding, damp and insanitary housing, a poor diet and defective public provision of services, such as water and sewage disposal. These in turn led to chronic ill health and shortened life expectancy, and in particular to a high infant mortality rate. The Victorian public health and planning reforms were aimed at some of these consequences, but in themselves did nothing to deal directly with poverty as such – simply with some of its consequences which had public health implications.

However, arguments that the personal health of the poor also required attention were advanced as early as 1844 by the Royal Commission on the Health of Towns, which itself was fundamentally arguing for solutions to collective problems rather than individual ones. Personal health treatment was very fragmented and involved a mixed model of state, private and voluntary/charitable provision and funding. Poor people only had access to a patchwork of Poor Law infirmaries, voluntary hospitals (which were of higher status and increasingly became more interested in acute and 'interesting' diseases rather than in chronic conditions) and charitable efforts by doctors and medical missionaries. The means tested voluntary (charity) hospitals normally took *only* patients unable to pay for medical care and who had been nominated by one of the financial supporters of the hospital. They were not spread evenly throughout the country, took only acute as opposed to chronic cases and, even then, were selective in the cases they took on. Apart from these, the poor in casual, unskilled jobs and the unemployed, were thrown entirely onto the Poor Law provision. There was a strong tendency to identify Poor Law infirmaries with workhouses. In short, the poor received preventive health measures (mainly through sanitary reform and education measures), but curative care was extremely uncertain and only readily available to those of the skilled working-class and tradesmen who voluntarily insured with Provident and Friendly Societies or with the craft trade unions. The middle- and lower middle-classes could buy personal health care according to their means; the amount of health care received depended on their ability to pay for it.

Personal health measures came much later than public health ones, resulting from the confluence of several different strands in the debate about the causes of ill health between the *laissez-faire* lobby and the interventionists. Edwin Chadwick, although a noted sanitary reformer and therefore interventionist in the matter of public health measures, was also Secretary to the Poor Law Commissioners and a strong supporter of the new Poor Law and its principle of lesser eligibility aimed directly at forcing the poor into employment and amending the previous legislation, which it was thought pandered to the very moral defects which led to poverty and unemployment. The same moral defects of the poor, which were responsible for their poverty, also showed themselves in poor hygiene, poor parenting, drunkenness and poor household management. All were defects which might have public health implications, given the slum housing into which the poor were crowded, following the rapid urbanization during the industrial revolution.

The growth of social work in late nineteenth-century Britain

The 'remoralization' of the poor was also a driving force for the growth of social work. Two particularly notable organizations involved in this provision were the Charity Organization Society (COS) and the Ladies' Sanitary Reform Association. These two associations can be seen as the outcome, both of a growing feminism in Victorian times (Banks 1981) and, of class-conscious philanthropy associated with the evangelical revival. Philanthropic good works were an outlet for upper middle-class Victorian women who were denied a role in production, were no longer satisfied with themselves as wives and mothers but continued to share Victorian middle-class attitudes to women. Philanthropy can be distinguished from charity: while the latter means the outright support of the poor by individuals or state agencies, the former in nineteenth-century Britain was a private intervention in the problem of poverty, a strategy for intervention under the liberal state. It deflected the problem of poverty and pauperism from being seen as a political rights issue, to one related to personal conduct and responsibility. Philanthropy was provided in two ways: assistance and aid, and the diffusion of medical and hygienic norms. It was based on an ideology of self-help and self-reliance.

The Charity Organization Society

The COS was the originator of the idea of 'case work', whereby a case worker made direct interventions into individual families to 'remould' them, in exchange for charitable payments. Thrift, temperance and habits of industry were what the poor needed. It grew out of the view that some of the poor – the 'deserving' poor – could be helped to become respectable, self-supporting members of society if given the right blend of assistance and advice. It was also influenced by the evangelical Christian argument that charity *per se* demoralized the poor. They argued that the deserving poor (the sick, the elderly and widows) should be trained in thrift and self-help. The COS, founded in London in 1869, was concerned to ensure that a clear distinction was drawn between the deserving and the undeserving poor. It was underpinned by moral values that were used to determine which individuals were 'in real need' and which were 'playing the system'. The dominant *laissez-faire* ideology that underpinned its moral values saw two causes of poverty: some were poor through natural disasters (such as widowhood) and some through their own 'moral failing' (unwillingness to work, or spending money on drink and gambling). The deserving poor were those whose poverty was no fault of their own and who displayed a willingness to help themselves – those who exhibited the moral values of thrift, sobriety and self-discipline were to be assisted. An officer of the COS assessed and classified different kinds of applicants. A 'case work' approach to individual applicants developed, whereby they were exhorted and encouraged to conform to 'virtuous' middle-class models of what the family life of the poor should be like. Only those assessed as deserving were given assistance, and they were followed up to see how the money was spent; the officers kept 'case notes' for all those who were assisted.

Ladies' sanitary reform societies

This spirit of personal moral challenge in social work ruled in health matters also, particularly where hygiene and the removal of squalor and filth were concerned. It was the mothers who were the first target for change. The Ladies' National Association for the Reform of Sanitary Conditions was a philanthropic organization established to educate the poor with specific reference to hygiene and cleanliness. The Association was founded in London and Brighton in 1857, based on the view that the mother is the key person in health education and that the instruction of mothers, especially working-class mothers, in hygiene was essential. The main aim of the Association was the preservation of child life – to reduce mortality rates among children under five – and the main target was mothers. Many of the lady members already visited the poor on behalf of the parish, the Bible Society etc. and they started to take 'sanitary tracts' with them as well as religious ones. In London, Mrs Raynor, a founding member of the Ladies' National Association, felt that *lady* visitors might not be able to influence poorer women, and she began to use working-class women to visit the poor as female sanitary missionaries. This idea spread to other parts of the country as local branches of the Association were established. However, the Manchester Ladies' Sanitary Reform Society (founded in 1861), which employed working-class women to visit mothers at home and instruct them in the need for cleanliness and good diet, is often thought to be the first organized hygiene movement. Its example spread widely in Britain in the late nineteenth century, and most cities came to possess charitable societies with the same purpose.

These organizations, like other similar Victorian ones, were founded, run and charitably supported by middle-class Victorians, out of a sense of a duty to help the deserving poor. They can also, however, be seen as the precursors of social work and health visiting – both services that have been developed and provided by the state in twentieth-century Britain. The latter became a mandatory and universal service. Until recently the majority of health authorities required their health visitors to have regular contact with all families with children under the age of five, but since the 1990s these services have become increasingly targeted on poorer and disadvantaged families, and families where children may be more at risk. Social work has remained a selective service, targeted now not so much at those in financial need but at those who are deemed to be unable to cope with their daily lives. A key concept here was the idea of dysfunctional families – families unable to cope and thus neglecting or abusing their children (Abbott and Wallace 1990).

From the nineteenth to the twentieth century

Towards the end of the nineteenth century, the view that poverty was the result of individual failure came increasingly to be challenged. Particularly influential in the debates surrounding the causes of poverty were the results of surveys carried out by Charles Booth in London and Seebohm Rowntree in York. In his first study, Booth divided the population into eight classes (see Box 2.2).

Box 2.2   Classes of the poor in Booth's London survey

A   The lowest class – occasional labourers, loafers and semi-casuals
B   The very poor – casual labourers, hand-to-mouth existence, chronic want
C, D The poor, including those whose earnings were small because of irregularity of employment and those whose work, though regular, was low paid
E, F The regularly employed and fairly paid working class of all grades
G, H Lower- and upper middle-class and all above.

Booth found that 30.7 per cent of the population fell into classes A–D and were in 'poverty'. Classes E and F, in which 51.5 per cent of the population being surveyed fell, were in 'comfort'. In York in 1899, Rowntree found that over 50 per cent of those living in poverty were poor because of a large family. He also found that the chances of being in poverty varied over the life course – those most likely to be living in poverty were young single people, families with dependent children and people over 60. Those least likely to be in poverty were married couples with no dependent children, with both partners in employment. Booth and Rowntree argued that not all – or even a majority – of the poor were responsible for their plight: the main causes of poverty were a lack of regular employment, low wages, sickness and old age.

By the late nineteenth century the poor had come to be viewed as a health problem in a wider sense than the perceived public health threat of the earlier period. The private sickness of many of the poor was now seen as a problem demanding public intervention – at first charitable intervention but, increasingly, provided by the state. The principle of non-interference was eroded further by the enormous outcry after the Boer War (1899–1901), when a high proportion of potential army recruits had had to be turned away as unfit for service (Abbott and Sapsford 1990). However, the debate continued between those who saw poverty and want as a result of individual failing and, those who argued that it was a result of factors beyond the control of individuals.

National efficiency

The debate on 'national efficiency', as it was called, was the immediate background to the Liberal government's health and welfare reforms in the Edwardian period, reforms now widely acknowledged as the beginnings of the British welfare state (see Box 2.3).

The state's interest in children as a resource followed on the revelations about the health of Boer War recruits, but it also intermeshed with a more general debate on national efficiency and eugenics – a fear that the decline in the racial stock meant Britain was losing out to its competitors both commercially, industrially (the USA and Germany) and militarily (particularly Germany). For the first time, the working-class were seen as a national resource, and the health and physique of working-class children as requiring state intervention. Health measures were increasingly targeted at individuals rather than, as in the case of sanitary reform, whole populations. The first responses were free school meals (1906), the medical inspection of schoolchildren (1907) and the Notification of Births Act 1907. (This last measure, whose provisions were made mandatory in 1915, was to enable health visitors to visit the homes of all newborn babies and give advice on hygiene and child care.) More generally, there was a commitment to improving 'the quality of mothering', for example, by the provision of mother and baby clinics and health visitors by local authorities.

Box 2.3   Key developments in Edwardian Britain

1904   Report of Interdepartmental Committee on National Efficiency
1905   Royal Commission on the Poor Law established
1906   School Meals Act
1907   School Medicals Act
       Workmen's Compensation Act
       Notification of Births Act
1908   Old Age Pensions Act
       Labour Exchange Act
       Children Act
1909   Majority and Minority Reports of the Royal Commission on the
       Poor Law published
1911   National Insurance Act

These interventionist reforms continued to be opposed, however, by those who argued that state welfare resulted in dependency. The COS, for example, said of school meals provision, that '*to feed the children is to debase the moral standard ... by prudently inviting parents ... to spend in idleness or drink the time and money which should have been given to making provision for their family*' (from an 1883 COS pamphlet, quoted in Owen 1965: 242).

This concern that parents, and especially men, should be encouraged to take their responsibilities seriously, or at least not be deterred from doing so, underpinned the legislative reforms to a large extent. Health visiting, for example, was introduced as a result of the inquiry in 1904 set up to investigate why many working-class recruits were not physically fit enough for military service. It found that the major factors were poverty and poor housing, although inadequate mothering was also seen as contributory. The committee made a large number of recommendations designed to reduce poverty and improve the housing conditions of the poor. In addition, the School Medical Service was established although it remained the responsibility of parents to ensure that their children received medical care.

The Liberal reforms

Other welfare measures of this period included the Workmen's Compensation Act 1907; the Children Act 1908, which was concerned with measures to combat cruelty to children; the Probation of Offenders Act 1908, which first introduced probation as an alternative to imprisonment; the Labour Exchange Act 1908; and the Old Age Pensions Act 1908, which introduced a non-contributory means tested pension of five shillings per week at age 70 for both men and women. Those who had an income of less than £21 a year received a full pension, and those whose income went up to £31.50 received a proportion of it. However, these reforms retained the centrality of the distinction between the deserving and undeserving poor, as those who had been habitually drunk, served a prison sentence in the previous ten years, been on poor relief or habitually failed to support themselves, were excluded on moral grounds. The Widows, Orphans and Old Age Pensions Act 1925, introduced additional contributory schemes to cover the risks of bereavement and old age.

The Liberal government did not, however, reform the Poor Law. The Royal Commission on the Poor Law, which was set up in 1905, resulted in a majority and minority report. The majority report (reflecting the views of the COS) was opposed to any state intervention and argued that every case of poverty needed to be investigated in order to distinguish between the deserving and the undeserving. In contrast, the minority report (reflecting the views of the Fabian Movement, represented on the commission by Beatrice Webb) argued that much poverty was not the fault of the poor and that the state should make provision. The Fabian view had been influenced by the surveys of Booth and Rowntree, which had demonstrated that a substantial proportion of poverty could be attributed to the unavailability of jobs, low pay (preventing saving), sickness and old age. A report written for the commission by Professor William Smart showed that poverty affected women, more than men and children, and the elderly more than the young. In a sample of paupers, 27 per cent were men, 29 per cent children and 43 per cent women. About 3/1000 people aged 15–20 years were in poverty, less than 7/1000 aged 25–34, 16/1000 of those aged 65–74, 276/1000 aged 75–84 and 353/1000 aged 85+. A report on 150,000 children

on poor relief found that they were undernourished, poorly dressed and
bare-footed (Jones 1994). Despite evidence of the extent of poverty, the
arguments and research on its causes, no major reform of the Poor Law was
undertaken until the 1940s. The argument that state relief would demor-
alize the poor and that outdoor relief would greatly increase costs to
ratepayers held sway.

The poor still relied on charitable medical care, although the number of
hospitals offering free care to acute cases expanded slowly but steadily in
Edwardian Britain, as local authorities took over many Poor Law infirmaries (following the abolition of the Poor Law wards in 1929) and built new
ones. A considerable and diverse range of local authority municipal hospitals was founded, including infectious diseases hospitals, hospitals specializing in the treatment of tuberculosis, maternity hospitals, mental
hospitals and general hospitals.

The most significant change in personal health care provision was due to
the Liberals' National Insurance Act of 1911, partly copied from Bismarck's
reforms in Germany. Lloyd George appealed both to the self-interests of
employers, in supporting reform, and to the hygiene movement's fear of
racial decline when he spoke in favour of the new Act. The Act was in two
parts: Unemployment Insurance and Sickness Benefit. Contributions were
made by employees, employers and the state.

The unemployment provision applied only to workers in fluctuating
trades (e.g. building and shipbuilding) and no benefit was paid for non-
working wives or children. Benefits were paid at the new labour exchanges,
where the genuineness of the claim was tested by ensuring there was no
suitable work available. In 1920, the scheme was extended to virtually all
manual workers earning less than £250 per year. However, as unemployment rose during the 1920s, benefits were cut and contributions increased
(Jones 1991). At the same time, dependents' benefits were introduced and
transitional benefit, at a lower rate, was introduced for workers who had
exhausted their benefit right. In 1930, the term 'Poor Law' was replaced by
'public assistance', 'paupers' became 'rate-aided persons' and workhouses
(now controlled by local authorities) became 'public assistance institutions'. In 1934, an Act of Parliament established the Unemployment
Assistance Board, which provided benefit for those whose entitlement to
unemployment benefit had become exhausted. Benefits were paid at a
lower rate than public assistance, with a considerably harder means test –
the Household Means Test – which included calculations based on the
income of the total household, including working children, aged parents
and lodgers. The health scheme was administered by local insurance
committees, which included representatives of approved societies, local
authorities and GPs, with a residual scheme organized through post offices
for those refused by the voluntary sector. Similarly to unemployment
benefit, the sickness provisions applied to all manual workers (both men
and women) aged 16–70 years who were earning less than £250 per year –
about two million people – although this was later increased to £420, and
non-manual workers earning less than £160 a year were included. The
benefits, however, were restricted to GP care, drugs and medicines, a
modest entitlement to sickness and disablement benefits and maternity
grants. Hospital services were originally excluded, but they were gradually

covered, and by 1939 about half the population was entitled to hospital care through one scheme or another.

The Act aroused opposition from employers, because of the contributions they had to pay and, from the British Medical Association (BMA), who believed that the remuneration for GPs under the scheme was inadequate. The middle-classes were excluded from the scheme, partly because the doctors feared losing their private patients and partly because the Liberals insisted that the scheme would be funded entirely from contributions – the insurance principle. Only working people were in the health scheme; non-employed wives and children were excluded, as were the unemployed and the self-employed. (It was feared that if married women and children were included, this would deter men from working to provide for their families.) Those who could not afford the fees for private treatment had to turn to the local authority hospitals (the old Poor Law infirmaries), which provided care mainly for 'the chronically sick, the elderly and the mentally ill', or rely on charitable medical treatment, which was in general available only for acute illness. However, by 1939, 43 per cent of the population were covered by National Health Insurance and about 90 per cent of GPs participated in the scheme (Webster 1993).

The 1911 Act was the forerunner of the 1946 National Health Service Act, which established universal health care funded from general taxation. However, the insurance principle remained a strong influence on future welfare policy and was retained by successive governments for sickness benefit and extended to unemployment, old age pensions and maternity benefits in the post-war welfare state.

Personal health care between the wars

The Liberal reforms and the slow extension of local authority hospitals, left a patchy and cumbersome system of personal health care in Britain in the inter-war period. Access to health care in the pre-war health service depended on geography and money. Access to high-quality health care varied throughout the country. The poorest, who were entitled to free care, and the wealthy who could afford to pay for it, received medical care, although even then the quality of the care they received varied considerably. Others depended either on insurance with Friendly Societies and Provident Associations or hoped they would not need medical care.

The poor then, although provided for in the public and voluntary hospitals and under National Insurance, had an unhealthy and insecure existence and there were many gaps in the services designed to satisfy their needs. The middle-classes were the major source of finance and paid more than their fair share of doctors' fees and hospital bills. The rich voluntarily excluded themselves from some of the best hospital care, preferring instead the small private hospital or nursing home, with sometimes poor facilities and inadequately trained staff.

Pressure for reform came from the Labour Movement and from middle-class fears of medical costs. The organized medical profession, however, resisted further reform, as it had resisted the 1911 scheme, on the grounds that what was being advocated was a system of state-salaried doctors. The BMA opposed the wartime proposals for a national health service; the Labour government's Bill was accepted only after a lengthy opposition. The eventual terms were much more favourable to the BMA's position than the Labour Party had wanted – GPs were to remain independent contractors rather than salaried employees, and hospital doctors were permitted to combine private practice with employment in the NHS. However, the NHS radically altered personal health care in the UK, providing a universal, comprehensive service free at the point of delivery, therefore substantially extending health care provision across the UK through a national, publicly funded and provided service (see Chapter 3). Ironically, as health care became part of the collectivist welfare state, views about public health were shifting towards more individualistic perceptions and explanations about the causes of ill health. The medicalization of public health was a key feature of the post-war period – a situation accelerated with the shift of public health from local authorities to the NHS in 1974 (Baggott 2000).

The classic welfare state

The NHS was only one element of the reform that was undertaken in the 1940s, which resulted in a considerable extension of the state provision of welfare and was accompanied by a commitment to full employment. The aim was to eliminate Beveridge's 'five giants' – want, disease, ignorance, squalor and idleness (Timmins 1995). The main measures included: universal free primary and secondary education, the NHS, compulsory insurance benefit for all employees and self-employed to cover for unemployment, old age and disability, as well as non-contributory benefits for those not covered by insurance, local authority children's departments staffed by qualified social workers, and increased provision of council housing (see Box 2.4). However, the linchpin of providing for the welfare of the population was the commitment to full employment – paid employment for all adult men of working age who were fit to undertake it. It was thought at the time that the government could ensure this by economic policy and the provision of labour exchanges to ensure that those seeking employment could be put in touch with employers with suitable vacancies. As Lowe (1993: 99) indicates, *'the maintenance of full employment was both a direct contribution to individual welfare and an essential support for other welfare services, because it simultaneously maximized revenue and minimized demand for them'*.

The legislative period between 1946 and 1949 continued, rather than redirected, the legislation of the pre-war period, making the state provision of welfare more comprehensive and more rational, with a more coherent coordination of services. The commercial sector was not abolished; private schools, private health services and private insurances, for example, were not curtailed by the legislation. However, there was a national pooling of risk, with all those in paid employment making flat-rate contributions to the insurance schemes for unemployment, sickness,

> **Box 2.4 Main legislation of the 1940s**
>
> 1944 Butler Education Act
> 1945 Family Allowance Act
> 1946 National Insurance Act
> National Health Service Act
> 1947 Town and Country Planning Act
> New Towns Act
> 1948 Children Act
> 1949 Housing Act

maternity, widowhood and old age, and all receiving the same rate of benefit. Other state provision was funded out of general taxation, and given the progressive taxation system in Britain (tax increases with income) the better-off contributed relatively more than the less well-off to the provision of education and health services. There was also the safety net of means tested income maintenance for those who fell outside the insurance network (see Chapter 5). The voluntary sector also continued to play a role, and informal care played a significant part in meeting welfare needs (see Chapters 7 and 8).

The legislation, introduced in the 1940s, founded what has been called 'the classic welfare state', one in which the state took the major responsibility for organizing and delivering welfare services and maintaining full employment. Welfare was paid for mainly out of taxation and from National Insurance contributions, although the latter have never been sufficient to cover the costs of insured benefits. The welfare provision that was introduced was service-led and professionally dominated. It was assumed that experts knew the 'best' ways to organize and deliver services to meet the welfare needs of all citizens. There was a considerable degree of consensus about the desirability of the welfare state between the Conservative and Labour Parties, although there were dissenting voices in the Conservative Party.

Basically, the shape of the welfare state remained as established in the 1940s, with the expansion of some services – especially personal social services in the 1970s (following the 1968 Seebohm Report) – the building of new hospitals, reforms to the organizational structure of the NHS and the introduction of new income maintenance benefits. There was a shift in emphasis from the late 1950s from residential to community care (see Chapter 9). An unanticipated development was that the number of people dependent on non-contributory benefits, which Beveridge had anticipated would decline, actually increased. What had been intended as an 'interim measure' now provides for the largest proportion of welfare expenditure (see Chapter 4).

It was not until the election of the Conservative government to power in 1979 that the classic welfare state was fundamentally challenged. The Conservatives carried out a major programme of reform, critically reviewing all aspects of the welfare state. The programme of legislative reform was concerned with moving away from the state provision of welfare (though not necessarily from state funding for it), to target benefits and services at those most in need, to introduce commercial sector management techniques (the 'new managerialism') and to open up the provision of services to competition. The reforms were underpinned by a will to challenge collective provision and to encourage the mixed economy of welfare, but with the state retaining an increasingly regulating role (Wilding 1992). The state's role was in future to be one that set the framework and regulated welfare provision but it became increasingly less involved in direct provision (Powell 2000).

New Labour and the welfare state

As outlined in Chapter 1, the election of New Labour in 1997 marked an important shift in welfare policy. The new government did not sweep away or 'turn back' the reforms of the Conservative government but, incorporated many aspects of Conservative philosophy such as the responsibility of the individual and the increased role of the private sector. However, this was combined with a renewed commitment to tackling poverty, social injustice and social inequalities. The new welfare state programme was to be based on the philosophy of the Third Way (Giddens 1998; Powell 2000). This approach would see a new way of developing a welfare state that was not dominated by the paternalistic, centralized bureaucracies of the post-war welfare state, nor shifted to the uncertainties of the market (Powell 2000). Labour's programme aimed to recast the relationship between the citizen and the state and, central to this philosophy was strengthening the link between welfare and work, with an emphasis on opportunity with responsibility (Lewis 2004).

Much of the shape of New Labour's approach was visible in the report of the Commission on Social Justice, established by the Labour Party in the 1990s, while in opposition. The Commission provided a template of an 'Investor's Britain' (Commission on Social Justice 1994), which emphasized economic opportunity as the basis of social justice and economic prosperity. This would then provide security through investment, underpinning redistribution of *opportunities rather than ... income*' (p. 95). Pressure for reform of the social security and welfare system came from a number of important developments in society during the late twentieth century. These included:

- rising female labour force participation;
- increasing divorce and relationship breakdown;
- the growing number of lone-parent households;
- the shift from manufacturing to service employment;
- growth of part-time work;
- increasing longevity.

New Labour's rhetoric was imbued with the language of welfare reform, to modernize social security and welfare, to cope with the new social risks of post-industrial society (Taylor-Gooby 2004). The government drew on traditional welfare concerns and the concept of full employment. There was to be work for those who could work and security for those who could not. Social security was to be rebuilt around the work ethic (Deacon 2002). These ideas can be seen in the changes to the way financial support is given to families with the Child Tax and Working Tax Credits, the minimum wage and also changes in delivery structures, such as the replacement of job centres and social security offices with Job Centre Plus (Lewis 2004). Drawing on Giddens' idea of the Third Way (1998), New Labour was to put in place a social investment state. This had four key characteristics:

1 Linking economic and social policy.
2 An active preventive welfare state.
3 The centrality of work.
4 The distribution of opportunities rather than income.

The framework for New Labour's approach was set out in *A New Contract for Welfare* (DSS 1998) which stated that '*the Government is determined to build an active welfare system which helps people to help themselves and ensures a proper level of support in times of need*' (p. 16). These changes have been characterized as 'progressive universalism'. New Labour have developed a mix of targeted and universal benefits in an approach that attempts to build on the ideas of universal solidarity but which gives more help to the worst-off members in society. As mentioned in Chapter 1, the Child Tax Credit system, for example, gives benefit to the majority of the population (those earning less than £58,175 a year in 2006/07) but is on a sliding scale so that poorer families receive substantially more help (Kemp 2005).

Another key theme of New Labour's approach to welfare, has been the recasting of the debate about inequality into one of inclusion and exclusion. However, the key emphasis is on inclusion through paid work and education. Levitas (1998) has identified three discourses (ways that something is conceptualized, examined and debated) of social exclusion:

1 A redistributive, egalitarian discourse that embraces notions of citizenship and social rights.
2 A moralistic discourse that focuses on individual behaviour and values.
3 A social integrational discourse that focuses on social cohesion through employment.

The centrality of work also has implications for the position in society of people with disabilities. While there has been a clear acknowledgement of the existence of differences and diversity, the key problem is how to overcome such differences to enable 'those excluded from society' to breach the barriers that prevent people from 'becoming like us' (Powell 2000). Society is to be diverse, but inclusive. However, while the 'responsible' are to be included, the irresponsible (those that abuse the welfare system, fail to look after their own health or their children) will be subject to more authoritarian measures (Levitas 1998). The social integrational discourse, while inclusive, does incorporate '*old individualistic ideas about the causes of, and the solutions to, poverty*' (Heron and Dwyer 1999: 101) and individuals who do not do the right thing risk being excluded from the

state welfare system (Powell and Hewitt 1998). The shift from unemployment to the increasing numbers of people with a long-term illness has
been a particular concern of the government and, proposals in *A New Deal
for Welfare* (DWP 2006d) highlight the fact that while unemployment rates
have been falling, there has been a substantial growth in claims for incapacity benefit (see Figure 2.1). These proposals need to be seen alongside
measures promoting self-care and prevention, in *Choosing Health* (DoH
2004a) and *Our Health, Our Care, Our Say* (DoH 2006), which demonstrate
an increasing focus on ensuring that citizens take responsibility, while it is
accepted that: people may need help in doing this and; that the state
should support those who want to return to work or take responsibility for
supporting themselves.

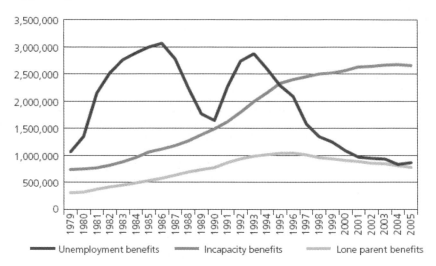

Figure 2.1   Numbers of people on benefits, 1979–2005
Source: Department of Work and Pensions, 2006

This distinction between 'deserving and undeserving' remains a key
focus for debate in current welfare policy. One strand of New Labour
thinking has been *communitarianism* and a focus on ideas of social inclu-
sivity. The role of the government is to ensure that people who need services or are members of society are not excluded from them or it. These
ideas are also key elements of the recent resurgence of *localism* – more local
control of services, a focus on neighbourhoods, more community
engagement. This approach is seen as a counterbalance to increasing
centralization and big government. In the last few years, government
ministers, such as John Reid, Alan Milburn and David Blunkett, have
advocated a more decentralized approach with a commitment, rhetorically
at least, to different shades of 'new localism', which has become a key
element of the government's strategy across a number of sectors including
local government, employment, the police and health (Pratchett 2004).

Since 1997, there has been a whole raft of area-based initiatives (health
and education action zones, neighbourhood renewal, Sure Start, single

regeneration budget areas) that have attempted to deal with social problems at a local level, bringing together local public and private organizations and local communities. Two principles have driven such approaches. The first is the recognition that social problems are complex and need to be addressed in a joined-up way (Glendinning *et al.* 2002). Second, tackling social exclusion requires a focus on where people live and work and how they relate to their local communities and services. Of particular interest has been the potential of *social capital*: the development of communities to address social inequality and social exclusion (Putnam 2000). This approach has not been without criticism (Navarro 2002) but fits well with New Labour's attitude to welfare and ideas of responsibility, although it may not sit easily with the idea of choice in public services (see Chapter 4).

Conclusion

In this chapter, we have considered the ways in which welfare has been provided, especially with respect to health services, during the nineteenth and the first half of the twentieth century. We have focused in particular on the ways in which the state came to be a major provider of welfare services during that period, including the debates as to whether and why the state should be responsible for the collective funding and provision of welfare services. Those who have advocated the state provision of welfare have not always done so for purely humanitarian reasons, but on grounds of national efficiency. We have explored this in relation to health, but it is equally true, for example, that the arguments for introducing and expanding state education have included the need to inculcate habits of industry and diligence in children and young people, enabling Britain to compete with its industrial rivals and not 'wasting' talent. Arguments for the state provision of welfare have, as often included reference to social control and meeting the needs of society, as reference to humanitarian concerns for the welfare of individuals.

The legislation passed in the 1940s laid down the framework for the state provision of welfare, that continues to underpin welfare provision to the present day. Most subsequent changes have taken place within that framework, although the future pattern of the welfare state is now on the political agenda (Gladstone 1995). Until 1979, when the first of Margaret Thatcher's administrations was elected, the main changes were to administrative structures and the extension of services; subsequently, the main changes have been in who actually provides welfare and the increased use of charging consumers for social care services. As we shall see in subsequent chapters, the main provider and funder of welfare services in Britain continues to be the state, although the informal sector continues actually to provide most welfare care. The roles of the commercial and voluntary sectors have become more prominent, with successive governments emphasizing the role they should and do play, and increasingly the state is purchasing services from these sectors on behalf of clients. The actual increase in the purchase of services from the commercial sector by individuals and families, apart from private pension plans, has been modest to date.

It is important to recognize, however, that the current New Labour government is committed to the development of alternatives to the state supply of welfare services, and is increasingly targeting those services supplied or purchased by the state at those most in need. New Labour have shifted the welfare debate but, as Powell (2000) has observed, many of the strands of New Labour's welfare state echo the past. The importance of work was a key element of the Beveridge post-war welfare state and even of the New Poor Law of the nineteenth century. New Labour's approach also builds on developments instigated by the Conservative governments in the 1980s and 1990s. The welfare state of the future will be increasingly pluralistic in nature, with benefits more work-focused, and a much stronger emphasis on individual responsibility. These points will be discussed in more detail in the following chapters. Equally though, there is a strong thread of ideas that can be linked to universalism and social solidarity, but these are expressed in terms of social inclusion and social capital. Currently a key challenge for the government is how universalism and solidarity can be sustained, in an environment where increasing choice is seen as a key component of social policy in areas such as health, education and social care and, where people are seen as consumers of public services (Clarke *et al.* 2005). Lewis (2003) has argued that this means that the difference (between individuals and groups in society) has been collapsed into diversity where people have equivalent but different needs and wants, rather than being positioned by structured and mainly unequal differences (Clarke *et al.* 2005) – an issue returned to in later chapters.

Summary

- This chapter has mapped the evolution of the welfare state in British social history, from the Industrial Revolution to the present day. It has used the example of the development of medical care provision to illustrate broader trends and influences affecting social policy.
- The chapter shows the important contribution of the mixed economy of welfare provision since the nineteenth century, in particular the contribution of voluntary sector hospitals and the dominance of the informal sector throughout British history.
- Through an analysis of health care policy, the chapter evidences the influence of political ideology on social policy, from a period of *laissez-faire* in the nineteenth century, to a period of concern about poverty (in the early twentieth century), both in terms of 'contagion' and its impact on public morality. This led to the development of social policies whose primary function was to control and reinforce certain patterns of social behaviour (such as the work ethic and 'normal' family relations).
- Post-war Britain witnessed the development of a political consensus during a period of social reconstruction resulting in more interventionist social policy, founded on principles of social justice and

> citizenship. This period saw the birth of the 'modern' welfare state. Using the example of the development of the NHS, this chapter has shown how institutional welfare provision may both promote social equality and reduce individual freedom, through increasing the powers of welfare professionals and new forms of regulation and surveillance.
>
> - The 1980s saw a return to *laissez-faire* principles under the policies of the New Right committed to monetarist economics, a 'return' to ideas about individual responsibility and the role of the welfare state in encouraging a dependency culture.
> - New Labour has attempted to reform the welfare state, drawing on ideas of personal responsibility and with a strong emphasis on welfare and work. There has also been an emphasis on the role of the State in addressing inequalities and social exclusion.

Further reading

Hill, M. (1993) *The Welfare State in Britain: A Political History Since 1945*. Cheltenham: Edward Elgar.

Jones, H. (1994) *Health and Society in Twentieth-Century Britain*. Harlow: Longman.

Jones, K. (1991) *The Making of Social Policy in Britain 1930–1990*. London: Athlone.

Lewis J. and Surender R. (2004) *Welfare State Charge: Towards a Third Way?* Oxford: Oxford University Press

Lowe, R. (1993) *The Welfare State in Britain since 1945*. London: Macmillan.

Powell, M. (1999) *New Labour, New Welfare State? The 'Third Way' in British Social Policy*. Bristol: Policy Press.

Thane, P. (1982) *The Foundations of the Welfare State*. Harlow: Longman.

Timmins, N. (1995) *The Five Giants*. Harmondsworth: Penguin.

HEALTH POLICY IN THE POST-WAR PERIOD

Introduction

This chapter focuses on recent health policy developments in the UK. However, it is important to understand these policy changes within the overall context of health policy over the last 150 years. This history has been amply dealt with elsewhere (Webster 1988, 1996, 2002; Ottewill and Wall 1991; Klein 2001) but it is useful to understand the background to the NHS in terms of the discussion in the previous chapter about personal and public health, the reforms leading to health insurance and public health measures, and how the NHS was established as part of the welfare state by the Labour government after the Second World War. In fact many of the policy developments since 1947 have been to address key tensions which continue to haunt the delivery of health care in the UK today, such as:

- the tension between central or local control and management;
- the tension between medical and management power;
- the tension between treating individuals and providing a population-based service within a capped budget;
- the tension between treatment and prevention of ill health.

In addition, each time a change is instigated to solve problems, it tends to throw up new problems due to unforeseen circumstances or failure of policy implementation to achieve what is desired. The last two decades have seen some fundamental changes in health care policy in the UK, which have had important implications for patients and those working in the NHS and social care organizations. However, these changes continue to reflect these basic tensions. Devolution and decentralization, key themes of current policy, highlight tensions between the centre (or now multiple centres) and local delivery of health care and public health. The recent debates about professional regulation, are at the centre of discussions about the role of managers and patients in health care, and about the introduction of patient choice, in various guises across the UK, demonstrating a continuing focus on individual patients. Yet at the same time there has been an increasing awareness of the limits of the NHS and the renewed focus on public health, prevention and self-care reflect a concern about both where responsibility lies for tackling health issues and, also the need to shift the NHS from a treatment service, to one that can support patients and the wider community. These themes are clearly set out in reviews of health care and public health in England, Wales, Scotland and Northern Ireland (Wanless 2003, 2004; Appleby 2005, Kerr 2005) and, in proposals for the English NHS set out in *Building on the Best: Choice, Responsiveness and Equity in the NHS* and *Choosing Health: Making Healthy Choices Easier* (DoH 2003a, 2004a).

This chapter discusses the broad sweep of policy since the establishment of the NHS after the Second World War and how developments, particularly since the 1970s, have led to current debates about the path of health policy in the UK today. The aim of the chapter is to set out broad themes relating to NHS policy developments and, the extent to which such changes represent a break from the past. The chapter also examines how wider changes to the welfare state have affected health policy.

The birth of the NHS

The NHS was a key plank of the post-war welfare reforms that created the welfare state. Poor health was one of five giants to be tackled by the welfare state and at the time, it was assumed that improved health care would lead to lower benefit costs and, eventually lower health care costs, as disease and ill health were tackled and eradicated (Timmins 1995). There was also a recognition that the previous health care system was uncoordinated and provided uneven cover. The experience of the war years demonstrated that it was possible to establish a national health service with central control which, in fact, established the regional system incorporated into the NHS in 1948. The reality, however, was that from the beginning, the NHS represented a compromise between competing forces and ideas and it has continued to consume increasing proportions of public expenditure. Nevertheless, the NHS has been seen as perhaps one of the greatest achievements of the post-war welfare state and established a service which was free at the point of access, universal (as it covered the whole population) and comprehensive in coverage. The achievement in providing health care for all, compared to the partial and patchwork health care service of the pre-war period, was enormous (Baggott 2004).

The architect of the NHS, Aneurin Bevan (the Minister for Health), had to accept a scheme about which he had doubts, concerning independent contractors (the GPs) and patients' freedom to choose the doctor they wanted, and also concerning the continuation of private practice. The need to extend health services to the dependants (primarily women and children) of the insured contributors (mainly men), and the need to provide hospital and GP care in those parts of the country (predominantly the poorer parts) where provision had been very thin, overrode the Labour Movement's doubts, so that legislation founded the health service that we have today, funded mainly out of general taxation.

The NHS, established in 1948, was under tripartite control (see Figure 3.1). Local authorities were responsible for community and public health.

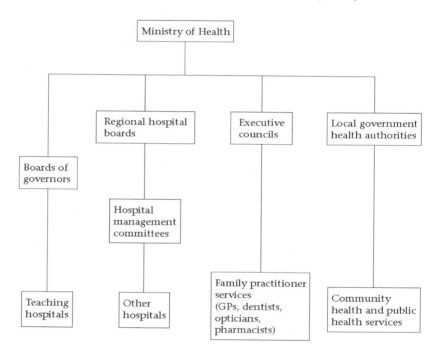

Figure 3.1   The structure of the NHS in England and Wales 1948–74

Executive councils made up of part-time appointees nominated by the Ministry of Health, the local authorities and the independent contractors themselves were responsible for GP, dental, ophthalmic and pharmaceutical services. Hospital services, with the exception of the teaching hospitals, were administered by Regional Hospital Boards (RHBs), responsible for the overall planning, coordination and supervision of services. Hospital Management Committees (HMCs) were responsible for the day-to-day running of local hospital services. Members of the RHBs were appointed by the Minister of Health after consultation with local authorities and the medical profession. HMC members were appointed by the RHB following consultation with local authorities, the medical profession and voluntary associations. The teaching hospitals were administered by boards of governors appointed by, and accountable to, the Minister of Health.

1950s to 1970s: growth and stability

The period of the 1950s and 1960s was one of expansion and renewal of health care services. Rapid budget growth in the first few years of the NHS, and the instigation of the Hospital Plan in the early 1960s (aiming to replace old, often Victorian hospitals in poor condition), set the course of health care development to the 1990s. There was a general consensus about the need for the NHS, despite the introduction of charges for prescriptions, dental and opticians' services. Over the next 30 years, the NHS remained a publicly-funded service that was comprehensive, universal and free at the point of access. The post-war settlement meant that doctors continued to have a key role in the organization and management of the service, with the government's role seen as supplying the funding. Klein (2001) has described this pact between the medical profession and the government as the 'politics of the double bed'. The policy focus was predominantly on the secondary care sector, so advances in medical technology and expertise led to enormous improvements in medical care in areas like heart disease and stroke, leading to improved survival rates. Other breakthroughs occurred in orthopaedics, especially joint replacement, cancer treatment and general surgery. These advances in medical technology created, however, a budgetary pressure and the demand for health care became predominantly driven by advances in medical care.

While hospitals and acute care remained the main focus of policy, there were important developments in primary and community care. The Doctors' Charter of 1965, led to an increasing interest in the quality of primary medical care and by the 1970s there were GP training schemes established (Moon and North 2000). Practices began to expand to deal with an increasingly aged population, and to provide services for those people who were now surviving acute illnesses due to improved care, but who the required ongoing medical treatment. Further expansion occurred in the 1970s and 1980s with the development of the primary health care team and the employment of an increasing range of health and administrative practice-based staff (Peckham and Exworthy 2003).

Cracks in the consensus

By the 1960s and 1970s there were increasing concerns about the quality of care provided – especially in the 'Cinderella' services, such as those for people with mental health problems, learning disabilities and older people (Baggott 2004). There was also the discovery that the NHS had, in effect, institutionalized many of the inequities of provision established before the war, in terms of availability of hospital beds and GPs, dictating how regional budgets were allocated. There was also continued concern about the organizational structure of the health service, in terms of communication and coordination, as well as its relationship with local government and welfare services. Finally, the government and the newly-expanding consumer health group sector (especially in the areas of mental health and physical disability), were increasingly concerned about the provider dominance of health policy.

These issues reflected a growing concern about the welfare state in general, with the rediscovery of poverty and the recognition that many of the problems that the welfare state had been set up to address, were still there (Timmins 1995). The growing complexity of social problems also created a pressure to revisit the delivery of services and, in particular, the division between health and social care services came under renewed scrutiny in the late 1960s. Two key developments were the growing pressure to unify health services and to develop social care services. The latter was achieved with the creation of social services departments in local authorities from 1972, following the publication of the Seebohm Report (Ottewill and Wall 1991). This brought all social care under local authority management, while moving public health and community health services to the NHS – a move widely seen as damaging the role of public health by further medicalizing the role of the public health physician.

These reforms also led to the establishment of Community Health Councils in 1974 (Community Health Boards in Scotland), to provide stronger local patient and public representation in the NHS and address ongoing criticisms about the lack of accountability within the NHS. In 1976, in response to wider concerns about the NHS, the Labour government established a Royal Commission to examine the funding and organization of the service (the Layburn Committee) and another committee to examine health inequalities under Sir Douglas Black (Townsend *et al.* 1992). However, both the Royal Commission and the Black Committee reported to a new Conservative government, which had very different views about the nature of society, the delivery of public services and the relevance of inequalities (Baggott 2004).

As discussed in the previous two chapters, the Conservative government of Mrs Thatcher elected in 1979, heralded major changes in the direction of welfare. While the NHS was initially unaffected by the new thrust of public service management and privatization, by the mid-1980s there were concerns about the dominance of provider-driven services and the power of the health professions. In addition, the rise of HIV and AIDS stimulated a new debate about public health and what the government's role should be (see Chapter 5). Finally there was also increased concern about the cost of social security payments arising from residential care – especially for older people – and an acceptance of the need for improved community care (see the next section and Chapters 6 and 7). Initial approaches to the NHS centred on improving the management and organization of the service, with Sir Roy Griffiths (the then chief executive of Sainsbury's) being commissioned to write a report on managing the NHS (DHSS 1983). His report was highly influential, leading to the introduction of general management, the development of business units (a key foundation for later reforms) and the increased use of patient satisfaction surveys (Baggott 2004). Rising public concern about NHS care, highlighted by media coverage of specific cases, led to an assertion from the Prime Minister that the NHS was 'safe in our hands' and the announcement of a review. This was an entirely internal review and the subsequent White Paper *Working for Patients* (DoH 1989a), set out a new approach to health care with the separation of purchasers (district health authorities) and providers (hospitals, community health services and other NHS providers which were already separate business units following the Griffths reforms). However, a unique development, in relation to the UK, was the establishment of GP fundholding, which let GPs hold a purchasing budget for their patients. The central idea was that money should follow the patient, as in a market, but this was an internal, or quasi-market, as it was between NHS organizations and essentially GPs acted as agents for their patients (Baggott 2004). It was this development and subsequent developments, such as multi-funds and total purchasing, that became key drivers in health policy in the UK and helped refocus attention away from hospital care to the concept of an NHS that was primary-care led, laying the foundations for the future (Le Grand *et al.* 1998; Peckham and Exworthy 2003; Baggott 2004).

The NHS and equity

The founders of the NHS envisaged a first-class health service for all. The service was to be funded out of direct taxation in order that the better-off classes contributed more towards its costs, while the poor, it was assumed, would benefit most. A Ministry of Health publication in 1944 stated that the aims of the NHS were '*to ensure that everybody in the country – irrespective of means, age, sex and occupation – shall have equal opportunity to benefit from the best and most up-to-date medical and allied services available. To provide, therefore, for all who want it, a comprehensive service covering every branch of medical and allied activity*' (Ministry of Health 1944: 47).

A leaflet circulated to every household in Britain in 1948, explained the purpose of the new health service: '*It will provide you with all medical, dental and nursing care. Everyone – rich or poor, man or woman or child – can use it or any part of it. There are no charges, except for a few special items. There are no insurance qualifications. But it is not a "charity". You are all paying for it, mainly as taxpayers, and it will relieve your many worries in times of illness*' (COI 1948).

The NHS was founded, then, on a principle of equity, and it was assumed that it would improve the health of the nation and more specifically of the poorer classes, who had previously had access to less comprehensive health care than the more advantaged classes who had been able to pay. It is certainly the case that the overall health of the population has improved since the NHS was introduced, although to what extent this is directly attributable to the service is more difficult to determine. Part of the general improvement in health is undoubtedly the result of improved living standards in Britain after the Second World War and elements of welfare provision other than the NHS itself. Indeed, Jones (1994: 53) has suggested that *'Good Health Services do not produce a fit and healthy population overall; they produce an aging population with a higher proportion of handicapped and infirm'*. Increasing longevity has become a key challenge to health and social care services and the changing socio-demographic and epidemiological profile of the UK population, has led to important changes in the way health services are organized (see below), but also the costs of old age care, an increasingly infirm group of older people and increases in the extent and range of long term conditions, have impacted on health and social inequalities (see Chapters 4 and 5). Tudor-Hart (1988) has also suggested that there is an inverse care law, where those in most need of health care receive less care, further exacerbating inequalities in health.

Despite increased spending on health care, there seems to be ever-increasing demand for more spending, partly because of the increasing proportion of elderly people in the population, partly because of advances (and higher than inflation cost increases) in medical science and particularly 'hi-tech' medicine (new equipment, specialist drugs), and partly because wage inflation (staffing costs) have been higher than the general growth in the economy. These issues have been particularly relevant in debates about why the NHS is in such a poor financial condition in 2005/6, despite record levels of investment by the Labour government in the preceding three years, (with some NHS organizations facing huge multi-million pound deficits), further exacerbating resource inequalities between different areas. There has also been a need, since the foundation of the NHS, to replace old hospital buildings and provide hospital and other services where the existing provision proved inadequate. The recognition in the early 1970s that the NHS had, to all intents and purposes, institutionalized inequitable patterns of provision that existed before the Second World War, was addressed through the Resources Allocation Working Party, which has gradually shifted resources throughout the UK, although not without some controversy, leading Powell (1997) to conclude that the NHS has largely failed to meet its goal of equity. This rediscovery of inequity (of service provision and use) and inequalities (of health outcome – see also Chapter 5) was closely associated with the rediscovery of poverty and a recognition of the link between poor health (particularly chronic ill health) and poverty (Townsend 1979).

From hospital to community

Current policy developments can also be seen as part of the continuing response to developments in health and welfare, which have been termed as the 'crisis in health' (Ham 2004). In the 1970s, there was an increasing recognition of a growing number of problems and issues facing health care systems in developed countries. While labelled as a 'crisis', this was not a single incident but the coming together of a range of factors. Many of the features of the 'crisis in health' were visible in all industrialized countries and had their roots in concerns about the rapidly escalating costs of health care (Saltman and Von Otter 1992), although the 'crisis' reflects concern about a range of issues of which those given in Box 3.1 are seen to be the most significant.

Box 3.1 Factors in the 'crisis in health'

- Demographic changes – the UK has an ageing population while at the same time a reduction in the proportion of the population of working age, leading to an increasing demand for health care at a time when health systems will be limited in their ability to respond to this demand.
- Epidemiological transition – a move from a major preoccupation with infectious diseases to one concerned with long-term conditions.
- Changing relationships between patients and health care professionals.
- Concern with social factors – the biomedical or curative approach to health is being questioned with a search for a broader approach which takes into account social factors, recognizes the harmful effects of the environment and shifts the emphasis onto prevention of ill health.
- Continuing concerns about inequalities in health and the recognition that these are deep-seated.
- The ever widening gap between demands made on health care services and the resources which the government is prepared to make available.

Part of the response to the 'crisis' was the recognition that changes in the epidemiology and demographics of disease (see Figure 3.2), required a different approach from one which focused on the delivery of acute care.

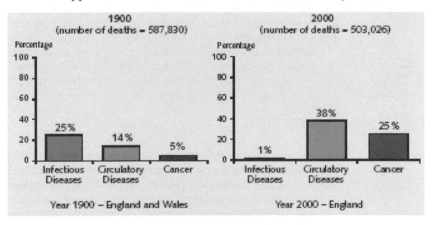

Figure 3.2 Shift from infectious to chronic diseases as the main causes of death over the last century. DoH (2004: 9)
Source: Brock and Griffiths 2003.

Thus in dealing with chronic illness and supporting older people, the role of general practice and community health services became more central. In the UK, the response was to develop general practice and primary health care teams. This led to an increasing engagement of government and the NHS in developing the quality and role of primary care (DHSS 1986, 1987; Ottewill and Wall 1991). There was also a retrenchment with an initial focus on high-spending hospitals but a recognition that control also needed to be exercised over the gatekeepers to the NHS, namely GPs.

Together with the financial pressures on the social security budget, the forces for change pushed the government to commission a report on community care from Sir Roy Griffiths (DHSS 1988). He identified severe weaknesses in the delivery of community care and recommended key changes to the organization and management of care, with a lead minister and making social services departments the coordinators and managers of care – transferring social security funding to these departments to develop packages of care based on the assessed needs of people. While politically unpalatable to the government who mistrusted local authorities, the recommendations were accepted and it published as the White Paper *Caring for People* (DoH 1989b) outlining its community care policy but also including a strong commitment to developing a market in community care services, pushing social services departments (SSDs) to contract with private and voluntary groups to provide home-based and residential care (Baggott 2004). Community care itself was not a new concept, as since the 1950s there had been a move to shift people with learning disabilities, out of large long-stay institutions and, this policy had been extended to other care groups (physical disability, mental health and older people), creating pressure for the development of community services, although progress towards this had been slow. The new community care arrangements attempted to provide a more coordinated approach to the closure of long-term institutions.

This process also led to an increasing overlap between primary and community care services, as more and more people were provided with care in their own homes. The issue of collaboration between health and social care agencies is not a new one but, there has been an increasing emphasis on health and social care partnerships since the 1990s (Lewis 2001; Glendinning *et al.* 2002; Rummery and Coleman 2003). The Labour government placed partnership at the community level, at the centre of its proposals and developments for the NHS and social services (Glendinning *et al.* 2002), leading to developments in primary care across the UK.

More recently, there has been a recognition that the NHS and social care agencies need to provide services and support, that help people to self-care and take preventive health measures (DoH 2004a, 2005a, 2006). Managing long-term conditions (chronic disease management) has also become a key element of new developments in health care, with the recognition that a small group of people consume the majority of health care resources. The British Household Surveys of 2001 and 2002 and the Health Survey for England 2001, suggest that over 50 per cent of the population have some form of chronic health problem. People with chronic disease are more likely to be users of the health system, accounting for some 80 per cent of all GP consultations, and 10 per cent of inpatients account for 55 per cent of inpatient days (British Household Panel Survey 2001). Older people are more likely to have multiple chronic problems and be intensive users of health care services – '15 per cent of under 5s and 20 per cent of the 5–15 age group are reported to have a long-term condition' (Wilson et al. 2005: 658). In addition, it is also estimated that as much as 40 per cent of general practice consultations and 70 per cent of accident and emergency (A&E) visits are for minor ailments that could be taken care of by people themselves (DoH 2005a). The Expert Patient Programme and patient support networks are one approach to this but, the recognition of the important role of carers and informal care has also been explicitly addressed by government policy since the mid-1990s (see Chapter 9). Central to all of these developments is the fact that the focus of care is more in the community rather than in hospital, and that health and social care need to support people at home as far as possible.

Primary care

The twentieth century saw the emergence of primary care as a specific area of health care, albeit dominated for the most part by general practice. However, this process was accompanied by a separation of the generalist model of primary care, from the specialist approach of secondary care services, formalized with the establishment of the NHS. This led to the independent practice status of general practice, outside of the mainstream NHS administration and, the retention of community and public health services within local authorities (Ottewill and Wall 1991; Timmins 1995; Klein 1998). This situation meant that the focus of government was primarily on hospital-based services in the new NHS and, health policy effectively overlooked the role of primary care (principally general practice) for nearly 40 years (Peckham and Exworthy 2003). This is not to say that these areas were ignored, as there has been a continuing debate within the UK about the relationship between community health and hospital services (Ottewill and Wall 1991) and, since the 1950s an interest in the development, quality and role of GP services (Moon and North 2000). Indeed, the GPs' gatekeeping role was considered vital to the functioning of the NHS. In many ways, other primary care professions (especially community nursing) experienced a similar separation from the rest of the health care system, by virtue of their distinctive professional development in local authorities. The integration of GPs and community nursing became most apparent with the effective development of primary care teams from the 1960s onwards, although the public health role of health visitors has not been well served by this (Moon and North 2000; Turton et al. 2000; Ottewill and Wall 1991; Peckham and Exworthy 2003).

While the managerialism of the 1980s and the internal market in the 1990s were seen as somewhat counter-intuitive to primary care teamwork, these two developments were instrumental in placing primary care medicine at the centre of health policy and had a pivotal role in the organization and management of health care (Peckham and Exworthy 2003). It is no surprise, therefore, that the 1990s witnessed the most concerted attempt to shape primary care through policy reform, in part because of the pressures and needs elsewhere in the NHS. This interest grew for a number of reasons but can be seen as arising from the coincidence of particular trends, as shown in Box 3.2 (Peckham and Exworthy 2003).

Box 3.2   Trends affecting the development of primary care

- Broader changes in the delivery of health care services associated with the 'crisis in health care' and the 'crisis of the welfare state'.
- An interest in the organizational relationship of general practice to the NHS, as the key to managing activity.
- A desire to extend managerial control over primary care and, following the failure of earlier cost-control measures, to engage GPs in financial management.
- The growth of 'new public management' and consequent changes in approaches to the management and organization of public services in order to curb expenditure, contain demand and increase efficiency and effectiveness.
- Changes in patients' expectations about being treated more promptly and closer to home.
- A fragmenting medical profession with changing professional expectations – especially for GPs – towards more flexibility in their working arrangements and career choices.
- The rise of professionals as managers and a desire to control the gatekeepers to the NHS, as general practice was seen as the last untouched bastion of clinical and medical autonomy.
- An increasing emphasis on localization and community-based services.

For much of the twentieth century, the government was wary about upsetting the medical profession (and particularly independent GPs), given their status within society and the power they wielded. However, with the rise of managerialism and the development of primary care purchasing in the 1990s, policies have made fundamental advances in shaping the organization and management of primary care. This has resulted in a wider and more inclusive definition of primary care (extending beyond the individual GP), a greater managerial role in what had been a professional enclave, and a more central role in meeting NHS objectives. General practice developments have also been supported by changes to the GP contract. Initially, this was an individual contract for medical services. From 1990, health promotion activities were added and with the development of primary medical services (PMS) contracts in the 1990s, new service developments (particularly the use of targets such as for heart disease) and new ways of thinking about primary care delivery were gradually developed on the ground and at a policy level (Peckham and Exworthy 2003).There have also been changes in the organization of primary care and the roles of health care practitioners, such as GPs and nurses and, though an increasingly inquisitive and sceptical public is placing more demands on practitioners, primary care has moved from the margins to the mainstream of health policy in the UK. In 2004, changes to the GP contract for general medical services, developed from PMS models, led to substantive changes in practice, with contracts now covering all principal GPs as a group rather than as individuals, and services split between core services (such as management of acute illness, chronic disease management and terminal care) and enhanced services – some of which are mandatory for each primary care trust (PCT) to organize (e.g. childhood immunizations), some of which are specialist (e.g. near patient testing) and others that are locally determined. In addition, a new performance framework which sets standards of practice was introduced and payment is made to the practice based on a mix of formula-based funding (the Carr Hill formula) and payment for the enhanced services.

In the UK, GPs have traditionally managed the care of their patients. They are the first point of contact for health care for the majority of the population, providing immediate health care to individuals and families and making referrals to secondary care (Fry and Hodder 1994; Starfield 1998). As Starfield notes, the UK system of general practice is the most universal and comprehensive in the world and although the distribution of GPs is unequal, with more patients per GP in more deprived areas (often single-handed in poor practice premises), it remains one of the most equitable primary care services in the world (Starfield 1998; Moon and North 2000; Peckham and Exworthy 2003). Thus, practices have a critical role to play in dealing with long-term chronic illness. Similarly, the UK has one of the most comprehensively developed community health services, which has increasingly become integrated with general practice. Interestingly, this integration combines both primary medical care and, to a certain extent, primary health care. Thus, the need to address changes in disease management, from mainly acute episodes to the management of chronic disease, placed a greater burden on primary care, contributing to the 'rediscovery' of the GP's role. At the same time, there have been significant changes in demand by patients, leading to pressure on consultation times, length of time waiting for an appointment and particularly out of hours work. The extent to which providers and patients contributed to this upturn in demand is not clear, however, nor is there any simple answer to dealing with these problems (Rogers *et al.* 2000). The situation is further exacerbated by the increasing introduction of performance targets in the general medical services, that reward more monitoring of patients with conditions such as diabetes, asthma, and hypertension. One result of the development of primary care is that from the 1960s, there has been a steady increase in the workload and consequently the numbers of staff. Today primary care is a major employer with over 100,000 people now working in general practice and over 40,000 additional members of the primary health care team who also work in, or with, practices (Peckham and Exworthy 2003).

The development of fundholding in the 1990s, total purchasing and primary care organizations arising from the Conservative government's introduction of the internal market, led to a clearer understanding of the important links between all community-based services and a drive towards closer partnerships with social care. The government's community care policy (DoH 1989b) also placed a greater emphasis on the need to work with community health services, particularly for people with mental health problems and those with a physical or learning disability. In addition, the increasing elderly population was placing greater demands on health and social care services and in an attempt to improve patient care, practices (especially fundholders) became interested in developing discharge processes and improving coordination between hospital discharge and community support services (Smith *et al.* 2004). This experience laid the foundations for primary care developments in England and Wales in the twenty-first century, with the development of primary care led commissioning and, in England, the introduction of practice-based commissioning, which are discussed further below (Peckham and Exworthy 2003).

New Labour's health policy

Since coming into office in 1997, the Labour government has placed priority on three policy areas which have impacted on health and health care in the UK. The first is *political devolution* to Scotland, Wales and Northern Ireland, with the emergence of four health services. The second is the *modernization* of the NHS, including organizational reform and an emphasis on standards and achieving clearly defined targets. Last, there has been a commitment to more *mixed approaches to coordination and service delivery* involving traditional NHS service structures, commissioning, developing the private and independent sectors, with increasing patient and public influence and engagement.

Devolution

Since the beginning of the NHS there have always been important differences in the organization and delivery of health care services between England, Northern Ireland, Scotland and Wales. Essentially England and Wales operated the same structure and organization, with Scotland having a similar structure, but with health boards rather than authorities, and Northern Ireland having combined health and social care departments. Many elements of the system were, however, the same including the GP system, role and location of public health, and delivery of community services. Since 1997 much has changed, with political devolution to the Scottish Parliament and Welsh Assembly and with political change now occurring in Northern Ireland.

The Labour government's political devolution has created the capacity for further spatial differences (Greer 2005). Moreover, other policies have supported greater diversity. The proposed NHS reforms, published in 1997 and 1998, incorporated different territorial policies. Although the capacity for policy diversity post-devolution will vary in each territory, some policy uniformity might be expected. On the one hand, in coming into power

New Labour stressed 'one nation' policies and greater uniformity through new institutions such as the National Institute for Clinical Excellence (NICE; England and Wales only) and the NHS Quality Improvement Scotland (although NICE guidelines are applicable to Scotland and the two organizations work together). The important role of NICE is underlined by the high media profile it has – especially regarding the sanctioning of use of new drugs (e.g. Herceptin in 2006) and its influence on services (such as choice in maternity services and place of birth in 2006). NICE guidelines are sent to all NHS trusts and, while not mandatory, it is expected that trusts take the guidelines into account. Details of all guidelines and how they are developed are on the NICE website (www.nice.org.uk). On the other hand, the government emphasized local targets and local responses to particular circumstances, for example, through developments in primary care. Political devolution has continued to increase diversity as it allows greater policy experimentation but, it may also facilitate uniformity through 'policy transfer' – the sharing of policy developments between one country and another (Dolowitz *et al.* 1999). However, while the impact of policy proposals upon *existing* systems is only emergent, devolution is likely to unleash a dynamic whose long-term impacts are currently unknown (Jervis and Plowden 2003).

Currently the Department of Health (DoH), for England, is the responsibility of the Secretary of State for Health, whereas elsewhere, responsibility lies with the Secretary of State for each territory. The DoH (in London) takes responsibility for UK-wide issues and for international health policy issues, such as liaison with the EU (Hunter 1998a; Jervis and Plowden 2000). This division of responsibilities is liable to change as devolved territories renegotiate their relationships within and outside the UK.

Scotland already enjoyed considerable administrative devolution, which is now complemented by political devolution, to the Scottish Parliament (Hazell and Jervis 1998: 31). The White Paper (Secretary of State for Scotland 1997) envisaged '*greater flexibility … over the pace and detail of the primary care changes*' (Hunter 1998b: 11). Hazell and Jervis (1998) foresaw the possibility that the Scottish Parliament could introduce radical changes, such as adding greater democratic input into health care commissioning or ending the independent contractor status of GPs and measures adopted in Scotland (e.g. the introduction of free personal care and student grants), have demonstrated that the Scottish Parliament is determined to set its own political course. In particular the decision to provide long-term care, free of charge, has had political and service ramifications across the whole of the UK, not just in Scotland.

The Welsh Assembly is responsible for allocating NHS expenditure in Wales but has no law-making powers. However, it can introduce structural changes (such as transferring powers to the Assembly itself) (Hazell and Jervis 1998: 34) or reorganizing health care organizations as it has been doing over the last five years. The Assembly cannot pass primary legislation and will have no tax-raising powers. However, by passing secondary legislation, it can '*dictate the detail of health policy*' (Whitfield 1998: 15). The NHS in Wales, underwent revision before the Assembly, was established by reducing the number of Trusts in Wales from 26 to 16 in April 1999

(Garside 1999). The Assembly was given a central role in health policy; for example, health authorities are held to account by it. The White Paper *A Voice for Wales* (Secretary of State for Wales 1997) defined its health remit as monitoring the health of the population, determining the scale of financial resources for health and the identification and promotion of good practice (para. 2.1). (This complements earlier innovations in e.g. health promotion services). In February 2001, *Improving Health in Wales* was published which proposed the abolition of heath authorities in Wales by April 2003 (NHS Wales 2001). The National Assembly was to take '*direct democratic control for its responsibilities providing leadership, direction and oversight through a newly-created Health and Well-being Partnership Council, which would be chaired by the Minister*' (NAW press release, WO1123, 2 February 2001). The Assembly has taken a stronger role in health policy and the local health board (LHB) structure, developed in Wales, has a stronger partnership focus than in the English PCTs. There is also a Welsh public health body responsible for coordinating public health activity across all LHBs. However, there has been recent criticism of the Welsh NHS performance, in comparison to England, as waiting times and other performance measures are substantially poorer (Audit Commission 2004; Healthcare Commission 2005).

Interestingly, both the Welsh Assembly and the Scottish Parliament have emphasized the development of public health measures and there are clear differences in the approach to public health in England, Scotland and Wales despite a similar emphasis on reducing health inequalities and tackling key public health problems. Historically, both Scotland and Wales have suffered poorer health status than England – particularly in the major industrial areas of southern Scotland and Wales. Thus, the increased focus on public health is not surprising. Differences in public health policy are characterized by the different approaches to partnership working and the development of public health practitioners, and the Scottish Parliament has passed legislation banning smoking in public that came into force in 2006, while in England only a partial ban is to be put in place.

Modernization

There is no one definition of modernization and it has frequently been used as a general term to describe organizational and service delivery changes in health care services. Each of the four NHS organizations has been pursuing organizational and structural change as a way of improving performance and patient care. The approaches between the four countries differ to a certain extent, with England focusing more on managerial changes, developing commissioning at a local level and introducing market-type approaches. Labour policy was initially developed in England with two White Papers, *The New NHS* (DoH 1997) on NHS organization and *Saving Lives: Our Healthier Nation* on public health (DoH 1999a), mirrored in Scotland and Wales with similar proposals for organizational change and public health development (NHS Scotland 2000; NHS Wales 2001). These were followed up in 2000/1, with development plans for each of the four countries and the development of a modernization strategy for the

NHS, which built on the White Papers. One key change was a shift away from competition within an internal market, introduced in 1991, to an approach based on partnership between agencies, while retaining the essential distinction between purchasers (health authorities and primary care organizations) and providers (hospitals and community health services) – although as will be discussed later, elements of the market have been retained and are now further developed in England. The other major change has been the increasing impact devolution has made on the shape of the NHS, with distinctive differences in policy development in Scotland and Wales. For example, in Wales there are 22 LHBs in addition to local commissioning partnerships; public health is led centrally under the direction of the Assembly. In England, organizational focus is on PCT size and coverage, reducing the number of strategic health authorities (SHAs), development of a new market with private sector service providers, practice-based commissioning (PBC), Foundation Trusts, payment by results (PbR) and patient choice. Nevertheless, there are important continuities of policy across the home nations which have focused on the development of primary care organizations, improved management performance, an emphasis on increasing quality through improved management systems and accreditation and, a focus on a national service with national standards brought about in England, through the instigation of national service frameworks (NSFs).

Coordination and service delivery

As previously mentioned, there has been an increasing focus on commissioning and the introduction of market-style mechanisms – especially in England. However, at the same time there has been an emphasis on partnership at an organizational level, joined-up policy at a national level and inter- and multi-professional practice in service delivery (including developing organizational and professional networks). Alongside these developments, all four home countries have retained a strong element of centralized control through the development of performance frameworks and through retaining control of funding. However, the NHS has moved in all countries (especially England) to more decentralized processes for managing health care, with a distinction between commissioners (those who pay for health care) and providers (those who deliver it). The exception is where primary care professionals (in England especially, but also in Wales) are also commissioners of care in LHBs, PCTs and in commissioning practices, where they engage with secondary care physicians about the individual care of the patient.

Before examining the key policy issues, the NHS currently faces, it is worth briefly reviewing the development of health services in each of the four countries.

The NHS in England

The publication of *The New NHS* White Paper (DoH 1997) in the autumn of 1997 set out the foundations of the new government's approach to the NHS in England, and was closely followed by a public health White Paper (DoH 1998a). *The New NHS* proposed to tackle the 'unfairness', 'unacceptable variations' and 'two-tierism' of the Conservative internal market (Powell and Exworthy 2000). It was followed later by *The NHS Plan* (DoH 2000a) and then by proposals for strengthening primary care commissioning and provision.

Partnership was also a central theme of *The New NHS* and the government was keen to support the development of partnership as an alternative to the internal market. This approach was emphasized as a 'Third Way': neither central planning (hierarchy) nor the internal market. It included developing local health economies and long-term service agreements between purchasers – PCTs and new care trusts (CTs) – and providers – hospital and specialist service trusts, other PCTs and provider CTs. The government also signalled a major investment plan in the NHS and stated its intention to modernize the service, improve standards and the quality of care. The health and social care system was to be shaped around the needs of the patient, not the other way round. There was to be an increased emphasis on developing partnerships and cooperation at all levels of care – between patients, their carers, families and NHS staff; between the health and social care sector; between different government departments; between the public sector, voluntary organizations and private providers in the provision of NHS services. Proposals included new approaches to partnerships to provide improved care for older people, especially by supporting intermediate care, developing 'one stop shops' (integrated health and social care services) and new children's trusts – combined health, education and social care organizations.

The framework for these developments was established in *The NHS Plan* (DoH 2000a) which has essentially provided the framework for current developments, such as increased decentralization to primary care, increased pluralization of services and greater patient choice. There was also a strong emphasis on the quality of services and proposals outlined in the *Plan* included new national standards, greater performance management, improved clinical governance and new national organizations to support high quality care (e.g. NICE) and, to ensure standards are maintained by service providers. The government also signalled its intent to support staff through additional education and training and, to expand the number of doctors and nurses. By 2003 it was reporting the additional employment of nearly 6000 doctors and 400 GPs (short of the target of an extra 2000), some 20,740 nurses and 2500 allied health professionals. However, financial problems in 2005/6 brought this expansion to an abrupt halt (see Chapter 10). Many of the new staff were recruited from overseas, raising concerns about international migration of health staff and the impact on developing countries. Change was driven by a new Modernization Agency (now the NHS Institute for Innovation and Improvement), which together with local modernization committees, led change throughout the service. Much of its work was based on using examples of 'good practice' within the NHS, such as NHS 'beacons' and through the use of 'pioneers', with lessons rolled out to the rest of the NHS. This approach has been evident in the Booked Admissions Programme, the collaboratives in cancer, orthopaedics, primary care and other services, and the 'Action On' initiatives for cataracts, ENT, dermatology and orthopaedics. In addition, numerous DoH documents now use brief 'case studies' to illustrate desired behaviour, although there is little indication of *how* they are to be used.

Building on the *NHS Plan*, the new five-year plan (DoH 2005b) emphasized shifting power from the centre – described by the Prime Minister as finding the balance between 'individual choice and central control'. These themes have been further developed in government policy on prevention, self-care, patient choice, practice-based commissioning and direct payments – where, for example, people with disabilities have been given funding to design and purchase their own packages of care (DoH 2005c, 2006). The government is committed to allowing patients a greater say in their own health care, for example, by choosing or sharing in the decision about where they should be treated, what kind of treatment to have or who should carry it out. Not only is it seen as right that patients should have such involvement, but that such a policy has beneficial consequences, for instance, making patients feel more satisfied because they get services which suit their needs better, improving the general quality of health services because of competition between providers or enhancing equity by giving more choice to those who have been disadvantaged in the past. This is perhaps the clearest attempt yet at 'market consumerism' (Greener 2004). This model, outlined in various policy documents (DoH 2000a, 2002a, 2003a, 2004a, 2005b), has also been supported by professional and consumer groups as it gives greater choice to consumers, though acknowledging that there are limits to, and adverse consequences of, choice (NCC 2004). PbR and developing a more pluralistic system of health care providers are seen by the government as providing the mechanisms through which patient choice will drive up the quality of care. It is assumed patients will choose hospitals providing the best quality care and that this will stimulate competition among health care providers to attract patients. However, the process of choice is dependent on a range of factors including knowledge and information, travel time, patient characteristics and the perceived reputation of local providers (Exworthy and Peckham 2006; Newman and Vidler 2006).

Similarly, public health policy sets out a strategy based on individual responsibility, rights and obligations, to others with state intervention (e.g. banning smoking in public places) only where necessary (DoH 2004a). Shifts to practice-based commissioning and the setting of national tariffs are key steps to opening up the English NHS to a wider range of providers, with the expectation that new private and voluntary sector agencies will enter the market. In addition there have also been proposals for developing new kinds of social enterprise organizations, run by doctors or nurses, that will move from the NHS into new contractual organizations (DoH 2006).

Klein (2005: 51–2) has argued that the NHS is moving towards '*a pluralistic, quasi-market model driven by consumer choice and shifting power to the periphery, where the role of central government increasingly becomes regulatory rather than managerial: setting priorities and targets, but allowing discretion in the way these are achieved'.* NHS policy is currently at a point of rapid development with a strong central drive towards a new, although not always clear, modernization programme. Two things appear to be happening at the moment which at first glance seem to be diametrically opposed. The first is the emphasis on decentralisation and devolution, with responsibility for the day-to-day running of the NHS shifting away from central government to front-line clinicians/managers within primary care organizations and the new providers in the private and independent sectors. There are also moves that appear to strengthen local accountability (such as Patient and Public Involvement Forums, lay involvement, foundation trust membership and the health scrutiny function of local authorities). However, such developments seem to remain at the mercy of whims by ministers and the DoH – for example, the abolition of the Commission for Patient and Public Involvement in Health or the action of the Foundation Trust Regulator (Monitor) which dismissed trust boards in Bradford and Sussex in 2005. At the same time, central government is also applying more central control on standards and quality through centrally-determined performance frameworks, suggesting that despite rhetoric that advocates decentralization the NHS, in England, has not escaped the yoke of central control. Thus, we will continue to see increasing diversity in organizational structure in the future (see Figure 3.3), including the development of market-type mechanisms such as patient choice, but clearer goals regarding standards, performance and quality of care, with nationally-driven guidelines and national inspection, all emphasizing a national health service to justify substantial increases in investment during the early years of this century.

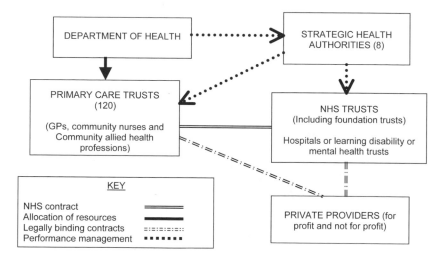

Figure 3.3 The structure of the English NHS

There still remains a tension between the moves to fragment and decentralize and the desire, and in some cases need, to retain central control – issues the service has been grappling with since the inception of the NHS in 1948. An example is the provision of community health services, which were incorporated into local primary care organizations (Peckham and Exworthy 2003) – but may now be removed, with debates raging about whether they should be privatized (DoH 2005b).

The financial crisis in the NHS in 2005/6 is a good example of where central government felt compelled to take strong executive steps to address financial deficits in some NHS trusts and PCTs. In addition, there was the imposition of national contracts for consultants (across the UK), centrally negotiated contracts for GPs and some services, with the reorganization of PCTs and SHAs, creating fewer, larger organizations. There was also the centralization and concentration of performance monitoring in the Healthcare Commission, moving policy in a different direction. In addition, the continuing development of NSFs, evidence-based medicine and national guidelines (through NICE) emphasize the importance of central approaches to standard-setting which restrict individual professional freedoms to practise and local variances in service delivery.

The NHS in Northern Ireland, Scotland and Wales

While there are clear similarities in policy proposals across the UK, such as the focus on primary care organizations, drawing clinicians into management and policy development, emphasizing partnership and developing national standards, there are still some very distinct and interesting differences. The establishment of the Wales Assembly Government and the Scottish Parliament had significant impacts on the structure of the NHS. Welsh organizational structures (see Figure 3.4) have resulted in LHBs matching local authority boundaries with broader LHB membership than

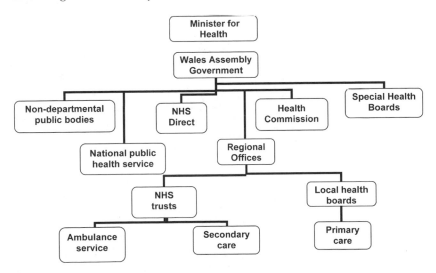

Figure 3.4   The structure of the Welsh NHS

in either England or Scotland. In Scotland, partnership arrangements are being developed through interorganizational arrangements rather than by unifying health and social care.

In Wales the emphasis on partnership has been particularly strong with collaboration formalized through membership of LHBs but also in approaches to integrated community and hospital services, such as in Powys (one of the largest Welsh counties). Key differences are also emerging regarding public health with the Welsh Assembly and Scottish Parliament placing more emphasis on this area of work, and with the Assembly government in particular taking a stronger role in addressing public health issues. For example, one important policy strand, set out in *Improving Health in Wales* (NHS Wales 2001), is the reduction of health inequalities. Another is the emphasis on 'localism' that is reflected in the decentralized LHB commissioning arrangements and closer links with local government. Some commentators (e.g. Greer 2004) have suggested that the stronger Welsh focus on health promotion and prevention has been introduced at the cost of relative neglect of the acute sector. Certainly, recent data on waiting times and ambulance response times appear to show Wales lagging well behind England in terms of performance (Audit Commission 2004). These problems have been directly addressed in *Designed for Life*, the current NHS plan for Wales, but concerns remain about the comparative poor performance of the Welsh NHS compared with England (Wales Assembly Government 2005).

Scotland has also seen substantial reorganization of the structure of the NHS, although to a lesser degree than in England (NHS Scotland 2000). A key difference is that the health boards, now unified boards, were retained as the main commissioners of health care, rather than shifting this function to primary care organizations. Within the unified boards there are operational divisions for aspects of the service, such as the primary care division that deals with GP contracts. Within each board area, there are community health partnerships that bring together general practice, community services and local authorities, to develop partnership working at a local level (see Figure 3.5).

By contrast, there has been little change in Northern Ireland, which has joint health and social care boards, rather than separate NHS and social care agencies. This structure is still largely intact and the boards commission health and social care from health and social care trusts of which there are 17. In addition, there are 15 local health and social care groups that bring together local health professionals, which were established to replace fundholding. These groups are committees of the health social care boards (See Figure 3.6).

This integrated approach between health and social care has been a long-standing feature of the system in Northern Ireland and, is seen to bring benefits in management and organization of care, although not all problems of partnership or integrated care have been overcome by this arrangement (Heenan and Birrell 2006).

Governments in Northern Ireland, Wales and Scotland have not been so determined to widen choices of service providers and have tended not to be in favour of introducing a consumer market approach. In Wales, the NHS plan identified the need to develop health services that comply with

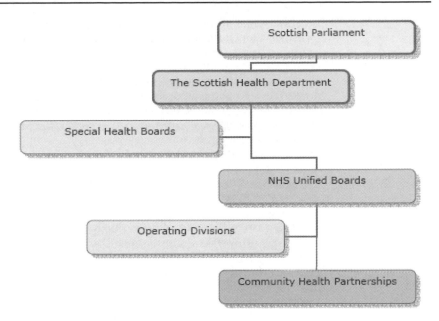

Figure 3.5 The structure of the Scottish NHS

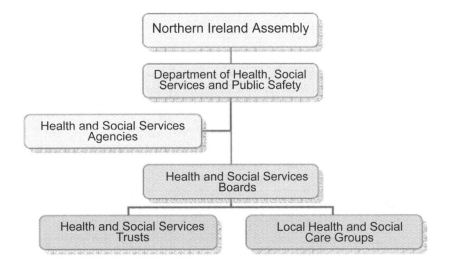

Figure 3.6 The NHS in Northern Ireland

patient preferences and there is the Second Offer Scheme where patients can be offered a second choice of treatment and/or location if they have waited for more than each of the national waiting time targets (generally 18 months, but 8 months for cardiac treatment and 4 months for cataracts). However, the Welsh Choice Scheme is centrally driven and is specifically

aimed at reducing waiting times, following criticism about the poor performance of the Welsh health care system (Wanless 2003; Audit Commission 2004). In Scotland, there has been an emphasis on patient choice
of secondary provider, facilitated by the establishment of the National
Waiting Times Database, to provide service users and their GPs information on which GP referral decisions can be based. In Northern Ireland, the
opportunity for choice is more limited given the size of the health system,
although it is proposed to introduce a Second Offer Scheme similar to that
in Wales (Appleby 2005).

While England has pursued a path of choice for patients, the emphasis in
Wales has been to 'empower the community to have its voice heard and
heeded, rather than simply being given a choice of treatment location'
(NHS Wales 2005). Thus, in Wales, patient and public involvement is seen
as central to the wider choice agenda. In Scotland, NHS boards are legally
required to involve members of the public in decisions about service
planning and, at the community health partnership level, there are public
partnership forums. Involvement by patients and the public is monitored
by the Scottish Health Council. This emphasis on engagement and
involvement provides a clear distinction between these countries and
England. However, the pressure to develop patient choice is strong and in
Scotland and Northern Ireland recent reviews have discussed the potential
for developing more patient choice (Appleby 2005; Kerr 2005).

The current context

As we move into the twenty-first century, we continue to see governments
grappling with what are somewhat traditional concerns of health care
policy – the funding and organization of health care systems – with a major
English review for the Treasury (Wanless 2001, 2002) and reviews in
Northern Ireland (Appleby 2005), Scotland (Kerr 2005) and Wales (Wanless
2003). In addition, governments across the UK are trying to improve
quality, tackling issues of accountability and addressing the roles and
regulation of health care professionals. Wanless (2002) described a vision
of a high quality health service in which a high level of clinical care is
delivered and the rising expectations of patients and the public are met. In
order to assess future resource needs of the NHS, he outlined three scenarios in the progress towards this vision: *solid progress*, *slow uptake* and
fully engaged (Wanless 2002: 35–41). While the focus of his report is on
health care, Wanless highlights the importance of a public health
approach (ultimately leading to his review of public health in 2004). Two
elements are essential if either the *solid progress* or *fully engaged* outcomes
are to be achieved. The first is progress towards achieving public health
goals on reductions in smoking, obesity, poverty and inequalities in
health; the second is the extent of public engagement, supported by
greater access, improved information and more involvement in health
care. The report concludes that the continuing development of NSFs across
the whole of the NHS will be central to improving the quality of services
over the next 20 years. Public health, and the emphasis on developing the

public health responsibilities of all staff, are key elements of the existing NSFs – an emphasis that is likely to continue.

Essentially all these reviews commit the UK to maintaining a publicly-funded NHS, free at the point of delivery to the public. While there has been some erosion of the free element (e.g. dental and optician charges, long-term care and prescription charges), this suggests that the founding principles of the NHS remain as relevant today as they did in 1948. Governments have therefore tended to focus on how the system is organized, in an attempt, to improve the efficiency and effectiveness of the service and there is no reason to see this changing. However, it is likely that significant changes relating to the way public services are structured and delivered – particularly with the development of non-public sector providers and increased choice for service users (discussed in Chapter 2) – will affect the NHS in significant ways. In addition, changing demography and epidemiology create enormous challenges for the delivery of health services. These include a greater emphasis on self-management of long-term conditions (see Chapters 6 and 9), an increasing emphasis on prevention, developing public participation ('voice': is a term commonly use to represent the ability of service users or consumers to complain or influence the way they receive services or goods), and patient choice ('exit': the ability of service users to choose an alternative service) in order to be more responsive to patients and users (see Chapter 9), and changes in professional practises and roles coupled with increasing regulation (see Chapter 10).

Increasingly, primary care organizations across the UK are becoming involved in a wider range of activities that encompass an ever-expanding range of primary care activities that move beyond traditional concepts of NHS primary care – the GP and the primary health care team – to include a range of community health services, community dentistry, pharmacy and public health. These developments have brought new practitioners into primary care. There is also an increasing diversification of organizational arrangements, often including the private and voluntary sectors. For example:

- healthy living centres;
- walk-in centres;
- telephone services (e.g. NHS Direct);
- one-stop shops;
- welfare advice services (such as Citizens' Advice Bureaux).

In addition there are an increasing number, and range, of private and independent practitioners who work in the community and provide first contact services to individuals and their families, such as complementary and alternative medicine (CAM) practitioners and private physiotherapists and counsellors. Again these practitioners work across the private, public and voluntary sectors and increasingly there is a blurring of the boundaries between them. These developments raise important questions about the nature of primary care itself and also about how this changing environment needs to be managed to maximize benefits for people's health.

New services, such as walk-in centres and NHS Direct, offer additional points of access to the NHS. Studies suggest that NHS Direct tends to provide an additional level of service, used predominantly by younger people, parents of young children – who use the service for reassurance in the evenings and at weekends when other services are not available – and older people who use the service during out-of-hours but for more serious complaints (Munro *et al.* 2000; Payne and Jessop 2001). The number of people contacting NHS Direct has increased from 1.65 million in 1999/2000, to 6.32 million in 2002/3 with an increase of 1.4 per cent in the number of contacts in the first half of 2003/4 (DoH 2003b). Walk-in centres have also added another route for consultations and, in 2002/3 1.373 million people attended the 42 centres in England, with figures for the first half of 2003/4 showing a growth in consultations of 14.3 per cent over the same period for the previous year. These consultations are in addition to the estimated 261 million consultations with GPs per annum in the UK, equivalent to roughly five visits per person per year.

There has also been an enormous growth in the range and availability of CAM practitioners. Some of these have long-established practices – such as acupuncture, herbalism and homoeopathy. More recent developments, such as chiropractic and osteopathy, are now considered mainstream provision and have regulatory general councils with statutory recognition. There is also a wider range of practices including aromatherapy, hypnotherapy and faith healing (Zollman and Vickers 1999). Of these, only homoeopathy has any formal recognition within the NHS, with five homoeopathic hospitals (London, Bristol, Glasgow, Tunbridge Wells and Liverpool) operating within the NHS since its inception, but the relationship between CAM and the NHS is becoming increasingly more complex.

While the values of the NHS remain the same as those established in 1948, what many people find strange is the fact that many of the problems of the 1940s remain, and today many of the issues that policy seeks to address are similar to those that were under discussion in the 1940s. These relate to the role of the medical profession and how accountability is built into the system, the stronger emphasis on cure than prevention, whether the NHS should be run centrally or locally, who should run the NHS (politicians, professionals, managers) and the relationship with the patient or service user and carers. The NHS also has many enduring features that have created problems over the years including inequalities in provision and access, rigid professional boundaries with a hierarchal clinical structure, poor buildings (often in the wrong locations) and a strong focus on individual medicine. There has also been a long-recognized deficit of underfunding which, while being addressed by increased funding in the first years of the twenty-first century, does not make up for lower funding (by comparison with other developed countries) from the mid-1960s. Finally, health is becoming more international. More people are travelling across the world, creating new contexts for public health and treatment. For example, there are increasing international movements of health professionals (especially from developing to developed countries, such as the UK and USA), faster communication (so that ideas and new technologies, especially drugs, are more easily known about) and a growing recognition of the important role of the private sector in all aspects of health care (which can bring benefits but also creates new problems and tensions). There is a need, therefore, for the UK to engage in international health policy at a European and world level, to develop common standards (such as for professional practice), regulatory frameworks and agreements (e.g. relating to pharmaceuticals, health care and professional migration) to collaboration on issues of public health.

Conclusion

The post-war history of health policy is fundamentally one dominated by the development of hospital-based acute care. This placed consultants and specialist medical care at the heart of health services. Since the 1970s there has been a shift, based on the recognition of the shortcomings of acute services and the need to address new long-term health conditions. Thus, the current emphases on self-care and prevention are clearly major issues that health policy will continue to address in the foreseeable future. However, while the need to address long-term health conditions, support prevention and self-care is widely accepted, the difficult task continues to be reorientating the NHS and medical practice away from hospital and acute-based practises. This creates real challenges for the NHS, in terms of the way it is organized, who should deliver care and what kind of relationship needs to be developed with patients and carers, the public, non-NHS health care providers and (increasingly) CAM practitioners (see Chapters 6, 7, 9 and 10).

While diversification through devolution is a key component of health policy in the UK, there remain strong unifying structures such as professional groups. In addition, the close proximity and links between the four countries have a strong unifying pressure. Policies adopted within one country will clearly be publicized and discussed in the other countries. Patient choice is a good example of this, taking a key place in the reviews in Northern Ireland and Scotland (Appleby 2005; Kerr 2005). Other policy initiatives in individual countries have also sparked fierce debate such as the abolition of charges for long-term care (Scotland), reducing the cost of prescriptions (Wales) and the use of targets (England). Thus, new tensions have been introduced into the NHS system. It is no longer a national NHS but a series of national NHSs, that on the one hand provide for experimentation and diversity but on the other retain a strong centralist tendency.

Summary

- Devolution has created substantial differences in the organization of the NHS between England, Northern Ireland, Scotland and Wales.
- Governments are pursuing major organizational changes to the NHS which seek to involve professionals, change working practises, involve patients/public, decentralize decision-making and establish national standards of quality of care.
- Management responsibility for the NHS is being moved away from

central government to devolved elected assemblies and primary care
organizations.

- There has been a renewed emphasis on public health, although there
  are concerns about how far the NHS can develop a public health
  approach, and whether sufficient resources will be dedicated to this –
  especially given the financial problems of 2005/6.
- There is a shift towards a wider range of providers with a growing
  private sector involvement in the delivery of services.
- Patient choice is a central feature of the Labour government's health
  policy developments.

Further reading

Baggott, R. (2000) *The Politics of Public Health*. Basingstoke: Macmillan.

Baggott, R. (2004) *Health and Health Care in Britain*, 3rd edn. Basingstoke:
    Palgrave Macmillan.

Klein, R. (2001) *The New Politics of the NHS*. London: Longman.

Peckham, S. and Exworthy, M. (2003) *Primary Care in the UK: Policy,
    Organisation and Management*. Basingstoke: Palgrave Macmillan.

POVERTY, INEQUALITY AND SOCIAL POLICY

- Introduction
- Social divisions and social diversity
- Poverty
- Inequality
- Implications for policy
- Universalism, selectivity and social security
- Poverty and inequality in the UK today
- Conclusion
- Summary
- Further reading

Introduction

While the last chapter specifically examined developments in health policy and the NHS, this chapter examines poverty and social inequality and how the state has responded to these in the post-war period. The discussion is set within the context of social diversity and difference, drawing on the concepts introduced in Chapters 1 and 2. In Chapter 1, we demonstrated how attitudes about the role of the state in social policy reflect perspectives on the causes of social problems. We also saw how different explanations of the causes of social problems reflect ideologically motivated perspectives on the extent and nature of any state intervention. These are recurrent themes in this chapter.

The chapter begins by considering social diversity and social inequality, examines competing definitions of poverty and some of the problems of measurement. The chapter also examines the incidence and distribution of poverty and inequalities in Britain. The links between poverty, inequality and social exclusion are explored. The chapter then goes on to examine how the state has responded to these issues, through welfare programmes, drawing on the concepts introduced in Chapter 1 and setting the scene for the discussion on health inequalities that follows in the next chapter.

Clearly, income inequality is only one aspect of social inequality, although it is arguably the most important consideration in terms of individual freedom, as equalization of income provides individuals with the widest range of choices within the mixed economy of welfare. This raises a number of issues that we shall consider in this chapter: what is poverty? Which groups are poor? Is poverty a major problem in Britain? What social policies are there for countering poverty? And how successful are they?

Social divisions and social diversity

Traditional discourses about poverty and inequality in the UK have focused on differences between social classes. As discussed in Chapters 1 and 2, however, it is clear that even before the establishment of the welfare state, differences between gender and age were also highly relevant to debates about inequality and poverty. In the post-war period, society is increasingly seen as being more diverse in nature and contemporary debates are characterized by a recognition that simple socio-economic distinctions, while useful, do not reflect the reality of poverty and inequality in British society (Anthias 1998; Braham and Jones 2002).

Ultimately from a social policy perspective, we are particularly interested in how such diversity and divisions in society develop and become structured and, lead to poverty and inequality. There is also an increasing concern that some individuals, by virtue of their difference (age, ethnicity employment status, sexuality etc.), are socially excluded (see Braham and Jones 2002). Recent debates have also centred on the relevance of the existence of social capital within groups and communities in society (e.g. Putnam 2000), and how absence of social capital leads to disadvantage and the need to find ways of including people and groups associated with the existence of bridging capital (a form of social capital that brings different groups or communities together).

One critical issue is how society is classified in official data. Identity and social categorization are complex and relate to how we are seen by others, as well as how we see ourselves (Braham and Jones 2002). Translating difference and divisions in society into formal classifications for official purposes is therefore a complex, although necessary, process for both the development of (and measurement of the effects of) social policy. The most common method has been by using the Registrar General's Social Class grading system (RGSC) – the principal classification of socio-economic status used in the UK since its first appearance in the Registrar General's *Annual Report* for 1911. Analysis by RGSC has consistently shown social gradients in health (see Chapter 5), and particularly in premature mortality by working age, infant mortality and birth weight. However, it was recognized that these groupings (see Box 4.1) were increasingly unhelpful. Two key issues were of concern. The first was the limited differentiation between groups that no longer matched the way people's socio-economic status was reflected in contemporary Britain. The second was that certain groups had always been excluded from the RGSC including unemployed people, single mothers and those in the armed forces.

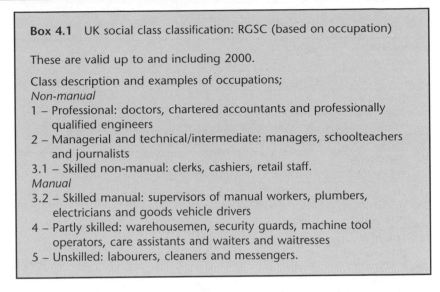

Box 4.1 UK social class classification: RGSC (based on occupation)

These are valid up to and including 2000.

Class description and examples of occupations;
Non-manual
1 – Professional: doctors, chartered accountants and professionally
    qualified engineers
2 – Managerial and technical/intermediate: managers, schoolteachers
    and journalists
3.1 – Skilled non-manual: clerks, cashiers, retail staff.
Manual
3.2 – Skilled manual: supervisors of manual workers, plumbers,
    electricians and goods vehicle drivers
4 – Partly skilled: warehousemen, security guards, machine tool
    operators, care assistants and waiters and waitresses
5 – Unskilled: labourers, cleaners and messengers.

From 2001, RGSC was replaced by the new National Statistics Socio-Economic Classification (NSSEC) in all official statistics, which also replaces Socio-Economic Group (SEG) that has also been used in official statistics. These new socio-economic classifications are based on occupation, in combination with employment status and, in some circumstances, size of workplace. There is no direct mapping between the old and new classifications, demonstrating the substantial nature of the change.

Table 4.1 illustrates the construction of the various analytical class breakdowns of the new NSSEC used for analysing official statistics. For example, the three-class version is the one used to define the DoH's public service agreement target on infant mortality.

While official classifications have evolved to reflect changing social circumstances, the collection of data that reflects a range of divisions and difference in society remains complex. How distinctions are made and differences defined are subject to substantial debate. The identification of ethnic groupings for the last national census in 2001 took many years and the final version was still criticized.

The collection of data on different groups in society is important if we are to identify the existence of inequalities, or measure the success, or otherwise of policies. However, the debates surrounding the construction of such data are complex and involve making assumptions about the nature of society. In this way much official data is seen as being socially constructed but this does not make it less useful or important (Braham and Jones 2002). The following discussion of poverty and inequalities demonstrates how making measurements and defining categories is complex but ultimately necessary.

Table 4.1 NSSEC operational categories and analytical classes

Operational categories	Analytical classes			
	Nine-class version	Eight-class version	Five-class version	Three-class version
1 Employers in large establishments	1.1 Large employers and higher managerial occupations	1 Higher managerial and professional occupations		
2 Higher managerial occupations				
3 Higher professional occupations	1.2 Higher professional occupations		1 Managerial and professional occupations	1 Managerial and professional occupations
4 Lower professional and higher technical occupations				
5 Lower managerial occupations	2 Lower managerial and professional occupations	2 Lower managerial and professional occupations		
6 Higher supervisory occupations				
7 Intermediate occupations	3 Intermediate occupations	3 Intermediate occupations	2 Intermediate occupations	
8 Employers in small establishments	4 Small employers and own-account workers	4 Small employers and own-account workers	3 Small employers and own-account workers	2 Intermediate occupations
9 Own-account workers				
10 Lower supervisory occupations	5 Lower supervisory and technical occupations	5 Lower supervisory and technical occupations	4 Lower supervisory and technical occupations	
11 Lower technical occupations				3 Routine and manual occupations
12 Semi-routine occupations	6 Semi-routine occupations	6 Semi-routine occupations	5 Semi-routine and routine occupations	
13 Routine occupations	7 Routine occupations	7 Routine occupations		
14 Never worked and long-term unemployed	8 Never worked and long-term unemployed	8 Never worked and long-term unemployed	Never worked and long-term unemployed	Never worked and long-term unemployed

Poverty

One of the five 'giants' that Beveridge argued that the welfare state would (should) eliminate was 'want' (poverty). There is considerable debate as to whether poverty persists as a social problem in Britain. The Conservative government of the 1980s consistently denied that poverty was a social problem and, to the extent that some people lived in need, it was because they chose not to spend their income appropriately. In contrast, Peter Townsend (1993: 18) argued that in Britain, '*Ill health, disability and premature death are ... outcomes of inadequate resources underlying material and social deprivation. Poverty kills'*. Between 1979 and 1989, the incomes of the richest tenth of the population rose by over 60 per cent, while the real incomes of the poorest tenth fell by 14 per cent (House of Commons 1993). Not only were the incomes of people at the top rising faster than those of people at the bottom, but tax reforms differentially benefited the better-off. As a consequence of reforms in the 1980s, the top 10 per cent paid 32 per cent of their income in tax, while the bottom 10 per cent paid 43 per cent (Oppenheim 1990; Abbott and Wallace 1992; Davies *et al.* 1992). Inequalities widened more in the UK between 1980 and 1985 than in any other member state of the European Community (Eurostat 1990). Indeed, Townsend, along with other commentators (e.g. Johnson 1990; Walker 1995), argued that not only did inequalities increase in the period from 1979, but that the proportion of the population in poverty also increased as a direct result of government policy (Townsend 1993).

Measures introduced by New Labour aimed to tackle some of these issues head on. There was, in particular, a commitment to reduce child poverty and a number of new measures were introduced targeting worst-off families, such as the Child Tax Credit and Working Tax Credit. In addition, nursery costs were met. This has led to a reduction in children living in poverty and while recent data suggests that the gap between the richest and poorest in society is still growing, although at a slower rate, the worst off in society are substantially better off (Brewer *et al.* 2005; Palmer *et al.* 2005; Pantazis *et al.* 2006). However, the proportion of the population on or below average incomes in 2003/4 was about 50 per cent (Brewer *et al.* 2005).

What is poverty? Issues of definition

The key issues in dispute here are the definition of poverty and the causes of poverty. Those who take the view that poverty is a minor problem, in contemporary Britain, argue that only those who are unable to provide for much more than the basic needs of food, clothing and shelter are poor (*subsistence poverty*) and tend to see poverty as the outcome of individual failures, inappropriate behaviour patterns or the inappropriate spending of available income. Those who argue that poverty persists as a significant social problem take a *relative* view – poverty is defined relative to the living standard of the population of the country under discussion – and they generally see poverty as the result of structural factors outside the control of the poor (*structural dependency*).

There is general agreement that those who do not have access to the resources to provide themselves and their families with basic needs, such as shelter and food, are living in poverty. Nor is there disagreement that inequalities exist in modern Britain. The debates are more concerned with what the basic needs are that must be met and what constitutes an adequate level. Nor is there much debate that needs, and the ways that they can adequately be met, are historically and cross-culturally variable. What would have been considered an adequate diet in Victorian England would not be thought adequate today. Similarly, what is considered adequate housing in Britain, with planning and building regulations, is very different from what is considered adequate in some countries, where it is possible to construct a house out of freely-available materials, on land occupied as a squatter. Consequently, the debate is not simply between those who argue that there is only subsistence poverty and those who argue for the concept of relative poverty; it is a more complex debate, about what needs should be met and at what level. Those who argue that there is 'no such thing as poverty in contemporary Britain' are saying that everyone has access to sufficient resources to meet minimum needs at a basic level. Those who argue that there *is* a significant problem of poverty, are arguing that some people do not have access to sufficient resources to meet socially agreed needs at a socially acceptable level. We can think of the debate as positions on two continua. One is a continuum of needs, with at one end, a small number of essential needs and, at the other a much broader range of socially agreed needs. The second continuum is one from provision at a minimum level (e.g. a diet that provides basic nutritional requirements), to one of provision at a socially acceptable level (e.g. the diet enjoyed by the majority of the population).

It is possible to identify four points along the continua to assist us in understanding the main definitions of poverty:

1 *Absolute poverty*. This is where individuals are unable to meet their basic needs at a minimum level. At the extreme are those who are starving and without shelter. Once we move away from this extreme, the question becomes what counts as an adequate diet and adequate shelter.
2 *Subsistence poverty*. This is where individuals are unable to provide for themselves and their families, a minimum number of agreed basic requirements at a minimum level. For example, Rowntree, in carrying out his survey in York at the beginning of the twentieth century, used a minimum standard that enabled him to determine the proportion of the population living at or below the absolute minimum level (see Box 4.2).
3 *Social coping*. This suggests that the poor are those who cannot enjoy the standard of living of the average working-class household. On this definition, a family would be living in poverty if they could not afford to buy the children birthday presents or new clothing. Piachaud (1979) has calculated that to achieve this standard of living, income must be substantially above benefit level. When he calculated the amount

necessary, he found, for example, that it would be necessary to provide 50 per cent more than the assistance benefit paid for each child.

4 *Social participation.* This defines the poor as those whose standard of living falls below the prevailing living standard. Townsend (1979: 3) summed it up by suggesting that people are living in poverty '*when they lack the resources to obtain the types of diet, participate in the activities and have the living conditions and amenities which are customary or at least widely encouraged or approved in the society in which they live*'. The EU has accepted this as a means of defining poverty and has defined as poor those who have a disposable income of less than half the average *per capita* income in their own country (Hantrais 1995).

Box 4.2   Minimum standards in Rowntree's survey of York

A family living upon the scale allowed for in this estimate must never spend a penny on railway fares or omnibuses. They must never go into the countryside unless they walk. They must never purchase a halfpenny newspaper or spend a penny to buy a ticket for a popular concert. They must write no letters to absent children, for they cannot afford to pay postage. They must never contribute anything to their church or chapel or give any help to a neighbour which costs them money. They cannot save, nor can they join a sick Club or Trade Union because they cannot pay the money subscription. The children must have no pocket money for dolls, marbles or sweets. The father must smoke no tobacco and must drink no beer. The mother must never buy any pretty clothes for herself or her children, the character of the family wardrobe as for the family diet being governed by the regulation '*nothing must be bought but that which is absolutely necessary for the maintenance of physical health, and what is bought must be of the plainest and most economical description*'. Should a child fall ill, it must be attended by the parish doctor; should it die it must be buried by the parish.

(Rowntree 1901: 334)

Problems of measurement: the poverty line

Not only are there different definitions of poverty, but also problems of how to measure it. There are basically three ways in which it can be measured:

1 *Professional*: for example, dietitians can provide details of an adequate diet that can then be costed. Those whose resources mean they cannot afford to purchase this diet, prepare and cook it are said to be in poverty.

2 *Conceptual*: for example, expenditure studies can determine how people live and this information can be used to determine the minimum adequate income. Townsend (1979), for example, constructed a 60-item deprivation index which he used as a basis for determining the minimum income necessary to enjoy an average standard of living. This

index was correlated with income, and he suggested that a threshold existed at incomes near 150 per cent of supplementary benefit levels.

3 *Public opinion*: for example, Mack and Lansley (1985) asked a random sample of people to indicate which of a list of 35 possible items they considered to be necessities. From this they constructed a list of essential items (see Box 4.3). Using this list they were then able to work out how much money a family required in order to be able to afford them. They defined the poor as those who lacked three or more of the 14 items which the large majority agreed to be necessities.

Box 4.3   Items considered essential to standard of living by the public (in rank-order of importance)

1 Heating	14 Carpets
2 Indoor toilet	15 Celebrations on special
3 Damp-free home	occasions
4 Bath	16 Roast joint once a week
5 Bed for everyone	17 Washing machine
6 Public transport	18 New, not second-hand, clothes
7 Warm waterproof coat	19 Hobby or leisure activity
8 Three meals a day for children	20 Two hot meals a day (adults)
9 Self-contained accommodation	21 Meat/fish every other day
10 Two pairs of all-weather shoes	22 Presents once a year
11 Sufficient bedrooms for	23 Holiday
children	24 Leisure equipment for children
12 Refrigerator	25 Garden
13 Toys for children	26 Television

Source: Mack and Lansley (1985)

To summarize, we have suggested that in order to determine who is in poverty, it is necessary to determine how many of a person's requirements should be met and the quality of the provision. At one extreme, a minimum number of requirements would be met at a minimum quality, and at the other, a maximum number of requirements would be met at a maximum quality. It is not essential, for example, for adequate nutrition to include a roast dinner once a week, but it is considered normal in modern Britain. Purchasing new as opposed to second-hand clothes is not essential, but it is generally seen as desirable. In contemporary Britain, we generally define as poor those who cannot afford to purchase the goods and services to participate in normal activities. There is, nevertheless, debate as to what is the basic minimum.

Poverty research in Britain has generally taken the level of state benefit as a proxy for a 'poverty line'. State benefit, or more properly the income support level, has been seen as an official definition of what income is necessary for subsistence. This is nonetheless a relative measure, as the real value of benefits has increased over time (though not as fast as the real value of wages).

It is now accepted by most researchers that benefit levels are too stringent a measure of poverty. The Social Security Advisory Committee argued in 1983 (DHSS 1983) that assistance benefit level was *'too near the subsistence level to provide an adequate standard of living for the poorest people in our society'*. Perhaps the most commonly used measurement is that of income poverty being income 60 per cent or less of the average (median) household income (Palmer *et al.* 2005). In 2003/4 this was:

- £180 per week for a two adult household;
- £100 per week for a single adult;
- £260 per week for two adults living with two children;
- £180 per week for a single adult living with two children.

What is evident is that, whatever definition and measure of poverty is used, there are still people living in poverty in contemporary Britain, and the absolute number and the percentage of the population living in poverty has increased (Brewer *et al.* 2005). At the same time, inequalities have also increased, so that the differences in living standard between those at the top and bottom of society have widened. Poverty has increased in Britain not only because of the widening gap between benefit levels and average pay, but also because the proportion of the population on benefits has increased and the number of people in low-paid jobs has also risen. Looking at the period since the Conservative government came to power in 1979, indicated that:

> the precise amount by which poverty has increased depends on the measure used. If relative measures and a low threshold are used (40 per cent of the contemporary average equivalent net household income) ... the poverty grew by a massive 333 per cent between 1979 and 1990/1. Assuming an 'absolute measure' is used, that is, holding the level of output constant at the 1979 threshold, poverty still increased by 40 per cent.
>
> (Walker 1995: 1)

Poverty and social exclusion

Poverty, however, is about more than income; it is about multiple deprivation (see Box 4.4), although not all those on low income are necessarily living in poverty. There are at least two reasons for this. One is that people's standard of living is determined by their immediately available resources, and people may have access to resources they do not have to purchase (e.g. housing, meals and/or food provided by their employer, transport and recreational facilities as part of their remuneration package). The second is that people may have savings and other 'stored' resources on which they are able to draw. Pensioners are an obvious example, they may have savings to supplement pension income as well as high-quality owner-occupied accommodation. They may also be assisted financially or in other ways by children. University students are another group who have low incomes but who are at the worst only temporarily in poverty, most having come from homes where they have not experienced poverty. On gaining degrees most will enter employment with income well above the poverty level. The Church of England Working Party (1985) defined poverty as *'not only about shortage of money. It is about rights and relationships, about how people are treated and how they regard themselves, about powerlessness, exclusion and loss of dignity. Yet the lack of an adequate income is at the heart'*. To be poor is to be multiply disadvantaged and to be excluded from participation in normal day-to-day activities that are taken for granted – the poor are not simply those who lack basic goods and services, but those who are unable to meet their needs from their own resources. They cannot make the same choices as the majority of the population regarding purchasing presents, taking holidays, buying clothing etc. People on low incomes often have to make undesirable or unpleasant choices; for example, whether to buy food or pay the rent, pay the electricity bill or buy shoes for the children. The income and other resources needed to provide basic necessities also vary. For example, transport costs are much higher in rural than urban areas; indeed, those living in rural areas may experience severe hardship if they do not have access to a car. However, changing patterns of shopping in modern Britain make food shopping difficult and expensive for many women with families if they do not have access to a car, as more and more supermarkets move to out-of-town locations. The reduction in extra-curricular sporting activities in schools in recent years has meant that children are deprived of participation in sport and other activities, if their parents cannot pay for them out of school. Furthermore, reductions in public transport mean that it is often necessary for parents to have a car if their children are to take part, for example, in swimming clubs, judo classes, ballet lessons, football training, the Girl Guides or even just a recreational swim. Elderly people also face social isolation because of their level of access to transport, which prevents them from participating.

Box 4.4   What is poverty?

- Poverty is not having sufficient money to buy the necessities of life and to participate in the life of the community.
- Poverty is constantly having to make choices about which necessities a person and the family shall go without.
- Poverty directly affects mobility, housing, leisure and social interaction, and it dramatically affects life chances. It is socially disabling.
- Poverty is closely linked to ill health.
- Poverty disproportionately affects working-class people throughout their lives, particularly when they are young or elderly, and especially if they are women, black or disabled.
- Poverty affects individuals and communities, but it is entirely preventable given the will on the part of government.

Source: Derbyshire Welfare Rights Service (1993: 1)

Thus it is important to recognize that it is impossible to have a 'poverty line' below which people are poor, whereas above it they are not poor (Piachaud 1979). It is possible to define income levels (see below) that are sufficient to enable people to live in varying degrees of discomfort, and indeed to indicate a level of income that permits social participation (Townsend 1979, 1993). Cut-off points are always arbitrary, however, leaving some people only just above the line and not noticeably better off than those just below the line. It is probably more appropriate to consider people as more or less deprived, when they have a standard of living below the societal norm, with the most deprived living in absolute poverty. All of the poor are excluded in different ways from full membership of society, however; they lack the resources to obtain access to the conditions of life considered necessary not to be deprived.

More recent debates about concepts such as multiple deprivation, inequality and poverty have been framed by the concept of social exclusion. However, the use of social exclusion is also not without problems, as it is necessary to define who is excluded, what they are excluded from and why (Levitas 2006). The government has been particularly concerned about the interconnectedness of different exclusions (e.g. work, jobs or education) in the same way that debates in the 1970s and 1980s were about who was poor and how multiple poverties affected their lives. However, poverty and social exclusion are not the same things. While poverty has an important effect on social participation, poverty and low incomes do not in themselves mean that people are excluded from social relations, raising doubts about policies that focus solely on employment as a route to social inclusion, as seen in UK policy (Levitas 2006).

Social exclusion is now a central element of UK and EU social policy. Within the EU, four key objectives for tackling social exclusion have been set out:

1　Facilitating participation in employment and access by all to resources, rights, goods and services.
2　Preventing the risks of exclusion.
3　Helping the most vulnerable.
4　Mobilizing all relevant bodies in overcoming exclusion.

While there are important links between poverty, social exclusion and social inequality (and substantial overlaps between people who are poor, socially excluded and experience the worst inequalities), social exclusion lacks substantive definition unless it is made clear what type of exclusion is being discussed (see Box 4.5). Importantly, people excluded from one aspect of society may in fact be included in others. For example, while a person with a disability may be excluded from employment, they may be included in a number of social networks through common experiences with other people with disabilities. What is critical, therefore, is to identify whether social exclusion is detrimental and, like inequalities, there are multiple exclusions from different aspects of society. So, a person with a disability may be excluded from work, which leads to a lower income and, is therefore excluded from doing things through lack of resources. They may also be socially isolated and excluded from their community as there is no appropriate transport. This is likely to lead to increased inequalities which may compound or increase other health and social problems.

Box 4.5   Examples of the social exclusion of older people

- Those affected by persistent disadvantage and poverty (e.g women without occupational pensions, older homeless people, some older ethnic minority people).
- Those affected by contracting social networks (e.g. without informal carers).
- Those living in disadvantaged inner-city or remote rural communities (over 2 million pensioners, mainly women, have no access to a car).
- Those marginalized through physical and mental ill health.
- Those affected by ageist beliefs and practises.
- Those cut off from new technologies, such as the internet.
- Those with difficulty exercising their civic rights.

Source: Phillipson and Scharf (2004)

Explaining the persistence of poverty and inequality

As Spicker (1993) points out, we do not have to understand the causes of poverty (or indeed, of any social problem) in order to respond to it. Nevertheless, the understandings of poverty that people have, shape their responses. Those who see it as the outcome of individual failures suggest different policies from those who see it as the outcome of structural factors. Murie and Forrest (1980) provided a useful comparison of the different theoretical approaches and explanations in relation to urban problems (see Table 4.2).

Inequality

Inequalities between different sections of society remain a key social policy concern but, as argued in Chapter 1, the analysis of inequalities is now more driven by a recognition of the many differences and divisions in society (Braham and Jones 2002). Of particular interest is the interaction between these divisions and inequalities. Much of the discussion in this text has so far identified class or socio-economic position as the key denominator to identify inequalities in society. Poverty is clearly linked to lower socio-economic status but is also influenced by factors such as gender, age, ethnicity, health and disability. However, inequality is not simply an issue of economics and income. There are links between inequalities and poverty that affect overall life chances in society. For example, as Figure 4.1 shows, 16-year-olds who are eligible for free school meals (as their parents are on a low income) obtain fewer GCSE grades

Table 4.2 Differing explanations of poverty

Theoretical model of problem	Explanation of the problem	Location of the problem	Key concept	Type of change sought	Method of change
Social pathology and culture	Problems arising from the pathology of deviant groups	In internal dynamics of deviant groups	Poverty	Better adjusted and less deviant people	Social education and social work with groups
	Individual psychological handicaps and inadequacies transmitted from one generation to the next	In relationships between individuals, families and groups	Deprivation	More integrated self-supporting families	Compensatory social work, support and self-help
Management and planning	Failures of planning, management or administration	In relationships between disadvantaged and the bureaucracy	Disadvantage	More total and coordinated approaches by the bureaucracy	Rational social planning
Resources	Inequitable distribution of resources	In relationships between under privileged and formal political machine	Underprivilege	Better allocation of resources	Positive discrimination policies
Structural	Divisions necessary to maintain an economic system based on private profit	In relationships between working-class and political and economic structure	Inequality	Better distribution of power and control	Changes in political consciousness and organization

Source: Murie and Forrest (1980)

A*–C, thus affecting their chances of going on to further and higher education and limiting choices about employment.

Figure 4.2 shows the results for educational attainment by ethnic group. This illustrates that there are also significant differences in achievement between ethnic groups. Importantly, it can be seen that significant gains have been made by some ethnic groups but, for black and Pakistani children these gains have been limited. Thus, childhood patterns affect life chances so that children from poorer families, or those from black and Pakistani communities, have more chance of being less well educated and, therefore, more poorly paid and at risk of greater social exclusion as

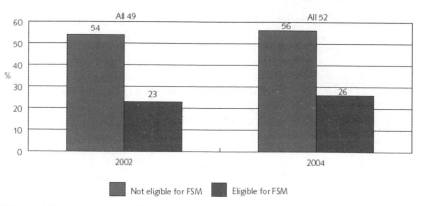

Figure 4.1 Percentage of 16-year-olds achieving five or more GCSE grades A*–
C (or equivalent) by free school meal (FSM) eligibility, England
Source: DoH 2005d, figures 20 and 21

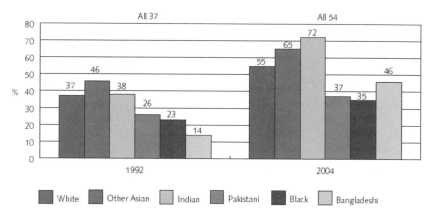

Figure 4.2 Percentage of 16-year-olds attaining five or more GCSE grades A*–
C by ethnic group, England and Wales
Source: DoH 2005d, figures 20 and 21

defined by the government. This affects their well-being and thus they are
likely to suffer poorer health (see Chapter 5).

Implications for policy

The competing explanations of poverty are not mutually exclusive, nor do
they necessarily result in completely different kinds of policy outcome.
Nevertheless, there is a relationship between seeing poverty as the result of
individual characteristics on the one hand, or structural ones on the other,
and the type of social policy advocated. Those who attribute poverty to the
laziness and attitudes of poor people, are likely to argue that poor relief
must be accompanied by measures to change the behaviour of 'the poor'.
Conversely, those who view poverty as the outcome of an unequal society

in which the poor are disadvantaged in economic, social and political terms, would argue that it is inappropriate to structure the relief of poverty through systems that indicate moral responsibility. Structural problems imply that some change in the social structure is desirable. This, however, is often difficult to achieve. The consequence is that the policies adopted by governments tend to rely on the redistribution of income, income maintenance, fiscal policy and social work. The emphasis placed on different forms of policy initiative will depend on the political ideologies of the government in power, but the basic outcome is that the vast effect of structural disadvantage is unchanged by social policies.

Social security

Social security is concerned with financial support, from the cradle to the grave. Beveridge's plan was tied to a policy of full employment, whereby employees and employers paid insurance contributions to provide for men and their families in times of unemployment, sickness, disability and old age. In addition, there was to be maternity benefit, widows' benefit and death grants. These insurance benefits were intended to support individuals and families at subsistence level. As a safety net, a non-contributory social assistance scheme was to be financed from taxation. Its aim was to meet the needs not covered adequately by insurance, but it was seen as less desirable than insured benefits and was based on a means test.

A clear distinction was drawn between universal benefits and means tested (targeted) benefits. State benefits were to provide a national minimum, people being free to make private arrangements; there continued to be a mixed economy of provision. State insurance was compulsory, but individuals and their employers could still provide additional protection (e.g. employer pensions, sick pay, health insurance, private pensions, mortgage protection and permanent disability income). Indeed, in the last 25 years, governments have tried to encourage people to make private provision for health, sickness, debt protection and pensions.

Social security benefits have a number of different facets, the four most important of which are compensation, personal insurance protection, employment protection and integrated social and economic development (TGWU 1994). Compensation is provided, for example, for disabilities and industrial injuries. Personal income protection is based on the insurance principle; regular weekly contributions paid while in employment provide for protection in old age, sickness, disablement and unemployment.

The social security system in Britain was changed incrementally in the 1950s, 1960s and 1970s (e.g. the option for women to pay lower contributions was withdrawn in 1975) and a number of new benefits introduced (e.g. mobility allowance and attendance allowance). In the 1980s, the Conservative government argued that the benefits system had become too complex with the mixture of insured and targeted benefits, and that the poverty trap provided a major disincentive for people to come off benefit and take available jobs. It undertook a number of reforms in the 1986 Social Security Act, implemented in 1988. However, it was not clear that the new system was any less complex or that it removed the poverty trap (Johnson 1990; Hills 1993). The aim of the new system of benefits was to target payments at those most in need and, to provide incentives to individuals to take the available jobs, provide for their old age and reduce 'dependency', and to do so by changing people's behaviour – to make them more self-reliant. In many ways the Labour government built on these reforms but has stressed the joint responsibilities of the individual and government. The social investment state places emphasis on employment as a path out of poverty, reliance on the state and social exclusion. Thus, there is an emphasis on helping people into work but also approaches to tackling family poverty. New Labour has also viewed general fiscal and economic policy as important in tackling poverty and inequality. Measures to introduce a low tax rate band and the minimum wage have been important social policies.

As a field of study, social security is a wide one, embracing the distribution of income, the taxation system, private insurance provision and the system of income transfers organized by the state. To understand the implications of social policy fully, we must consider not only the contribution of statutory provision, but also the role of the commercial sector and of occupational welfare. This is particularly important in relation to social security and recent developments in pensions policy (see below).

The British social security system

The UK government pays out more than £100 billion a year in social security benefits and pensions to around 30 million people. There are about 40 different sorts of benefits, allowances and grants, and the delivery system is complex, with different eligibility criteria, different payment dates and methods. A recent National Audit Office report (2005) estimates that the Treasury loses £2.6 billion a year from fraud and error in the system, which is caused largely by its complexity. Particular concern has centred on the complexity of new Tax Credits for families and the minimum income guarantee for pensioners. Both of these are means tested and have been subject to criticism about the complex claim and administration processes which affect take-up of the benefits, as well as leading to problems in terms of errors in awards. For example, take-up of the minimum income guarantee for pensioners was between 63 and 74 per cent in 2002/3. In fact the overall estimate for take-up of income-related benefits in 2002/3 was between 72 and 80 per cent, leaving between £3,300 million and £6,260 million unclaimed (DWP 2005a, 2005b).

The British state systems, of income support, fall into three categories: contributory benefits; non-contributory benefits, which are not means tested as such, but are allocated according to some 'needs' criterion (e.g. age or disability); and means tested benefits (see Table 4.3). It is important to stress that a person or a family may depend on both contributory and non contributory support simultaneously. Indeed, one of the most significant recent trends has been to displace contributory schemes with means tested ones. The Beveridge plan envisaged that contributory benefits would provide the main source of support in old age, sickness and unemployment, although in fact the actual insured benefits were paid at

Table 4.3 Main social security benefits

Contributory (paid only to those who have paid insurance contributions)	Non-contributory (and not means tested)	Means tested (paid only to those on limited means)	Discretionary (to deal with urgent or exceptional needs)
Statutory maternity benefit	Family allowance	Income support	Social fund
Retirement benefit	Mobility allowance	Income maintenance	
Unemployment benefit	Attendance allowance	Death benefit	
Widows' pension	Disabled living allowance	Supplementary pension	
Widowed mother's allowance	Invalid car allowance	Childrens' Tax Credit	
Incapacity benefit	War pensions	Working Tax Credit	
		Housing benefit	
		Council tax rebate	
		Free prescriptions	
		Free dental treatment	
		Free eyesight test	
		Disability working allowance	

much lower rates than those recommended by Beveridge (Timmins 1995). In addition, the limited period for which sickness and unemployment benefits are paid, has meant that the idea of insurance was compromised from the start, with a significant number of people dependent on means tested benefits for topping up inadequate insured benefits. However, government policy in recent years has been to argue for the targeting of benefits to those most in need, and this has meant an increasing emphasis on means tested income support, as opposed to contributory and universal benefits by, for example, making the contribution requirement for entitlement to retirement pension more stringent.

A major concern about means tested benefits has been lack of 'take-up'; that is, people failing to claim benefits to which they are entitled. As Spicker (1995) points out:

For many years this was described as a problem of stigma, because some claimants felt humiliated by claiming, but the problem is rather more complex than this suggests. Reasons for non-takeup include ignorance about benefits, the complexity and difficulty of the process, previous problems in

*attempting to claim, limited marginal benefits and the costs to the claimant
of proceeding.*

(Spicker 1995: 155-6)

A good example is welfare policies designed to help families with children. Child benefit is universal and has virtually 100 per cent uptake. However, Child and Working Tax Credits, introduced by Gordon Brown in 2003, provide a sliding scale of support to parents in work with most help targeted at poorer families. Tax Credits need to be applied for and are complex to administer, leading to criticism about both the nature of the benefit and how it has been delivered. In particular, those most in need have had erratic payments. Underpayments and overpayments are common, due to the way the system estimates income over a year, and then has to adjust for changes in income during the year.

Contributory benefits

Contributory benefits are those for which employees make weekly or monthly payments through their wages, on an earnings-related basis, to the National Insurance scheme. Employers also have to make contributions on behalf of their employees. These contributions go towards a range of benefits covering sickness, maternity leave, unemployment and pensions (see Table 4.3).

Contributory benefits are not without controversy. A good example is pension entitlement, where many older women paid a lower National Insurance rate (the old married woman's rate) and did not get National Insurance Credits while looking after children and, therefore, have received lower pensions with the consequence that many women pensioners experience poverty in old age. The government is now addressing this and is encouraging women to ensure that they review their National Insurance contributions. It also provides a home carer credit for National Insurance to cover periods of looking after children or another family member, to ensure that women receive the basic state pension they are entitled to. Many black Britons who came to this country in the 1950s and 1960s, will also be entitled to only a reduced pension on retirement due to insufficient contributions. Pensioners who are entitled to only a reduced pension, who are often those who do not have an employer's pension or a private pension and have not earned sufficient to be entitled to an earnings-related pension, have to rely on means tested benefits to raise their income to subsistence level. The Labour government introduced the minimum income guarantee for pensioners, which was changed to the Pension Credit system in 2003 to address some of these shortcomings (see below).

Non-contributory benefits which are not means tested

A small number of benefits exist which require neither contributions nor means testing. They are, strictly speaking, 'universal' benefits, available to all individuals who fall within certain needs categories, irrespective of means. The most important feature of these benefits is that by removing the need to qualify by work record, some of the worst obstacles to more comprehensive coverage are also removed. The major reason that few have been introduced is that, because they are financed from general taxation, they are difficult to justify in terms of redistribution, because they do not necessarily redistribute income from the better off to the poor. When such benefits have been introduced, as with the disability living allowance, the eligibility criteria have been very stringent.

A distinction can be made between non-contributory benefits, which depend on some kind of qualifying test, and those which are available with no test of contributions, need or means. The latter generally depend on membership of a demographic category, for example, children or old people. Benefits of this type are paid universally to certain classes of people, providing them with a minimum income level. The major advantages of such benefits are that they are easy and inexpensive to administer and take-up is high. The best known and most hotly debated of them is child benefit, available to all parents, or guardians, of children under 16 and, children aged 16–19 who are still in full-time non-higher education. The only qualifying condition is a residence one (the child must 'generally' live within the UK, and either he or she must live with the applicant or the applicant must pay maintenance at the rate of at least the amount of child benefit).

Means tested benefits

Means tested benefits are paid only to those who have limited capital and earnings. Assessment for eligibility involves an investigation, by the authorities, into 'means' – a 'means test'. Following the 1986 Social Security Act, in 1990–1, means tested benefits accounted for 24 per cent of government spending on social security (DSS 1991: 8). The Social Security Act radically altered the structure of means tested benefits. A central objective in reforming support to those in employment on low incomes, was to ensure that they would not be less well off than comparable families on income support. The range of changes introduced did not have any significant effect on poverty. The Labour government has increasingly used targeted benefits, that are means tested, arguing that the priority is to help the poorest in society. Examples include Child and Working Tax Credit and the pensioner minimum income guarantees.

Universalism, selectivity and social security

Assuming that the role of social policy in general is to meet need and reduce poverty, it is possible to argue endlessly about the efficacy and desirability of different modes of provision. The debate over the balance of selective and universal services has a long history within social policy. Since 1979, however, the dominance of the ideology of the New Right has sharpened this debate, with increasing emphasis placed on notions of freedom, choice, efficiency and the elimination of dependency. On balance, the shift in the 1980s was away from contributory schemes and towards an increase in selectivism and means testing, on the grounds that targeting benefits reduces the cost and at the same time meets needs more effectively. The major problems with this kind of policy are low take-up and the poverty trap, where movement to work means that benefits and support are withdrawn, leaving people worse off.

Redding (1979) developed definitions of universalist and selectivist services that go beyond party political dogma, to consider the real issues at stake, and the implications for equity in social policy. In particular, he noted that one can have a very generous system of selective benefits or, conversely, a very miserly universal benefit (such as child benefit or the old maternity grant of £25), their existence being more symbolic than a real benefit to the recipient. Redding defined universal services as those which provide for a category of citizens, such as children or disabled people, without any direct regard for their incomes. Typically, such programmes are financed collectively and administered by government agencies. Universal services may discriminate on the basis of 'needs', but not on the basis of ability to pay. They are relatively inexpensive to administer and have a high take-up rate.

Selective services, on the other hand, are characteristically only offered to those individuals who are in some demonstrable need, usually defined by some form of means test. Selective services tend to be posed in the context of private market arrangements for the majority of citizens, with the provision of selective public services for a minority of definably poor people. (This comparison fits neatly into Titmuss' residual and institutional welfare model discussed in Chapter 1). They are relatively expensive to administer and tend to have a low take-up rate, partly because of the stigma associated with them and partly because of the complexities of claiming.

Redding argued, however, that there is some blurring at the edges of these definitions and, further, that there are no truly universal services in Britain. In particular, he pointed to the fact that we all *contribute* unequally through rates, taxes and wage-related contributions (we need to consider the financing of the system) and, also that very few services are actually *received* equally. Seeing a doctor, for example, is ostensibly free, but increasing prescription charges may introduce inequalities in outcome. In relation to social security, there are serious questions about the information available to the public about benefits, and questions about take-up rates.

Redding also argued that we must take account of the changing values of the wider community if we are to understand the impact of policies. This might include: attitudes towards the recipients of services by non-recipients (are they seen as scroungers, for example?), resulting in stigma and low take-up; the attitudes of the recipients themselves and their experience of means testing (an estimated 60 per cent of family credit goes unclaimed); and finally, the attitudes of the population as a whole towards taxation and the funding of services. Redding concluded that what we have in practice is 'selectively financed universal services, selectively used'.

The debate surrounding the balance of universal and selective provision, then, takes place on two levels: first, on an ideological level and second, in terms of administrative feasibility and effectiveness. Collectivists have typically favoured universal services as an important instrument in the achievement of equality through redistribution, while anti-collectivists have been fierce advocates of a residual model of welfare provision with an emphasis on non-intervention, the promotion of choice and the remedial treatment of poverty. For many proponents on the Right, universalism discourages thrift and erodes incentives to work.

However, accepting for the moment that we have a finite 'pot of money', some of the arguments in favour of selective services bear consideration. The principal arguments are as follows:

1 The selective approach enables existing money to be focused on the needy (targeted).
2 It prevents money being squandered on the already well-off (an argument often used in relation to child benefit).
3 It reduces public expenditure and stimulates the commercial sector, thereby increasing consumer choice.

One of the most problematic aspects of selective approaches, however, concerns the administrative difficulties of identifying and defining 'the poor'. Titmuss (1987) suggested that selective services operate as a form of social control and deliberately discourage take-up through the imposition of stigma, the denial of information and the sheer complexity of procedures. As such, they reinforce the work ethic and induce a sense of personal failure in their recipients. Jones (1992: 46), however, stressed that not all selective services are stigmatizing (giving the example of selective benefits for disabled people), while the recent use of Child and Working Tax Credits offers selective benefits to everyone with family incomes below £58,175 (2006/7), although with progressively higher levels of support to those on lower incomes. However, the complexity of the system has caused problems for many people with erratic incomes as the system is based on annual earnings.

Poverty and inequality in the UK today

In 2003/4, 12 million people lived in poverty, as defined by the measure of income poverty (60 per cent or less of average household income). This total includes 3.5 million children, 2 million adults living with children, 2 million pensioners and 3.5 million working age adults without dependent children (Palmer et al. 2005: 10). However, it is not just the total numbers that are important. The concentration and distribution of poverty across Britain impacts on how poverty, inequality and social exclusion are experienced, with important consequences for people in poverty and for health and social welfare services. For example, 50 per cent of people on low incomes live in just 20 per cent of small local areas and, 50 per cent of children of primary school age entitled to free school meals, are concentrated in 20 per cent of schools (Palmer et al. 2005: 10).

In addition, certain groups in the population are more likely to experience poverty including women, lone parents, people on low pay, unemployed people, pensioners, people with disabilities or long-term health problems and people from certain ethnic and cultural groups (Graham 1984; Palmer *et al.* 2005). The experience of poverty also tends to be cyclic, with people moving in and out of it across the life course, being most likely to experience it as children, as adults in a family with dependent children and in old age. Those who experience poverty at these stages of their lives, often have only barely adequate incomes at other times and, are therefore unable to save or otherwise provide for these stages. For example, a working-class couple who may have an adequate income when they are first married, but find themselves in poverty when they have children, experience a period of relative affluence when the children are older and both parents are able to hold down paid employment, but never earn sufficient to save or insure privately for old age. The risk of being in poverty, then, relates to the stage in the life course, but also to gender, ethnicity and social class.

Families, children and poverty

When elected in 1997, the Labour government made a substantive commitment to reducing the numbers of children living in poverty to 3 million by 2004/5, to halve child relative poverty to its 1998/9 level by 2010 and eradicate it by 2020 (DWP 2003). Families with children represent nearly half the total amount of people living in poverty in the UK today. There have been significant changes in the levels of poverty experienced by people in families with dependent children due to changes in the benefit system, such as the new Child and Working Tax Credits, the introduction in 2004 of the minimum wage and moves to get more people into work. However, complexities in administering the new tax credits, created (and continues to create) problems for many families and has contributed to a slowdown in the reduction of child poverty, so that the government missed its first target. While support for work has been an important element of the government's strategy for tackling child poverty, the UK still has the highest proportion of children living in workless families in the EU (Palmer *et al.* 2005).

Lone parent families are particularly at risk of poverty (Brewer *et al.* 2005). For example, lone parents are more likely to be workless than couple families with children (53.2 per cent compared to 9.0 per cent in 2003/4), although the situation has improved since 1996/7 (66.5 per cent and 12 per cent respectively) (Brewer *et al.* 2005). In addition to direct financial support measures, to support parents in work, there is also support for nursery costs, the provision of after-school and breakfast clubs, and there have been substantial improvements in raising the income of the poorest families and reducing child poverty (see Figure 4.3). This has been a result of improvements in financial support for children, improved benefits and Tax Credits for the lowest income groups and the introduction of the minimum wage, although low pay remains a key factor in family poverty.

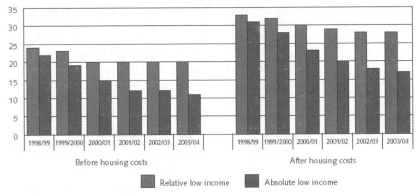

Figure 4.3 Percentage of children in England living in low income households (below 60 per cent of Great Britain median income) 1998–2004
Source: DoH 2005c, figures 26

Employment and poverty

The changing structure of UK employment has been dramatic over the last 30 years. Central to this is the shift from long-term stable male full-time employment, to more temporary and part-time employment, with many more women in the labour market. There has also been a shift from higher paid industrial employment, to lower paid service jobs. Low pay and employment instability are key factors in creating family poverty. In March 2006, 1.68 million people were officially unemployed, representing an unemployment rate of 5.5 per cent (ONS 2006). However, the trend in unemployment in 2006 was upward, while the numbers of people in employment was falling suggesting further increases in unemployment. While average wages increased ahead of the inflation rate, many people remain in low paid work. It is estimated that over 5 million employees, aged 22 or over, are low paid and that 50 per cent of part-time workers earn less than £6.50 an hour. The introduction of the minimum wage, by the Labour government, has gone some way to improving wage poverty but, the rates (in 2006) are still fairly low (£5.35 per hour aged 22 and over, £4.45 for those aged 18–21 and £3.30 for those 16–18).

Unemployment is a major cause of poverty in contemporary Britain. When it is short-term, it is unlikely in itself to be an indication of poverty. The Beveridge system of benefits was not designed to deal with long-term unemployment yet, by mid-1993, 40 per cent of registered unemployed men and 26 per cent of registered unemployed women, had been unemployed for over a year (see Hills 1994). (This is probably an underestimate of long-term unemployment for women, as women are less likely to register as unemployed than men.) The long-term unemployed are likely to experience considerable poverty. Furthermore, the longer they are unemployed, the less likely they are to be re-employed. The way in which the benefits system works means that a household headed by an unemployed man is likely to have less income if the female partner has employment. Some groups of the population and some areas of the country are more vulnerable to unemployment than others.

Of particular interest is the fact that there are work-rich areas and work-poor areas and, where someone lives may be more important than their qualifications, in determining the type of work they do, with the best paid jobs in London and the South East (although living costs are higher in these areas as well) (Wheeler *et al.* 2005).

Women and poverty

Women predominate among those who are poor – as low-paid workers, as pensioners, as disabled people and as lone parents. Glendinning and Millar (1992: 60) have suggested that '*Women bear the burden of managing poverty on a day-to-day basis. Whether they live alone or with a partner, on benefit or low earnings, it is usually women who are responsible for making ends meet and for managing the debts which result when they don't*'. Glendinning and Millar noted that when looking at women's poverty, we should not be concerned solely with the disparate levels of *income* which exist between men and women, but also with their *access* to income and other resources, the *time* spent generating income and resources and the *transfer* of these resources from some members of a household to others. While increases in employment for women have provided some security, they are more likely to be in temporary, part-time jobs. For example, of the 50 per cent of part-time workers earning less than £6.50 an hour, three-quarters are women (Palmer *et al.* 2005). Overall, women's real gross weekly earnings are considerably lower than men's. For example, in 2002, men in the top decile earned over £836 per week, compared with £614 for women. In the bottom decile, men earned less than £238 and women less than £195 (ONS 2002: 648).

The benefits system was built on the assumption that married women would generally be dependent on their husbands for economic support. It is this ideological notion of dependency within the existing benefits system, despite the move to more formally equal treatment in the 1980s, which is the root cause of gender inequality. An important feature of the British benefits system is the division between benefits notionally funded from National Insurance contributions and means tested benefits. As long as sufficient contributions have been made, the former are paid on an individual basis regardless of income; means tested benefits are based on a test of income and capital. Women are less likely than men to be eligible for contributory benefits, failing to have made sufficient contributions either because of interrupted employment or because they had been earning insufficient to have made contributions. The result is that they, and all those who are unable to work as a result of domestic responsibilities, have no right to claim National Insurance funded benefits. Women are less likely than men, then, to be able to claim state benefits in their own right (and, for the same reasons, employer/private ones) and more likely to be dependent on the social security system (and thus on means tested benefits). In 1988, according to the Child Poverty Action Group (CPAG):

• over three times as many women as men over pension age were receiving income support;

- two-thirds of lone parents (mostly women) were reliant on income support;
- ninety-six per cent of lone parents on income support were women.

Furthermore, even when women live in a household with an adequate income, they may still live in poverty, as resources are not necessarily shared equitably (Davies and Joshi 1998; Himmelweit 2002). Since 1997, there have been moves to address the way the social security and tax systems treats women and changes have been made to restructure the social security system, so that it assesses individuals. Similarly, the tax system is now based on individual income with equal allowances for men and women and the ending of the married man's allowance. In effect these changes followed changes in working patterns rather than being introduced to remove inequalities.

Women are still at particular risk of having a low income when they retire, due to the way the National Insurance system worked in the post-war period. It is more likely for women to have a reduced pension, as their entitlement is based on National Insurance stamp payments, many women either paid a reduced stamp (relying on their husband's contributions) and/or paid no stamp as they were caring for children. There is now a credit system for a home carer's allowance, which will go some way to helping women claim better pensions in the future but, many pensioner women are forced into the benefit system because of inadequate provision.

Poverty and older people

The lives of most people change considerably on retiring from paid work and generally speaking, people have less money and more time than previously. To some extent, retirement is a fairly modern convention, creating a fundamental change in people's lives at the appointed time. For many, retirement marks the passage between 'useful work' and 'old age', between earning a wage and depending on a pension. The specific impact of these changes varies between men and women (particularly if the woman has not been engaged in paid work), between individuals of different socio-economic backgrounds (some have financial investments and company pensions, while others are reliant on a state pension alone), between able-bodied and disabled individuals and between different cultures. The material and psychological impact of retirement is therefore quite complex and generalizations, as always, have their problems. However, for the majority of people (including those who have looked forward to it), the onset of retirement is often experienced as a time of relative loss. People may lose the status and income gained from paid employment and the sense of companionship of workmates and colleagues – and, perhaps more importantly, the sense of purpose in their lives. Many people lose their role as workers and have no other positive role with which to identify (for further discussion, see Phillipson and Scharf 2004).

Since 1997, the position of older people has improved, with less people in income poverty. The minimum income guarantee has had a significant impact in reducing the number of pensioner households in poverty.

However, the majority of the fall in households in poverty has been among single pensioner households, while the proportion of pensioner couple households in poverty has remained about the same since 1996/7 (Palmer *et al.* 2005).

The increase in private pensions has also had an effect on pensioner incomes so that older pensioner couples, in particular, are more likely to have a low income than younger pensioner couples. However, about 1.2 million pensioners have no income other than state retirement pension and state benefits. The increasing shift towards non-state pension schemes is one significant feature of the past few years, as is the shift towards fully-funded pension schemes, with many funds having altered their pension arrangements by withdrawing final salary schemes. This has been particularly true in the public sector. Non-take-up of benefits remains a significant contribution to pensioner poverty. Pensioners are more likely to report a long-standing illness or disability, while the number of people receiving home care has nearly halved since 1994. Older people are more likely to report that they feel unsafe – particularly women from lower income households (Palmer *et al.* 2005: 87–93). This contributes to greater social isolation and exclusion (see Box 4.6 and Chapter 7).

Box 4.6   Growing older in socially deprived areas

- Older people in deprived areas face multiple risks of exclusion; poverty affects nearly half of people aged 60 and over in deprived urban neighbourhoods.
- About a fifth lack seven or more items that we think are necessities.
- Almost half of older people in poverty go without buying clothes; 15 per cent sometimes go without buying food.
- Almost 80 per cent of older Somali people and 70 per cent of older Pakistani people live in poverty; they are also more likely to be lonely.
- Older women are much more likely to be multiply deprived than older men, and older pensioners than younger.
- 28 per cent have had recent experience of property crime, for example, break-ins and vandalism. Nevertheless, three quarters can identify something that they like about their neighbourhood.
- More than a third see a child or other relative every day; a further 37 per cent see a relative at least weekly. Loneliness is more prevalent in those who have never married or are separated/divorced.
- A significant minority report a lack of services, such as clubs and post offices (the latter is likely to become more of a problem due to branch closures).

Source: Scharf *et al.* (2002)

Since 1997, the Labour government has made some moves to improve pensioner incomes but, there has been no return to matching state pension increases to average earnings and, they remain linked to the retail price index, which gives lower annual increases. Two main developments in state support have taken place. The first is one-off payments (e.g. the winter fuel allowance) paid once a year and, the second is the Minimum Income Guarantee, introduced in the first years of the government but replaced in 2003 by the Pension Credit. While welcomed, there has been a continuing campaign for better state pensions, as many pensioners still rely on social security support. In addition, many pensioners entitled to means tested benefits do not claim them. In 2002/3, the rates of uptake were about 87 per cent for housing benefit, 68 per cent for the minimum income guarantee and 59 per cent for council tax benefit.

In future there will be more emphasis on individual saving for pensions. The shift from state provision to individual private pensions has continued and the government expects people to save for retirement. The role of the state pension will be to provide a basic minimum. The introduction of stakeholder pensions was a major policy initiative, to extend pension provision to many lower paid people and those in small companies without pension schemes. The scheme provides a tax-free way of building savings to buy a pension, but take-up has been poor. Recent concerns have been about the viability of private pension schemes, due to rising costs resulting from longevity and shifts in the balance between those in work and those retired. Many schemes are concerned that there will be a shortfall in funding and a major pensions review, chaired by Lord Turner, was established by the government in 2004 to examine the 'pensions crisis' (see Chapter 11). The review in 2005/6 produced substantial debate about the need to simplify state pension systems, and ensure adequate and secure private pension schemes. However, perhaps the most contentious issue has been the discussion over retirement age and, whether it should be raised from 65 due to increasing longevity. Of concern here is another inequality between lower and upper socio-economic classes, with lower groups having lower life expectancy and, therefore, less retirement time (see Chapter 5).

Long-standing illness, disability and poverty

Disabled people are more likely, than other groups, to be dependent not only on state benefits – contributory, means tested and universal – but also on state welfare services. Changes in the levels of service and the way services are provided also affect disabled people and their ability to meet their own needs. The removal of the right to income support, to pay for residential care or housework, and its replacement with a system of care managers designing packages of care (see Chapters 6 and 7), has been severely criticized by disabled people.

Disabled people are disadvantaged in the labour market, and are more at risk of unemployment and low pay than other groups of workers. This means that they are likely to fare badly in occupational and private pension schemes (Groves 1991). Some 30 per cent of disabled adults are living in poverty and they are twice as likely to live in a low income household as non-disabled adults (Palmer *et al.* 2005). In addition, the proportion of people with a work-limiting disability, who are low-paid, is around 10 per cent higher than for employees without a work-limiting disability (Palmer *et al.* 2005: 75). Long-term illness and disability are associated with poverty: adults in the poorest fifth of the population, aged 45–64, are twice as likely to have a limiting long-standing illness or disability as those on average incomes and nearly three times as likely as the richest fifth of the population (Palmer *et al.* 2005: 79). The results for experiencing a mental health problem are similar except that women are more likely to suffer than men in all but the poorest fifth of the population (Palmer *et al.* 2005: 80).

People with disabilities are also more likely to have lower educational qualifications than non-disabled people. However, notwithstanding this, at every level of qualification, people with disabilities are more likely to be low-paid than non-disabled people, suggesting that there is discrimination in the labour market against people with disabilities (Palmer *et al.* 2005)

Race and poverty

Ethnicity and race are also linked to poverty. The health of Pakistanis, Bangladeshis and Afro-Caribbeans, is the poorest in the UK due to the fact that many are living in poverty (Nazroo 1997). People from ethnic minority communities tend to work in sectors where wages are low, and 25 per cent of Pakistani and Bangladeshi employees, 15 per cent of Indian and 11 per cent of black people are low-paid, compared to 10 per cent of white people (Howarth *et al.* 1999). Some 60 per cent of Pakistani and Bangladeshi people are poor – nearly four times the rate for white people (Berthoud 1998). Unemployment rates for people from ethnic groups are also higher, while benefit claimant rates are often lower.

Thus, race and ethnicity are important factors in relation to poverty. More importantly, we can see how race and ethnicity can exacerbate problems of low pay, unemployment etc. It is not surprising that employment rates for women are lower in these groups, and that pensioner poverty is greater. For migrant workers the situation is even more problematic, as they only have temporary status. However, analysis of benefit uptake and income for migrants is complex. Overall, it has been estimated that migrant workers contribute more to the economy than is claimed in services and benefits. Migrant families with children are, though, more likely to be worse off than their UK-born counterparts and, poverty in old age is also a problem (reflecting lower contributions over a lifetime towards pensions) (Gott and Johnston 2002).

The situation for asylum seekers is further exacerbated by their non-resident status and the high political profile attached to issues of immigration and illegal immigrants. Many asylum seekers have suffered major health problems and through the dispersal system, are often detached from their own communities. In the past few years, government policy towards asylum seekers has become increasingly restrictive, with the removal of welfare benefit entitlements in 2000, and support responsibilities transferred to the National Asylum Support Service (part of the Home Office). In 2002, support was withdrawn from those not seeking asylum status immediately they entered the UK, or cooperating with Home

Office enquiries as to their status, leading to increased homelessness (Heptinstall *et al.* 2004). The position of asylum seekers remains difficult and their numbers and nationalities fluctuates from year to year, but many asylum seekers find it difficult to access services, including the NHS, and rely on charitable support (Burnett and Peel 2001).

Conclusion

This chapter has provided a brief overview of poverty and inequality in the UK. An understanding of these issues is important for health and social care practitioners, as people's circumstances impact on their health and social circumstances and with their ability to engage in activities in society. In particular, it is important to recognise that people with health and social problems are also at risk of poverty and social exclusion. People with disabilities and long-term health problems are likely to be at greater risk of poverty, particularly if they move from employment to being supported on benefits. In addition, the rapid expansion of credit in society puts many working people at greater risk of poverty if they become unemployed or ill. The interrelationships between income, social position, educational attainment and health are complex but people disadvantaged in one area are more at risk of suffering multiple disadvantage.

Some universal services, such as the NHS, actually stigmatize in the way people are treated. As Abel-Smith and Titmuss argued:

> *The challenge that faces us is not the choice between universal and selective services. The real challenge resides in the question: what particular infrastructure is needed to provide a framework of values and opportunity bases within and around which can be developed socially acceptable selective services able to discriminate positively with the minimum risk of stigma in favour of those whose needs are greatest? There can, therefore, be no answer in Britain to the problems of poverty, ethnic integration and social and educational inequalities without an infrastructure of universal services.*
> (Abel-Smith and Titmuss 1987: 189)

However, 'universal services' also need to be both equitable and non-discriminatory in nature. The complexity of modern societies, which are marked by difference and division, creates enormous challenges for welfare services. It is difficult, for example, to address problems of race discrimination among users of welfare, when those very agencies supplying the services may discriminate against ethnic minorities in their employment (Carter 2003). For health and social care professionals, having a good understanding of how poverty and inequalities manifest themselves, is essential to the provision of good care and services. This is not just because of the interrelationship between poverty, inequalities and health, but also because of the way that differences and diversity can reinforce these inequalities, and affect the life chances and circumstances of people who are users of services. In addition, the way the state responds to these problems is an important factor in reflecting how people experience welfare support. The challenge to modern welfare states is how to combine concepts of universalism with an appreciation of difference and diversity. The development of choice in public services has been one response to this, and here, the idea is that increased choice develops opportunities for individuals to gain services relevant to them. However, as suggested in Chapter 2, this consumerist approach is not without problems, and how welfare states deal with poverty and inequality is perhaps one of the major challenges of this new century.

Summary

- There are long-standing tensions within UK welfare policy between the provision of universal or selective (targeted) benefits, that are associated with views about deserving and undeserving poor and the best way to tackle poverty and inequality.
- Despite the introduction of the Beveridge post-war welfare state by the Labour government in the 1940s, poverty and inequalities have persisted and, new divisions in society may have been created by the welfare state itself.
- While there are many divisions in society, structural inequalities between different socio-economic groups, men and women, different ethnic groups, those with and without disabilities or between older and younger people remain.
- Approaches to individualize welfare have been occurring since the 1980s. These address the uniform approach developed in the 1940s and 1950s, based on ideas of self-responsibility but also recognize the heterogeneity of society and changes in working patterns.
- While there is a continuing emphasis on self-responsibility, the New Labour government has emphasized the need for universal approaches and the role of government to address the inequality and poverty of particular groups in society, such as families with children, people with disabilities and older people.
- However, work and the need to link the benefit system to work, are central to the Labour government's approach.
- Social exclusion has become a key concept in examining the problems of poverty and inequality in society, and recognizes that exclusion from work and social life can exacerbate existing poverty and inequalities.

Further reading

Palmer, G., Carr, J. and Kenway, P. (2005) *Monitoring Poverty and Social Exclusion 2005*. York: Joseph Rowntree Foundation/New Policy Institute.
Pantazis, C., Gordon, D. and Levitas, R. (2006) *Poverty and Social Exclusion in Britain*. Bristol: Policy Press.

Smith, G.M., Dorling, D. and Shaw, M. (2001) *Poverty, Inequality and Health in Britain, 1800–2000: Reader*. Bristol: Policy Press.

Social Exclusion Unit (2004) *Breaking the Cycle: Taking Stock of Progress and Priorities for the Future*. London: Office of the Deputy Prime Minister.

Sutherland, H., Sefton, T. and Piachaud, D. (2003) *Poverty in Britain: The Impact of Government Policy Since 1997*. York: Joseph Rowntree Foundation.

Wheeler, B., Shaw, M., Mitchell, R. and Dorling, D. (2005) *Life in Britain: Using Millennial Census Data to Understand Poverty, Inequality and Place*. Bristol: Policy Press.

PUBLIC HEALTH AND HEALTH INEQUALITIES

Introduction

In Chapters 1, 2 and 4, we outlined debates about the extent to which the welfare state was introduced, to bring about greater equality rather than just to provide a 'safety net'. We have suggested that the provision of free, universal health care was intended to ensure that everyone had access to these services and that, at the very least, there would be a considerable reduction in the inequalities that were based on social class and the ability to purchase services (or not). Without doubt, the health of the UK population has improved substantially since the Second World War. However, as discussed in Chapter 3, we need to question the extent to which this is the result of the welfare state and, more specifically, the creation of the NHS.

The UK situation reflects the fact that the health of the world's population has improved faster in the last 50 years then at any other point in human history. When reviewing measures of human health, such as life expectancy or disease-specific mortality rates, we see remarkable increases in longevity, alongside a rapid decline in rates of what used to be killer diseases, such as smallpox or cholera. However, while gross statistics show what great progress has been made, they also hide highly variable pictures within countries.

The health status gap between the richest and poorest nations, and the richest and poorest communities within nations, has expanded in the last

30 years, as shown by the inequalities in the under 5 mortality rate between countries, shown in Figure 5.1, leading policy-makers in many countries to turn their attention to health inequalities. But what action should be taken? The concept of health inequalities is highly contested, precisely because of debates around what should be measured, how to measure it and what is causing health inequalities in the first place. This chapter reviews these debates, and discusses the response of the government to health inequalities and public health in the UK.

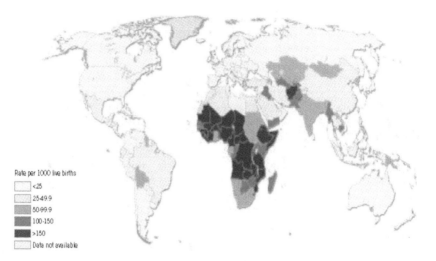

Rate per 1000 live births

- [ ] <25
- [ ] 25-49.9
- [ ] 50-99.9
- [ ] 100-150
- [ ] >150
- [ ] Data not available

Figure 5.1 Global distributional inequity – under 5 mortality rate, 2003
Source: WHO (2005: 9).

Equity and the NHS

As discussed in Chapter 3, equity was a key founding principle of the NHS and, since the establishment of the welfare state, social policy analysts have principally been concerned with the question of equity. Whitehead (1994) has indicated that the NHS was built on at least eight components of equity or fairness, and it is possible to evaluate the extent to which it has operated in an equitable or fair manner. The evidence available indicates that some of the principles have been achieved, at least in part, whereas others have not:

1 *Universal entitlement.* In general, this principle has been achieved; everyone who is resident in Britain is entitled to the services provided by the NHS. However, homeless people and new immigrants can find it difficult to register with a GP and gain access to health care. In recent years, it has become increasingly difficult, especially for adults, to find a dentist who is prepared to treat them on the NHS, though the NHS has

to provide people with details of a dentist who is prepared to take NHS patients.

2   *Pooling of financial risk.* The NHS continues to be paid for out of general taxation. Taxes are generally progressive in Britain, meaning that the better off, in general, pay more in taxes than those who are less well off, although since 1979 taxation became less progressive – with a shift from direct taxation (on income) to indirect taxation (on goods and services, such as VAT).

3   *Free at the point of delivery.* The principle of a free service was breached almost immediately and since then charges for medicine, appliances, opticians and dental services have gradually increased, and the rate of increase has accelerated since 1979. Charges are means tested so that the least well off, and children, are generally exempt. However, means tests act as a deterrent to the poor seeking services, and many people who are not entitled to a free service, have difficulty in meeting charges. Differences are now appearing within the UK, with Wales and Scotland having cheaper prescription charges and Scotland providing free long-term care (see below). Also, the hidden costs of health care are not taken into account, for example, the cost of getting to the service in the first place with loss of earnings resulting from time taken off work. Manual workers are more likely to lose earnings if they take time off, poor people, older people and women are more likely, than middle-class people and men, to have to use public transport (where it exists) to attend health care appointments, with the attendant costs in money and time which its use entails.

4   *Equality of access.* Everyone should have access to a comprehensive range of services – primary, secondary and tertiary care. However, the NHS nationalized the existing provision, resulting in considerable inequalities in spending on health care and the provision of services in different regions. Since the 1970s, there has been some reduction in inter-regional inequality following the introduction of funding formulae to redistribute resources, initially through the Resource Allocation Working Party (RAWP) and now via complex mechanisms to allocate resources based on socio-demographic factors (Mays and Bevan 1987; Royston *et al.* 1992; Dixon 2001). There are also distinct differences in funding levels between England, Northern Ireland, Scotland and Wales, with the English NHS receiving less per head of population than the other countries. There is also considerable evidence of 'distance decay and territorial injustice', which means that the greater the travel distance between the hospital and a patient's residence reduces hospital utilization – although this depends also on patient characteristics, such as age, gender, ethnicity, socio-economic status, the type of service (e.g. cancer services have become more centralized) and the type of condition (Mohan 1995; Exworthy and Peckham 2006). More resources in the NHS have been devoted to acute services than those for people with long-term conditions, although there has been some redistribution from hospital to community services since the early 1980s, in an attempt to restructure services to meet the growing need of addressing chronic, rather than acute, health problems. Current policy recognizes the need to develop self-care and support chronic disease

services in the community (Scottish Executive 2003; DoH 2006). As discussed in Chapter 7, there was an erosion of free NHS care for frail elderly people requiring non-acute health care, including continuing care beds, during the 1980s. Reforms, brought in under the Community Care Act 1990, focused attention on the relationship between health and social care and who should pay for it (Means *et al.* 2002). Most recently, this debate has centred on the payment for long-term nursing care, and following a decision by the Ombudsman, many English PCTs have had to review decisions about nursing payments. The issue has also been highlighted by the fact that in Scotland long-term care for older people is now free (Bell and Bowse 2006).

5 *Equality of care.* This is the principle that everyone should receive the same quality and level of service for the same need. In 1971, Tudor Hart argued that there is an 'inverse care law' in the NHS – those that have the greatest need for services have access to the poorest services. He suggested that this was because the more prosperous areas attract the greatest resources, including skilled health workers in primary and secondary care. Other research has suggested that middle-class people receive a better standard of care, are given more time by doctors and other health workers, also that doctors and other health workers are less likely to explain their health problems and treatment to working-class, than to middle-class people (Cartwright and Anderson 1983). However, recent research suggests that the UK has one of the most equitable primary care services in terms of provision (Shi *et al.* 2002).

6 *Selection on the basis of clinical need.* This is the principle that services should be provided on the basis of need and not ability to pay. It has generally been adhered to, although it is affected by inequalities between regions (discussed above) and clinical judgement of the likelihood of benefit. There have, for instance, been cases of people denied treatment on the basis of age or lifestyle. It has also remained possible for people to pay privately for treatment in order to avoid a wait and/or to have treatment that is not considered medically necessary. Recent policy attempts, to curtail waiting lists, have also led to concerns that people with less urgent medical needs are being treated at the expense of those with more urgent needs and patient choice adds an additional complexity to waiting list management (Fotaki *et al.* 2005).

7 *Non-exploitative ethos of science.* This is the view that medical care is based on value-free and objective knowledge. Concern has been expressed at the ways in which people, especially those from ethnic minority groups and women, have been controlled by medical professionals in relation to access to health care and treatment (Miles 1991; Coker 2001). At a more general level, it has been suggested that, the power of the medical professions has come from their successful claim to scientific status and the claimed efficacy of medical treatments (Foucault 1963; Armstrong 1984), which is not totally proven. Also, it has been argued, that doctors have extended their status and power by medicalizing more and more areas of life (Scull 1977; Witz 1992; Moynihan and Henry 2005) although Strong (1979) argues against this. This enables medical practitioners to maintain a high status, high economic rewards and a dominant position in the medical division of

labour. Patients are seen as something to be worked *on* rather than people to be worked *with* (Savage 1986).

8 *Feelgood factor*. A feeling shared by all citizens, that it is a good thing that all members of society have access to health care when they are ill. Despite all the criticisms and concerns that have been expressed about the NHS, there is a feeling that it should remain; it continues to be a popular service in Britain.

The NHS, then, while it may not have achieved equity – whether this is defined as equal access for all, equal spending on all, services provided on the basis of need, equal treatment or equal outcome – remains a popular institution, although there is still dissatisfaction with waiting times (British Social Attitudes Survey 2005). Furthermore, while the health of the population, as a whole, has generally improved since 1948 and the fear of having to pay for medical treatment has, in the main, disappeared, nevertheless, the relative inequalities between the more advantaged and the more disadvantaged groups, prior to 1948, have persisted and may even have increased. Since the 1970s, there has been an increasing concern, therefore, not only about equity, but also about identifying and measuring inequalities in health outcome, reflecting the wider concern of examining the impact of the welfare state. In addition, as discussed in Chapter 3, there has been a renewed interest in the role of public health and improving population health, a key element of which has been the priority placed on tackling health inequalities by the Labour government (Baggott 2000; Exworthy and Powell 2001). The setting up of the Acheson Inquiry (DoH 1998a) into health inequalities perhaps marked a key break with the position of the previous Conservative government, which had not placed inequality particularly high on its political agenda, although it had commissioned work on 'health variations' in the mid-1990s (DoH 1995; NHSCRD 1995). The Acheson Inquiry affirmed Labour's commitment to addressing health inequalities, and linked back to the previous Labour government of the 1970s, which commissioned the Black Report (Townsend *et al.* 1992). This first identified the continuing persistence of health inequalities in Britain, but was virtually ignored by the Conservative government, which replaced Labour in 1979 (see discussion below, and also, Berridge and Blume 2005).

Understanding health inequalities

One need only look at national and international statistics on maternal and child health, to understand that there is great variation within and between populations and that, therefore, the concept of health inequalities should be relatively straightforward. During the latter half of the nineteenth centrury in Britain, when vital statistics such as births and deaths were being systematically recorded for the first time, the country's first public health officers noted large variations in the health of different populations. William Farr worked as 'Compiler of abstracts' for the General Registrar Office in the mid-1800s, and reported stunning differences in

Table 5.1 Density of population, death rate, birth rate, excess of births over deaths and increase of population per 1000 persons, living in seven groups of districts, arranged in the order of mortality

Number of districts	Range of mortality rates per 1000 living	Persons to a square mile	1861–70 To 1000 persons living			
			Average annual deaths	Average annual births	Average annual excess of births over deaths	Average annual increase of population in middle of period
England and Wales 619	15–39	307	22.4	35.1	12.6	12.4
51	15–17	171	16.7	30.1	13.4	15.8
349	18–20	193	19.8	32.2	13.0	8.8
142	21–23	447	22.0	35.6	13.6	16.2
56	24–26	2,183	25.1	38.1	13.0	15.3
16	27–30	6,871	27.8	39.1	11.3	8.9
1	32	12,172	32.5	37.3	4.8	3.2
1	39	65,834	38.6	37.6	−1.0	−12.3

birth and mortality rates by area (according to population density) and by social class. Table 5.1 is taken from his report (Humphreys 1885).

There are stark inequalities in maternal mortality between developing and developed countries, with women in developing countries as much as 40 times more at risk of dying during pregnancy and childbirth as women in developed countries (see Box 5.1). The maternal mortality ratio in Eritrea for the period 1990–8 was 1000/100,000 compared to the UK's 7/100,000 (World Bank 2001). Within the UK, life expectancy for women varies from 82.26 years, in Kensington and Chelsea (a relatively prosperous area), to 76.58 years in Manchester. Infant mortality rates, in Manchester, are double the rates in Kensington and Chelsea (9.2 per 1000 live births v. 4.1 per 1000 live births) (ONS 2001). These rates, in themselves, mask variation within local areas and between different groups in local areas. In the USA, where health statistics are kept by ethnic origin, infant mortality rates within large cities can vary as much as 300 per cent between whites and ethnic minorities. For example, in Chicago, the infant mortality rate in the non-Hispanic white population is 6 per 1000 live births, while for the non-Hispanic black population it is 13.9 per 1000 live births (Margellos *et al.* 2004).

Central to the debate about health inequalities is whether attention should be given to health *inequality* or to health *inequity*. Those who concern themselves with health inequalities wish to see the closure of the health gap between rich and poor, while those focusing on health inequity wish to tackle the injustice of the most disadvantaged populations having the poorest health. However, any discussion of equity or equality, and thus inequality, needs to define the equality of what and between whom. The term 'health inequalities' encompasses two very loaded words – 'health' and 'inequalities'. Both need definition in order to understand the overall

> **Box 5.1   Maternal mortality**
>
> Every day, at least 1600 women die from the complications of pregnancy and childbirth. That is 585,000 women – at a minimum – dying every year. The majority of these deaths – almost 90 per cent – occur in Asia and sub-Saharan Africa; approximately 10 per cent in other developing regions; and less than 1 per cent in the developed world. Between 25 and 33 per cent of all deaths of women of reproductive age, in many developing countries, are the result of complications of pregnancy or childbirth. In addition to the number of deaths each year, over 50 million more women suffer from maternal morbidity – acute complications from pregnancy. For at least 18 million women, these morbidities are long-term and often debilitating.
>
> *Source*: WHO (1998: 1)

term itself. This area is well explored in the Black Report (Townsend *et al.* 1992), which considers the thorny issues of defining 'health' and 'inequalities' and then what indicators to use for measuring both (see Box 5.2). The writers of the Report opted for using the World Health Organization (WHO) definition of health as '*a state of complete physical, mental and social well-being and not merely the absence of disease or infirmity*' (WHO 1985). This definition allows the inclusion of indicators that reflect social, economic and environmental, as well as biological, determinants of health. The indicator of inequalities used by the Report is social class, which they define as '*segments of the population sharing broadly similar types and levels of resources with broadly similar styles of living and some shared perception of their collective condition*' (Townsend *et al.* 1992: 39). This view of health inequalities is summarized by John Mckinlay who wrote, '*While still largely overlooked in epidemiologic thinking, social system influences may account for as much (if not more) of the variation in health and/or illness statistics as do environmental influences, or even the attributes and lifestyles of individuals*' (1995: 2), although as we saw in the last chapter, these broad groupings have now been changed to more fully reflect these aspects.

Since the publication of the Black Report, numerous researchers have taken up the challenge of identifying the 'best' indicators for understanding the relationship between socially constructed inequalities and health. It is widely recognized that there are inequalities in health status between deprived and affluent communities, confirmed by numerous studies, and that inequalities exist not only in mortality but in morbidity (Davey-Smith *et al.* 1994; Blane *et al.* 1996; Eachus *et al.* 1996; Kaplan *et al.* 1996; Kennedy *et al.* 1996). However, the precise causal relationship between deprivation and health inequalities is unclear, but both individual characteristics, geographical and social factors are implicated (Duncan *et al.* 1993). The relative effect of these will vary according to specific circumstances and, interventions to reduce health inequalities will therefore require a range of approaches tailored to societies, communities and individuals. It has also been suggested that early life factors, and/or the

> **Box 5.2** The Black Report
>
> The controversial nature of discussing health inequalities is depicted by the history of the Black Report. A study of national and international evidence on inequalities was commissioned by the Labour government in the UK in the late 1970s, and the Report was presented in 1980 to a Conservative administration. The main policy recommendations featured in the report were:
>
> - A call for a total, and not merely service-oriented, approach to the problems of health.
> - A call for a radical overhaul in the balance of activity and proportionate distribution of resources within the health and associated services in favour of those most disadvantaged in British society.
>
> The Report was promptly buried by the Conservative government, who could not marry up its redistributive thrust and their own free-market agenda. The Report was published two years later, by Penguin Books, and generated tremendous interest beyond Britain's borders, where it influenced the WHO's European office, as it developed its own health promotion strategy focusing on reducing health inequalities.

cumulative effects of life events, including the effects of deprivation on social cohesion, play a significant role (Davey-Smith *et al.* 1997; Kawachi *et al.* 1997). More recently, the Acheson Committee called for a renewed approach to tackling health inequalities, that cuts across departmental boundaries and responsibilities – although it stopped short of calling for redistributive income policies (DoH 1998a).

Explanations for health inequalities

In Chapter 1 we introduced the concept of social divisions – the recognition that society is characterized by differences between people. We argued that such differences are linked to inequality, and discussed how this relates to poverty and social exclusion in Chapters 2 and 4. It is, therefore, not surprising that health inequalities are also linked to these differences. However, there has been substantial debate about the exact relationship between such population differences and their effect on health inequalities. There are two broad approaches to explaining how health inequalities arise.

Cultural/behavioural explanations stress differences in the ways in which different social groups 'choose' to live their lives – that is, the behaviour and 'voluntary' lifestyles they adopt. It has been suggested, for example, that lower social groups choose to smoke more, drink more, eat less healthy food and exercise less than those in more advantaged groups, all issues raised in *Saving Lives* and *Choosing Health* (DoH 1999a, 2004a). However, statistics have shown that even when we compare individuals from socio-economic groups 1 and 2 (see page 73) whose smoking, eating, drinking and exercise habits are broadly similar to those of the working-class stereotype, health inequalities by class still persist (Marmot *et al.* 1991; DoH 1998a).

Structural explanations stress the role of social circumstances that are outside the control of individuals. They maintain that the evidence indicates that the majority of health differentials between people defined on the basis of class, gender or ethnic group, are avoidable and are intrinsically related to the wider life chances of these groups. Structuralist explanations thus emphasize the external environment and the conditions in which people live and work. Research indicates that lay people are themselves aware of the effect that poor living conditions, low income, unsafe working conditions, pollution and so on have on their health. (Cornwell 1984; Ong 1993). They also stress the importance of socio-economic pressures on low-income households to consume unhealthy products (such as cheap food) as important determinants of health status.

In *The Health Divide*, Whitehead (1987) noted the interrelationship between behavioural and structuralist explanations, using as an example the incidence of childhood accidents. Here the behaviour of parents and children is clearly linked to structural issues, such as the lack of safe play areas and fenced gardens, and the problems of supervision in high-rise areas.

In a study by Marmot *et al.* (1984), which looked at health inequalities within the Civil Service, it was found that mortality rates of low-grade civil servants were three times higher than those of high-grade civil servants. Evidence of this sort suggests that poverty itself is unable to explain the persistence of health inequalities, for while low-grade employees have less disposable income, they are not 'poor' as such. This suggests that explanations which highlight the importance of social and psychological stress, as significant factors affecting health inequalities between different groups, may be more useful.

Other studies have focused on material deprivation and specifically on housing conditions, employment, poverty and an adverse environment. The explanation put forward by Marmot may be even more relevant when we acknowledge the relationship between these material factors and psychological and social stress. Furthermore, by looking at health inequalities from this perspective, we are able to appreciate the impact that all areas of social policy have on health, and the interdependence and relationship between them. Housing conditions are a major contributory factor determining health. It has been found, for example, that people from areas of poor-quality housing are in poorer health, have more long-standing illness and show more symptoms of depression, than those living in 'good' housing areas (see Chapter 8). The reasons for this include living in damp and mouldy housing causing: respiratory/bronchial problems; overcrowding leading to stress within families, family breakdown and mental illness; poor design and lack of play areas, contributing to ill health and accidents, especially among children; and problems associated with poor refuse collection and infestation (Marsh *et al.* 2000).

Employment status and unemployment have also been shown to be a cause of physical and mental ill health (Whitehead 1987). Manual workers such as miners, builders and others, whose jobs involve exposure to dust or toxic substances and possible accidents, are clearly at more risk of ill health or even death than those in the professional classes. Some studies have also shown that the stress caused by unemployment is an important factor in mental health and may sometimes lead to suicide, but that once the unemployed find their way back into work their, and their family's, overall health improves markedly (Fox and Goldblatt 1982).

Researchers have developed these concepts in more detail and developed a number of different explanations that draw on these two broad approaches, focusing on income, class, inequalities arising from health conditions, life course differences and inequalities of access (Marmot *et al.* 1997; Stronks *et al.* 1997).

Income inequality

More recently income has been seen as a key factor influencing inequalities in health (Kaplan *et al.* 1996; Wilkinson 1996, 2005; Lynch *et al.* 1998). Wilkinson, in particular, has argued that there is a direct relationship between levels of income inequality and health across more developed countries. In his book *Unhealthy Societies* (1996) he pulls together '*a growing body of new evidence which shows that life expectancy in different countries is dramatically improved where income differences are smaller and societies are more socially cohesive*' (Wilkinson 1996: 1), where life expectancy becomes his indicator for health. He explores data on relative income levels within countries and, compares these with life expectancy, arguing that in countries such as Japan and the Netherlands, where income disparities are relatively small, life expectancies are indeed higher than in countries where income disparities are much wider, such as the UK and the USA. In his later book, *The Impact of Inequality*, (2005) he argues that the absolute income poverty of less developed countries accounts for their appalling health statistics. For further health improvement in more developed countries, rather than focusing on increasing economic growth or improving living standards, the policy focus now needs to be on reducing the income gap between the highest and lowest paid in any given country. The policy implications, of accepting the arguments about income inequality, lead to a need for redistribution of income in any given population, so as to narrow the gulf between the highest and lowest earners in society (Wilkinson 2005).

Income also affects access to services and goods, such as the quality and quantity of food which people can afford. It is commonly found in studies of poorer families that when money is short, spending on food tends to be restricted (Dowler *et al.* 2001). Furthermore, given that the cheaper foods tend to be high in sugar and fat content, this leads to less healthy diets being adopted (see Box 5.5). Income also affects the type of housing a family can afford and the amount and type of heating available. Research data consistently demonstrates the link between income and poor health (see Figure 5.2). The issue of income inequality and health inequality was the subject of debate following the publication of the Acheson Report

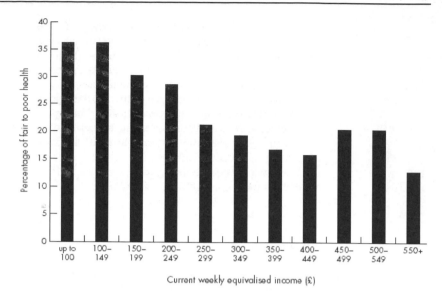

Figure 5.2 Prevalence of poor self rated health by net current weekly equivalized income
Source: Weich *et al*. (2002: Fig. 1)

(DoH 1998a) which was seen to shy away from explicitly linking income inequality and poverty specifically to health inequalities.

Class inequality

It has been argued that Wilkinson's approach is an insufficient explanation, and that the focus should be on social class and the differences in relative and perceived social status between classes (Muntaner and Lynch 1999; Coburn 2000). The emphasis, here, is on the study of social mechanisms that create income inequality in the first place – in other words, social class – as concentrating on income levels doesn't adequately explain other research findings that link different social *position* with differing health status. The relative effect of being of a certain social class can, in itself, influence an individual's health. Marxists and neo-Marxists consider the importance of class relations and exploitation of one class by another as a key feature explaining differences in income levels and other social welfare indicators. Those who own the means of production (e.g. chief executives and senior managers of large corporations), enjoy greater health because they can control how the wealth that is generated is then distributed. The policy implications of following this line of thinking would be to work on breaking down class structures, so that there can be greater social mobility and a greater sense of control for all parts of society. There are two theoretical approaches associated with such arguments challenging the dominance of class *per se* as the cause of such differences.

The *artefact explanation* of the apparent differences in health experienced by the lower and higher social classes, argues that the method of measuring occupational class, used by the Registrar General, inflates the size and importance of health differences (Jones and Cameron 1984; Illsley 1986). However, studies that tried to control some of the measurement problems involved with occupational class (Goldblatt 1990; Marmot *et al.* 1991), continued to demonstrate the existence of a clear occupational class gradient, and research using indicators of inequality other than occupation, has confirmed the pattern of health inequalities between the top and bottom of the social scale (Rose and Marmot 1981; Marmot *et al.* 1991).

Theories of *natural and social selection* (in terms of health selection) acknowledge the existence of health inequalities but attribute them to a process of 'natural selection' or 'the survival of the fittest'. In a way analogous to the theories of Darwin, it is suggested that those who are best fitted to survive are upwardly mobile socially, and those who are not are downwardly mobile. That is, people in poor health tend to move down the social class scale and become concentrated in the lower socio-economic groups, whereas those in good health experience upward mobility; in other words, it is health status that determines social class, not social class that determines health status. The gap between the higher and the lower classes is therefore inevitable, whatever overall improvements occur.

However, the downward social mobility of unhealthy people makes only a small difference in the overall figures. Indeed, other research has clearly indicated that health-related mobility between classes, cannot explain the difference in health between them. Fogelman *et al.* (1987), for example, found that differences in health between socio-economic groups of young people, who had remained static with respect to their parents, were the same as the differences for those who had been upwardly or downwardly mobile between the generations. Whitehead (1987) concluded that there is some evidence for health selection, but that it accounts for only a small proportion of the differences between social classes.

Inequality in individual health condition

Applying an economic perspective, Murray *et al.* (1999: 537) define health inequality as a '*composite measure of variation in health status across individuals in a population*'. By asking 'equality of what?' they considered whether they should focus on equality of 'healthy lifespan' (the number of years one lives in a state of good health), equality of 'health risk' (the level of health risks an individual faces in the course of their life) or 'health expectancy' (which measures expected levels of morbidity and mortality in individuals based on health risk) (Gakidou *et al.* 2000). They dismiss the usefulness of social class as an indicator of inequality, arguing that health should be considered as much of a 'commodity' as any economic commodity, and that therefore inequalities in health between individuals are valid to measure in and of themselves. While interesting, this argument does tend to leave aside the complexity of the interactions between an individual's social world and personal responses to it, that are better captured in both the social class and income inequality schools of thought.

Further, the implications of concentrating on health aspects alone might lead to inattention to wider societal determinants that result in health inequalities (Acheson 2000).

Inequalities in life course

While there is concern about focusing on individual health factors, there is evidence to suggest that individual life course factors can and do play an important role (Ben-Shlomo and Davey-Smith 1991; Elford *et al.* 1991; Davey-Smith *et al.* 1997; Kawachi *et al.* 1997). Research on birthweight has found that the risk for coronary heart disease and stroke falls with increasing birth weight (Frankel *et al.* 1996; Barker 1998). Similar observations have been made in relation to: accelerated ageing; the increased likelihood of a women born underweight giving birth to an underweight baby; and insulin resistance syndrome, which consists of diabetes, hypertension, dyslipidemia, cardiovascular disease and other abnormalities (Barker 1998).

Similarly, nutrition in the early years is also associated with life course health. Nutritional deficiency in the early years is associated with many adult diseases, such as cardiovascular disease, diabetes, cataracts and lower hearing acuity (Kuh and Ben-Shlomo 1997; Barker 1998). It is not surprising, therefore, that the WHO has highlighted the need to address such areas in its approach to well-being in later life (Stein and Moritz 1999). While such an approach does not deny the importance of wider social determinants on health, it is thought that the interaction of life course and social determinants experienced in life, are important factors when considering health inequalities (Stein and Moritz 1999).

Inequalities in access

As we explored in Chapter 3, one further dimension of inequalities, in relation to health, is access to services. For example, the 'inverse care law' (Tudor Hart 1988) states that the distribution of health care professionals is inversely related to the need for health services. The provision of a service which is theoretically 'free at the point of use' does not ensure that it is equally used in practice. Fees for some services and, for some people, the cost of actually getting to the surgery or clinic may be prohibitive. In addition, the need for knowledge about services is not equally distributed. All of these factors are particularly relevant in relation to the development of patient choice (Fotaki *et al.* 2005; Exworthy and Peckham 2006). These factors combine to create unequal access to, and use of, services. For example, there have been increasing concerns about differential access to pregnancy, maternity and postpartum support services between different age groups, different socio-economic classes, different cultural and ethnic groups (Social Exclusion Unit 1999; Bailey and Pain 2001; Davies and Bath 2001). This would suggest that both the absolute provision of midwives and skilled birthing attendants, their availability and accessibility, and the way in which they work are all important in addressing inequalities of access for women.

How do these social mechanisms interact?

Besides the debates regarding what are the most significant causal social mechanisms with regards to health inequalities, there has also been a fair degree of debate about how these mechanisms interact to create better or poorer health. A great deal of research has gone into explaining the links between social and health inequalities, with some interesting findings. The Whitehall Study followed a group of 17,000 civil servants, working in government offices, over a period of time and found that the employment grade of individuals proved to be far more important, as a risk factor for coronary heart disease, than the combination of 'class' risk factors, such as cigarette smoking, blood pressure or serum cholesterol levels (Marmot *et al.* 1984, 1991). Social epidemiologists, using the results of this and other long-term studies, speculate that there is an interweaving of psychosocial and biological factors that link social status with health.

There are several other factors, associated with poorer health status, that have an important bearing on the health inequality–health inequity debate. Besides income, education, occupation, gender and ethnicity have all been shown to correlate positively with health status (Nazroo 1997; Gwatkin 2000). Thus, health inequalities are intrinsically linked to difference and diversity in society. One approach, to addressing this, has been an increasing interest in the notion of social capital, which is seen as key to enhancing health outcomes, as it has been found that where there are stronger community ties, health is improved (Kawachi *et al.* 1997). Social capital describes the pattern and intensity of networks among people and the shared values which arise from those networks. While definitions of social capital vary, the main aspects are citizenship, neighbourliness, trust and shared values, community involvement, volunteering, social networks and civic participation.

Again, the reasons for the breakdown, of social capital or its absence, or how any of these aspects related to social capital, lead to differential health status are contentious, though social status provides an important link for all. What is remarkable is that in poorer countries where income levels are far lower than in the UK or other European countries but, where investments have been made in education (especially girls' education), health status indicators are impressive. *Support-led* economic processes, that focus on 'skilful social support of health care, education and other relevant social arrangements' have led to rapid reductions in mortality rates in countries such as India (Kerala State), Costa Rica and Sri Lanka, without any of these countries experiencing much economic growth (Sen 1999: 46). Yet survival rates within some African-American communities in the USA are lower than survival rates of people born in developing countries. (Sen 2001).

Health inequalities in Britain

Research in Britain, and elsewhere in Europe, has consistently demon-strated that disadvantaged groups have poorer health than more advan-taged groups and also, reduced access to health care. The publication of the Black Report, on health inequalities, had a significant impact on politi-cians and the medical and medical-sociology disciplines (Townsend *et al.* 1992; Berridge and Blume 2005). The working group's main finding was the apparent failure, of post-war social welfare and economic policy, to reduce the differences in health experience between the most affluent and the most impoverished in British society. Except in the case of child health, the differential between occupational classes I and II (professional and managerial) and IV and V (semi- and unskilled manual), in terms of life expectancy, grew until the mid-1990s, since when there has been a slight narrowing (see Figure 5.3). Mortality rates for the more affluent in society have fallen steadily, while the death rate for the poorest has fallen only marginally, thus widening the gap.

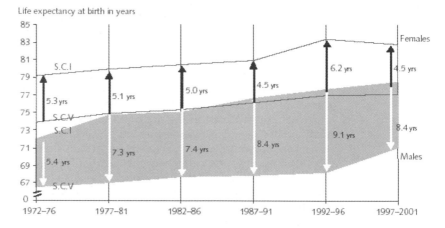

Figure 5.3   Life expectancy at birth in years, by social class and gender
Source: DoH (2005c)

The life expectancy of the least privileged in society is about eight years less than that of the most affluent. The most disadvantaged are also likely to experience more illness and disability (White *et al.* 1993). On election in 1997, the New Labour government announced that it would establish a committee of inquiry to update the Black Report and examine the more recent evidence on health inequalities. This work did in fact build on the DoH's work on differences in health (DoH 1995; NHSCRD 1995) but the general reluctance, by the previous Conservative government, to address health inequalities was based on their belief that these were the result of individual choice and lifestyle (Baggott 2000). The committee was chaired by Sir Donald Acheson (previously Chief Medical Officer from 1983 to 1991). It reported in 1998 and raised again questions about the relation-ship between population differences and health inequalities. Before examining the policy responses of the government, it is worth examining health inequalities in Britain in more detail.

Class, deprivation and health inequalities

As discussed earlier, class is problematic when used as a proxy indicator of household deprivation. The occupation of the head of household may not reflect the material circumstances of the household, if there are other wage-earning members. Conversely, those households in which there is no economically active member are excluded from analysis; this means, for example, that households headed by lone parents, who are not in employment, are excluded from analyses of inequalities in child health, despite being a group larger in numbers than either class I or class V. Studies that rely on social class, therefore, seriously underestimate inequalities in child health. Another problem emerges when social class is used in research into health inequalities among Britain's Afro-Caribbean and southern Asian populations. A final difficulty with using social class is with respect to older people. While social class, as measured by the occupation of the head of household prior to retirement, is a good indicator of health inequalities for the younger elderly, it is less so for older people. This may be because the economic circumstances of old age have an increasing impact, or because the relative importance of material factors in explaining differences in health experience declines with age. Small area studies have consistently found an association between ill health and deprivation (Kawachi and Berkman 2002), and Townsend et al. (1988) have argued that deprivation measures are more highly correlated with health status than is social class. While the reclassification of socio-economic groups addresses some of these issues, it still leaves questions about the interrelationship of difference (e.g. gender, ethnicity, age, employment status etc.) and its effect on inequalities (see Chapter 3).

For example, Moser et al. (1986) found that even after socio-economic position is taken into account, there remains more ill health among the unemployed than would be expected, and this is *not* due to health selection. Morris (1994) found significantly higher death rates among men whose unemployment was not obviously related to ill health, compared to men in employment. The stress associated with unemployment could be implicated in higher suicide rates among unemployed people, and mortality among women, married to unemployed men, is higher than among other married women. Wilkinson (1996) found that small changes in the living standards of families in occupational class V, literally mean life or death to the babies born to them. Shaw et al. (1999) have demonstrated that higher housing wealth is positively associated with higher life expectancy (see Figure 5.4). Homelessness is also associated with poor health (Stern et al. 1989), as is living in bed and breakfast accommodation (BMA 1987). Both homeless people and those in temporary accommodation have difficulty in gaining access to health care (Graham 1993a; Bines 1994).

Differences in health, between males and females, are usually so obvious that they are taken for granted, and as such they are easily overlooked. Male mortality is higher than female mortality from before birth, although

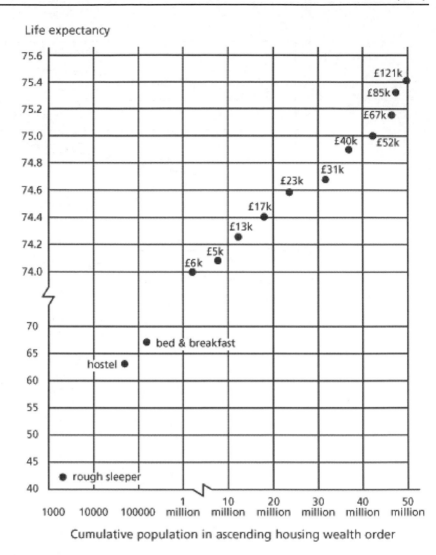

Figure 5.4 Life expectancy by housing wealth in England and Wales 1981–9.
Source: Shaw *et al.* (1999)

the difference has narrowed over the last 50 years (see Figure 5.5). While more men die from heart disease, cancer is the major cause of death among women. Women live longer than men but have a higher self-reported rate of morbidity.

There has been an increasing interest in the nature of gender inequalities and health, and the interrelationships between gender and other differences in society (Annandale and Hunt 2000; Cooper 2002). For example, when marital status is taken into account, married men have lower death and morbidity rates than men who have never been married, are widowed or divorced, but the reverse is true for women. Women have more physical

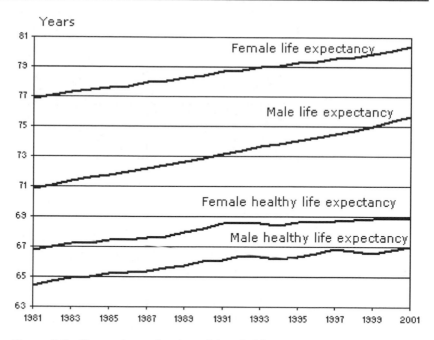

Figure 5.5 Comparison of male and female life expectancy 1981–2001
Source: National Statistics (2004)

illness and disability across the lifespan than men (Blaxter 1990), poorer psychosocial health, see GPs more often and are more frequently prescribed psychotropic drugs for anxiety or depression (Ashton 1991; Doyal 1995). We can sum up gender differences by suggesting that 'women get the quantity of life, men get the quality'.

Although, as we have already indicated, social class is not necessarily the best measure, and we should note that women do not always have equal access with men to household income (see Chapter 4), there are clear class differences in women's experience of health. Women who are married to men at the bottom of the class hierarchy, report more physical symptoms and illness than women married to men in higher social classes (Blaxter 1990). Women married to men employed in semi- and unskilled manual work (Registrar General's classes IV and V), are more likely to consult their GPs about health problems, than women married to men in professional or managerial occupations (classes I and II) (Chandola *et al.* 2003).

Motherhood also has an adverse impact on women's health. Mothers are more likely than fathers to report recent ill health and less likely to rate their health as good (Popay and Jones 1990). Women who are married or cohabiting and owner/occupiers are less likely, than tenants, to have a long-standing illness and more likely to rate their health as having been good over the previous 12 months. Married/cohabiting women who are tenants and on benefit are more likely to report a long-standing illness and less likely to report their health as having been good in the previous year; lone parent mothers' health status, controlling for housing tenure, is on the whole poorer than that of married/cohabiting women (see Box 5.3).

> ### Box 5.3   Health and the lone mother
>
> *I've never had a health visitor since the baby's been born. I can't get registered with a doctor. I've lived here a year without one, and with a baby. He's been in hospital twice. He caught a virus from the hotel which was growing in his bowel. He lost over six pounds in a week. Then he had a blocked intestine so he was in hospital for nearly two weeks that time . . . I feel so old, I mean I don't class myself as being young. I'm 34, but I don't know – I feel so old now, so very, very old.*
>
> (Graham 1993a: 175)

Women's own employment status and marital roles interact with their structural position to influence their health status. Married women in paid employment tend to be healthier than those who are not, and there is some evidence that paid employment 'protects' women from depression (Arber 1990).

Age is another variable which is frequently ignored as a factor in its own right. Age, like gender, carries with it a baggage of social meanings and expectations. There are difficulties in interpreting data of this kind, since we have very little information on how to differentiate between the physiological aspects of ageing and the social implications of 'passing age landmarks' – childhood, youth, years of fertility, middle age and old age. Mortality rates are high for the first four years of life and decrease thereafter; except for males, who have high mortality rates in the age range 15–24 years, accidents and violence being the predominant causes of death. There is also variation in self-reported illness with age. It is particularly high in the age groups 45–64 and 65–74 years. Health inequalities in old age relate to socio-economic circumstances prior to retirement (Goldblatt 1990; Arber and Ginn 1991), although the significance of social class declines with age (Wadsworth 1997). Cold and damp accommodation can also affect the health of older people, especially when the cost of heating means that they cannot afford, or are frightened that they cannot afford, to heat their accommodation adequately (Scharf *et al.* 2002; Phillipson and Scharf 2004).

The data available on ethnic groups are problematic, and the different age mix makes comparison of overall populations difficult. Apart from the incidence of diabetes and mental health problems, there are no overall differences between white and non-white populations. However, some ethnic groups, particularly from Bangladesh, Pakistan and the Caribbean, have higher rates of common diseases. There is a high incidence of hypertension and stroke among immigrants from the Caribbean, but the highest rates of ischaemic heart disease, infections and diabetes are among those from Bangladesh and Pakistan. British southern Asian mothers also have a higher perinatal mortality rate than non-Asian mothers. The black and Asian populations of Britain are disadvantaged in terms of housing, employment, education and other indicators of quality of social existence, when compared with the white population (Skellington and Morris 1992;

Philpott 1994). Nazroo (1997) has argued that poverty is the main cause of ethnic inequalities in health. As Figures 5.6 and 5.7 show, people from Pakistan and Bangladesh are also more likely to report poor health and a long-term disability.

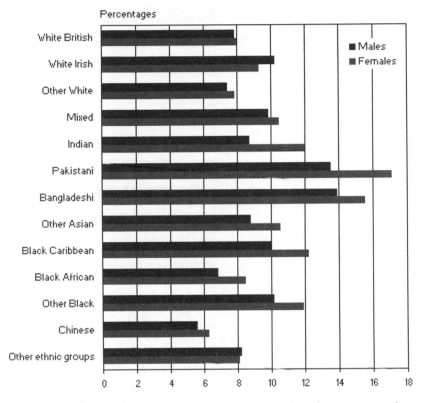

Figure 5.6 Age standardized 'not good' health rates: by ethnic group and sex, April 2001, England and Wales
Source: National Statistics downloaded on 13th December 2005 from http://www.statistics.gov.uk/cci/nugget.asp?id=464

It is also necessary to consider the effect that race and racial discrimination have on health and access to health services (Oppenheim 1990; Benzeval *et al.* 1992); the pressures of living in a racist society may have an adverse effect on health, especially mental health, and racial discrimination by service providers may deter people from seeking help, or at least delay them from doing so.

Of particular concern is the way that inequalities are compounded by the combination of difference. Thus, while inequalities are evident between different ethnic groups, when the analysis incorporates gender they are magnified for women (see Table 5.2). Cooper (2002) found that while socio-economic difference accounts for much of the disadvantage experienced by minority ethnic men and women, even after adjusting for socio-economic differences, gender inequality remains. Black women are

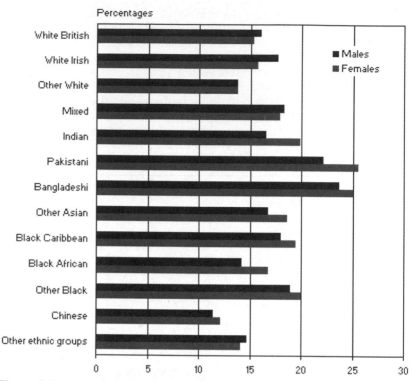

Figure 5.7 Age standardized rates of long-term illness or disability which retricts daily activity: by ethnic group and sex, April 2001, England and Wales
Source: http://www.statistics.gov.uk/cci/nugget.asp?id=464

Table 5.2 Standardized mortality ratios by country of birth, selected causes, men and women aged 20–69, England and Wales, 1989–92

	All causes		Coronary heart disease		Stroke		Lung cancer		Breast cancer
	Men	Women	Men	Women	Men	Women	Men	Women	Women
All countries	100	100	100	100	100	100	100	100	100
Scotland	132	136	120	130	125	125	149	160	114
Ireland	139	120	124	120	138	123	151	147	92
East Africa	110	103	131	105	114	122	42	17	84
West Africa	113	126	56	62	271	181	62	51	125
Caribbean	77	91	46	71	168	157	49	31	75
South Asia	106	100	146	151	155	141	45	33	59

Source: Wild and McKeigue (1997)

more likely to live in working-class households and be employed in lower-paid sectors of the economy, and to experience racism as well as economic hardship, all of which have an adverse effect on their health.

Area of residence has long been associated with mortality and morbidity. In Britain there is a health gradient from north to south, death rates being highest in the north and west, and lowest in the south and east. There is also an intra-regional gradient, with inner-city areas having higher mortality rates than rural areas (Fearn 1987); people from ethnic minority groups are often concentrated in these inner-city areas. There are also differences between wards in inner cities, the wards with the highest standardized mortality ratios being located in the most deprived areas, with the outlying suburbs having the lowest SMRs for preventable deaths (Abbott and Sapsford 1994; Curtis and Jones 1998).

Policy responses

Inequalities in health are amenable to direct policy interventions on four levels: strengthening individuals; strengthening communities; improving access to services; macro-economic change (Whitehead 1995). McKeown (1976) has argued that the main reasons for the decline in infant mortality rates in the twentieth century and, the improvements in our health generally, are to be found in the improved social, economic and environmental conditions in which we all now live. Although he recognizes that medical advances have been of some importance, he suggests that these have been of only marginal importance compared with improvements in our housing and working conditions, diets and general improvements in water supply and sanitation.

However, by the end of the nineteenth century, due to the influence of Social Darwinism, there was a shift in emphasis away from community interventions towards seeing individual behaviour as the major factor (see Chapter 2). Newman (1906), for example, suggested that:

> the problem of infant mortality is not one of sanitation alone or housing or indeed of **poverty** as such, but is mainly a question of motherhood ... death in infancy is probably more due to ignorance and negligence than to almost any other cause ... three measures are needed to be carried out (a) instruction of mothers, (b) the appointment of lay health visitors, and (c) the education of girls in domestic hygiene.
>
> (Newman 1906: 257, 262)

Subsequently there tended to be a bias towards blaming the victim, to see poor health as the result of individual failings, whether by biological constitution, unhealthy lifestyles or by not using the services provided. There has been a focus on what individuals should do to promote their own health. Women, as in the passage from Newman quoted above, were especially seen as negligent not only on their own behalf but on behalf of their husbands, children and other dependants for whom they were seen to be responsible. Even today, people from ethnic minority groups are often blamed because of their 'special diets', 'strange religions', 'funny habits' or 'inability to speak English'. There has consequently been a relative neglect, in public policy, of the social causes of ill health – unemployment, poverty, environmental pollution and so on. Service providers failed to recognize that their services may not meet the needs of many potential users, or indeed that the ways in which services are provided, are seen as patronizing and out of step with people's lived experiences. As a consequence, until recently, most policy initiatives fell in Whitehead's first category of policy responses but with limited success. For example Cornwell (1984) has indicated that many working-class people are well aware of the ways in which their work and the environment in which they live 'cause' their ill health. Health education that targets individuals and suggests that their chosen lifestyles are responsible for their ill health will not, in such circumstances, have much impact. It is notable, for example, that health education aimed at encouraging people to stop cigarette smoking has been most successful among the middle-classes and least successful at discouraging working-class men and women (see Figure 5.8).

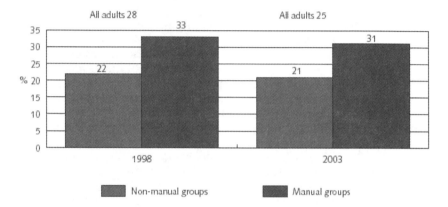

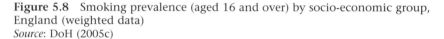

Figure 5.8   Smoking prevalence (aged 16 and over) by socio-economic group, England (weighted data)
Source: DoH (2005c)

Within the WHO's Health for All programme, many countries have begun to place more emphasis on issues such as inequalities. For example, in the UK proposals contained in *Saving Lives: Our Healthier Nation* (DoH 1999a) placed a greater emphasis on a broader strategic approach. This fitted with calls for new approaches to tackling inequalities, which move away from the disease model towards the promotion of social support and the development of family and community strengths (Wilkinson 1997; Campbell and Aggleton 1999). The focus of much of this debate has been on local areas and communities, with a strong emphasis on collaboration and participation. Within the current UK policy context, it is this approach that was central to developments in primary care in the late 1990s (DoH 1997, 2002a) but, the wider societal context is also at the heart of the UK's approach to tackling health inequalities (DoH 1998a, 1999a, 2002b). The UK's policy approach reflects a wider international agenda as well and builds on earlier programmes in the UK, such as the Healthy Cities Movement (Ashton 1992) and the WHO's Health for All programme which, while adopted widely in the UK, was never formally sanctioned and supported by the Conservative government.

The WHO formally adopted a programme to address health inequalities, within the Health for All programme (WHO 1985), although equity has long been seen as an important element of health policy and is one of the key pillars of primary health care (WHO/UNICEF 1978; Macdonald 1992). These developments also came at a time when HIV/AIDS was causing a rethink of the role and importance of public health in people's lives (Baggott 2000). The WHO also indicated that in health care, the principle of equal justice 'means equal access to available care, equal treatment for equal cases and equal quality of care', and in health terms it means that 'ideally everyone should have the *same opportunity* to attain the highest level of health, and, more pragmatically, no one should be unduly disadvantaged'. At the heart of these new approaches, to tackling poor health post 1997, have been the principles of what has been called the 'new public health' (Ashton and Seymour 1988; Baggott 2000). The new public health advocates a strong public health role that focuses on inequalities in socio-economic circumstances, inequalities in access and health, while addressing structural and individual causes of ill health. The adoption of this broader approach in the UK, represents a shift in how equity and health inequalities are addressed in policy in two key ways. The first is, a shift away from a focus on the role of the NHS in delivering equity and, the second is, the acceptance of the wider social determinants of health inequalities.

Policy responses in the UK

In addition to the emphasis on primary and community care, the 'crisis in health' in the 1970s (see also Chapter 3), and the new attention paid to health inequalities, led to a renewed interest in public health in the UK (Baggott 2000). The NHS has predominantly been concerned with caring for the sick, and medicine is primarily concerned with curing the sick. However, Sigerist (1943: 24) suggested that '*the task of medicine is to promote health, to prevent disease, to treat the sick when prevention is broken down and to rehabilitate the people after they have been cured*'. Increased health spending, since the Second World War, has not bought significant improvements in health (McKeown 1976; Baggott 2000). The post-war period has seen an increase in major chronic diseases and, as it became increasingly recognized that the major killer diseases of the late twentieth century – cardiovascular diseases, cancer, accidents and alcohol-related conditions – are preventable, there has been a recognition that the focus of health and health care should change. As we saw in Chapter 2, the same was true in the nineteenth century with the major killer diseases of the time – typhoid, smallpox and so on. A major concern of the nineteenth century was sanitary reform, with doctors prominent in the reform movement. It was recognized that reducing morbidity and mortality rates would be best achieved by environmental improvements, necessitating state intervention. A new development, however, is that prevention may now entail medicalization and a great expenditure on medicines, if, for example, the recommendations for prescribing statins are put into practice (Boseley 2006).

One key theme of the government's approach to public health, has been the renewed emphasis on tackling health inequalities. As previously noted, public health policy during the 1980s, ignored the findings of key reports on structural influences on health, and in particular the Black and Whitehead Reports (Townsend *et al.* 1992). Until 1995, the then Conservative government, made no explicit recognition of socio-economic issues relating to variations in health or health inequalities. In the mid-1990s, the government went some way to addressing these shortcomings, with the acknowledgement that there are variations in health and, a national research programme on variations in health was established (DoH 1995; NHSCRD 1995). However, this only related to the contribution that could be made by the NHS and DoH, and specifically avoided addressing the role of other areas of government policy, such as the environment, transport, employment and welfare benefits.

One of New Labour's first actions was to commission the Acheson Report (DoH 1998a). The report reviewed the research evidence related to health inequalities and made 39 recommendations. Only three of the recommendations were directed to the NHS, thereby, underlining the relative contribution of health care services, to tacking health inequality compared to what might be achieved by tackling poverty, education, employment, housing, transport and nutrition.

The government's commitment, to public health and tackling health inequality was also encapsulated in early policy documents such as *The New NHS* (DoH 1997), in which it was proposed to renew the NHS and to tackle the 'unfairness', 'unacceptable variations and two-tierism' of the Conservative internal market (Powell and Exworthy 2000). Central to government policy, has been the call for greater coordination of strategy and action. Since 1998, primary care organizations have been given a public health responsibility, that puts a much greater emphasis on local, community-based developments. (DoH 1999b). The government has developed many of these in collaboration with local health, local government and voluntary agencies. In addition, at the centre, there have been stronger links between departments, such as for programmes like neighbourhood renewal and Sure Start (see Box 5.4). However, public health initiatives may be more vulnerable to changes in priorities when there are ministerial changes.

This change, in the way the health of the public is addressed to secure healthier communities, focuses attention on the local context of health services – an arena now clearly identified with primary care organizations. However, this refocusing of public health also requires a wider understanding, one that encompasses the circumstances and social reality of people's lives, and their perceptions and experiences of these as factors that contribute to their illness and their health.

Box 5.4   Sure Start

In 2000 the Secretary of State for Health, Alan Milburn, highlighted Sure Start as making one of the most important contributions to health improvement in the UK (Milburn 2000). Sure Start is one of many community partnership approaches being developed in many areas around the country, which seeks to address individual problems through community-based responses, working with the local communities involved. Sure Start is based on a similar approach pioneered in the USA and has a strong neighbourhood focus, with each programme serving the local community 'within "pram-pushing" distance'. The programme was originally targeted on children and families in deprived circumstances, and was delivered through local partnerships with the aim of providing a range of support services, including child care, early learning and play opportunities, support with parenting skills, as well as improved access to primary health care. By the summer of 2003 there were 522 schemes up and running and the aim was to reach 400,000 children by 2004, including a third of all under 4s living in poverty. The political drivers changed in late 2004, when it was decided to extend the scheme to all children, and, there was a change of minister. By 2010 there should be 3500 Sure Start centres, although it is too early to tell what the outcomes have been. As in other areas of provision, it is likely that the voluntary sector will become more involved.

Both national policy and local action require that traditionally separate statutory organizations, including primary care, work jointly with each other, with other organizations (both private and voluntary) and with the individuals and groups comprising local communities. To date, little attention has been paid either to the public health role of primary care organizations (Mays *et al.* 1997; LeGrand *et al.* 1998) or, for that matter, to the role of communities in determining public health strategy and action. While the White Paper on public health *Saving Lives: Our Healthier Nation* (DoH 1999a), did not contain targets on health inequalities, the *NHS Plan* (DoH 2000a) flagged up the intention to develop inequality targets and these were published in 2001. Later in the same year the DoH published a consultation document addressing health inequalities, to stimulate debate about the relevance of the targets and to identify how these should be addressed (DoH 2001b). The document highlighted the role of primary care and the need to support disadvantaged communities.

However, while *Saving Lives* did not specifically address health inequalities, the emphasis on addressing inequality was central to a key government policy document aimed at the nursing profession. *Making a Difference* (DoH 1999b) placed an emphasis on the role of nurses, midwives and health visitors in tackling inequalities in health, stressing the need for midwives, for example, to take on a health promotion role with 'disadvantaged' women – although as Hart *et al.* (2001) have argued, there is no clear definition in the document of what this means. Central to *Making*

Box 5.5   Obesity as a public health problem

Obesity in England has grown almost 400 per cent in 25 years, and three-quarters of the adult population is now overweight. Childhood obesity has tripled in 20 years. The economic cost in England arising from its consequences, such as heart disease, could be £7.4 billion a year, with the Wanless Report (2003) predicting that our health care system could only remain affordable if we become fully engaged in maintaining our own health and therefore tackle issues such as obesity.

All governments need to consider the extent to which they are prepared to intervene to alter the individual behaviour of their citizens. In the UK, governments that do so are often accused of being a 'nanny state' (a term which has buried within it a set of assumptions about the unacceptability of being a fussy old woman). However, such are the concerns about the 'obesity epidemic' that such intervention is now being attempted. There have been several reports on obesity, such as the House of Commons Health Committee report (2004a), and the global plan from the WHO (2004). The Food Standards Agency has recommended curbing the aggressive marketing of food to young children.

There are also many debates on the extent to which we have real choices in the food we eat. Many poor people live in 'food deserts' where they have access to only a limited range of shops, with little fresh food, and parents with little money will not risk buying unfamiliar foods which their children may not eat. Poor people buy calories which are cheap, not vitamins and other micro-nutrients (Ralph 1997).

Blythman (2004) analyses the power of the large supermarkets, which sell more than 80 per cent of the food we eat. Five giant companies control three-quarters of the world's banana trade; two provide two-thirds of the bread in the UK. The food industry lobbies government intensively, for example, in delaying EU regulations for food labelling. It also seeks to improve its image; in 2002/3, Cadbury produced a Get Active Campaign of tokens for sports equipment, endorsed by Richard Caborn the Sports Minister, which required the consumption of large amounts of chocolate to get the tokens.

Inactivity is also a factor; in the UK only 40 per cent of men and 26 per cent of women take enough exercise (30 minutes of moderate activity on five or more days a week). The Department of Culture, Media and Sport therefore also has an important role, as has the Department for Education and Skills, in promoting sport in schools.

a Difference was the idea that nurses, midwives and health visitors should be working with the wider community and across organizational boundaries, undertaking health promotion activities. This reflects a commitment to widening the public health workforce.

However, the lack of clarity and huge scope of the public health function, and the organizational diversity of public health practice, makes the notion of 'a public health workforce' extremely complex. The Chief Medical Officer (CMO), in his report on the project to strengthen the public health function in England (DoH 2001c), considered people '*from a range of disciplines and at all levels of seniority*', to contribute to the public health workforce in their daily work (p. 6). Although many of these people may not have a 'public health' label, or even recognize that they have a public health role, they will, to a greater or lesser extent, be working to promote, protect and improve the health of populations and communities. The CMO describes such people as falling into three categories:

- *public health professionals*: consultants and specialists working at a strategic or senior management level or at a senior level of scientific expertise, such as in public health statistics;
- *public health practitioners*: professionals who spend a major part, or all of their time, in public health practice; and
- '*the wider workforce*': all those who, even if they do not at present recognize it, have a role in health improvement and reducing inequalities (e.g. teachers, local business leaders, social workers, transport engineers, housing officers, as well as other local government staff and health care professionals) (DoH 2001c: 6–7).

Each of these three categories has been further divided into two: strategic and operational/technical (Burke *et al.* 2001). Any attempt to 'map' a workforce using these categorical distinctions will soon encounter a great deal of ambiguity. A project to map the public health workforce in London, for instance, both within and beyond the NHS, brought to light the elasticity of boundaries, which could conceivably encompass a vast number of people (paid and unpaid) in all sectors and at all levels (Sim *et al.* 2003). As an occupational category, 'public health' is virtually impossible to describe, yet there is a clear recognition and expectation that public health will be a shared activity and responsibility, and that the NHS should take a public health approach.

Over the next ten years, distinct differences in the organization and shape of the public health workforce are likely to emerge in England, Northern Ireland, Scotland and Wales. In Scotland, the role of the Scottish Parliament is likely to become more significant and it may take a more multi-sectoral approach to public health. In many ways Scotland is becoming a distinctively different country. Since self-government came to Scotland in 1999, there have been almost 80 new pieces of legislation, free personal and nursing care, free bus travel for older people, no student tuition fees and a raft of policies on health, social care and education (see Box 5.6). This political coordination could well place a greater emphasis on a broader responsibility for public health, and thus prompt a wider view of who a public health worker is. While the health boards are likely to retain medical directors of public health, the strong emphasis on developing public health practitioners in the local health care cooperatives, provides an important focus for public health action (Scottish Executive 2001).

Box 5.6   The Scottish smoking legislation

Scotland has been more proactive than England in taking action on
smoking. The Smoking, Health and Social Care (Scotland) Act 2005 and
the Prohibition of Smoking in Certain Premises (Scotland) Regulations
2006 came into effect on 26 March 2006.

The intention of the new law is to save lives and prevent disease caused
by passive smoking, meaning the breathing in of other people's tobacco
smoke, which is also known as second-hand smoke or environmental
tobacco smoke (ETS). Smoking is no longer allowed in any workplace or
public place which is 'wholly or substantially enclosed'.

The only exemptions to the ban, which is more extensive than that
planned for England, are oil rigs, psychiatric and care homes, hospices,
police interview rooms and prison cells.

Scotland has the highest rate of lung cancer in Europe and smoking is
estimated to kill 13,000 Scots each year. The Scottish Executive decided
to go ahead with the Bill after a nationwide consultation revealed high
levels of support.

This clearer political involvement in public health is also likely to be
found in Wales, with the Welsh Assembly prioritizing public health. The
coterminosity of local authorities and the LHBs (established in April 2003),
with their broad memberships, provide opportunities for close cooperation
and coordinated activity. Moreover, the founding of the National Public
Health Services in Wales, which brings the public health resources of the
five former health authorities together under one national organization,
promises strong national leadership in public health to support multi-
disciplinary action that cuts across policy and organizational boundaries.

In Northern Ireland, where a second hiatus in devolution (from October
2002) has meant a period of relative inaction, future developments are less
clear. The suspension of the Assembly has hindered the implementation of
decisions arising from consultation on the future of primary care and the
alternatives to GP fundholding – new local health and social care groups
are, at the time of writing, just entering the start of their second year. These
new groups are expected gradually to take on more responsibility for
arranging and developing primary care services during the next few years.
Within the existing health and social care workforce, it is nurses who have
received most attention, and their existing and potential contribution to
the public health agenda has been both recognized and supported (Poulton *et al.* 2000; Mason and Clarke 2001).

In England, the Minister for Public Health is perhaps more politically
remote from the delivery of public health than in Scotland and Wales, and
the public health function has undergone successive reorganizations. The
structure of the public health function will be determined by the way
regional government offices and SHAs, with their medical directors of
public health, direct and performance manage the wider public health
workforce in PCTs and local authorities. Meanwhile, on the ground, public

health activity is likely to remain largely locked into funding structures which are influenced by political demands for reduced waiting lists, and which stress quick, 'measurable' outputs. Even in new quasi-autonomous structures, such as neighbourhood action areas, which aim to encourage bottom-up, locally sensitive, innovative activity, the reality is somewhat less than inspiring. In practice, they face the same political imperatives to secure tangible improvements and to meet performance targets as statutory agencies (Painter and Clarence 2001). Pressure from the centre for quick results, is likely to continue to undermine the conditions needed to build a sustainable collaborative infrastructure, and to develop meaningful partnerships with the local community. Where idiosyncratic differences emerge between localities, they will often depend on the experience and character of the key individuals within the organizations.

The first clear government commitment to tackling health inequalities came in *The NHS Plan* (DoH 2000a), which highlighted its importance and led to the establishment of targets. Progress against these targets has been mixed, as demonstrated by recent infant mortality statistics. Similarly in Scotland and Wales, there has been a focus on the need to address health inequalities which, in these countries, have been seen as key problem areas for many years (Baggott 2000). Following the Wanless Reports on health services in England and Wales (Wanless 2002, 2003), the Treasury commissioned a further report on public health (Wanless 2004), and a further White Paper *Choosing Health* was published in 2004 (DoH 2004a) setting public health policy. However, despite concerted government statements about developing public health approaches, financial constraints in 2005/6 tended to focus attention on the acute health care sector and limit resources for public health. In England, changes were made to GP contracts to stimulate greater preventive activity, but this was mainly on an individual basis. So, as we move into this new century, the role of public health and the commitment to eradicating health inequalities remain uncertain.

Conclusion

In this chapter, we have considered the basic principle of equity, on which the NHS was founded, and considered the extent to which this has been achieved. We have indicated that inequalities in access to health care and in health status have persisted, with more advantaged groups having better access to services and a better health status than materially disadvantaged groups. Further improvements in health, we have argued, are more likely to come from improvements in the general standard of living, and from health promotions that recognize the structural constraints on individual choices rather than from health care *per se*.

There is a danger that insufficient attention is paid to developing an adequate performance management structure for public health. Public health professionals, in England, are being absorbed into primary care organizations. At the same time, there is an emphasis on developing public health skills across all professional groups. Such moves may dilute public health activity or they might increase it. Two dangers are present. The first is that there is insufficient development of the notion of a multi-disciplinary public health force. In Scotland, there is an emphasis on the role of health visitors, but this is missing from England, where the health visiting role was narrowed in the primary care reforms of the early 1990s. Second, the preoccupation with service delivery (standards, quality, commissioning, professional regulation etc.) tends to overshadow public health policy and activity. It is not clear whether the potential for developing a broader public health approach – particularly for community nurses – will be fulfilled.

Summary

- Despite the institution of health services based on principles of universal entitlement, the pooling of financial risk, equality of access and quality of care, considerable evidence exists of the persistence of health inequalities in Britain – and in some cases increased levels of polarization between social groups and regions.
- Social reformists have attributed health inequalities to the institutional malfunctioning of the NHS and its failure to ensure equality of access, equality of care and territorial justice and to its focus on treatment as opposed to prevention.
- A variety of theories have developed to explain the persistence of health inequalities. Cultural/behavioural explanations have emphasized the role of individual responsibility; the NHS can only encourage healthy lifestyles and treat illnesses, it cannot force people to adopt them, e.g. to stop smoking or consume more healthy diets.
- Other theories have suggested that inequalities in health status are a function of broader structural problems, which cannot be remedied by changes in health care alone. Townsend's work demonstrated the impact of multiple deprivation on health status, in particular the impact of poor housing and unemployment. Employment status is also related to health status, with a close association between certain occupations and industrial disease or stress. Furthermore, low income itself restricts a household's ability to adopt healthy lifestyles.
- Public health policy in the UK has shifted towards addressing health inequalities, since the mid-1990s, and cross-governmental approaches to tackle health inequalities are being implemented.

Further reading

Baggott, R. (2000) *Public Health: Policy and Politics*. Basingstoke: Macmillan.
Townsend, P., Whitehead, M. and Davidson, N. (eds) (1992) *Inequalities in Health: The Black Report and the Health Divide* (new edn). Harmondsworth: Penguin.

WELFARE PLURALISM

Introduction

This chapter builds on the discussion in the previous three chapters and examines recent changes in welfare and health services that have been introduced in the last 10 to 15 years. It focuses on the increasing pluralization of welfare service delivery in the UK, addressing issues such as privatization, consumerism and individualization. In Chapter 1, we identified the different forms of social welfare, building on Titmuss' four divisions of welfare. In this chapter, we demonstrate how private and voluntary sector provision has become increasingly important as part of the delivery structure of welfare services. In addition, we will explore the increasing reliance on private funding of social support for old age. We also examine how these developments have incorporated notions of how people use services, and explore the concept of consumerism.

The chapter begins by examining the impact of the changing context of the British welfare state (discussed in Chapter 2) on welfare services and, how welfare services are coordinated and delivered. Previous chapters have highlighted the increasing diversity of service delivery in a number of areas, including health. Privatization of welfare has increased substantially since the mid-1980s and the increasing use of market models for the delivery of health and social care is a key feature of the UK welfare state. Increasingly this has also drawn the independent sector, in its broadest sense, into welfare provision and the role of voluntary agencies in service delivery in areas such as housing and social care, is an important feature of the UK welfare state and will increasingly be seen in health care. The last 25 years have seen a growth in more market-orientated approaches, to the way services are organized, in the delivery of welfare alongside more traditional public sector delivery. However, at the same time, there has been greater recognition that to tackle complex social problems, more collaborative approaches between different agencies – whether public, voluntary or private – is needed.

We have also discussed the many challenges that the welfare state has been responding to – particularly a diversifying society and the persistence of inequalities. However, there have also been key underlying themes about to what extent individuals are responsible for themselves (and their own misfortune or successes), and the extent to which responsibility for care is the individual's (and their family's) or the state's. These debates are particularly relevant given discussions about consumerism and welfare services. Alongside the development of private and voluntary services there has been a strong emphasis on the service user or patient as a consumer of services. Consumerism has therefore become an important element of debates about the nature and future of the welfare state.

This chapter sets the context for the discussion that follows. We discuss the growth of commercialization in health and welfare services and the impact on those using services, highlighting the important role of informal care and self-care. These concepts will then be applied to health and welfare services addressing topics such as consumer choice, commissioning, the Private Finance Initiative (PFI), individualism and how this all fits into the New Labour approach. These issues will then be explored in more detail in the following three chapters.

In Chapter 1 we introduced the concept of welfare pluralism, which is used to describe welfare systems in which social needs are met through a wide range of sources including the voluntary, commercial, informal and state sectors. We discussed Titmuss' divisions of welfare and in the following chapters, outlined how shifts in the relative contributions of the different sectors of welfare has occurred over time, with an increasing emphasis on non-public sector providers of welfare. While the concept is not new, recent debates about welfare pluralism have focused on two key aspects that characterize recent developments in welfare. The first is the increased emphasis on the role of private sources of welfare. This includes the increasing use of non-public sector agencies to deliver welfare goods and services, and shifts to private funding in areas such as pensions, fees for health care services and social care. The second change is the blurring of the different sectors with voluntary sector agencies competing with private agencies, the state contracting-out services to private and voluntary agencies, and state agencies in competition with each other and other private and voluntary agencies (Powell and Hewitt 1998).

The background to why these changes occurred, is set out in Chapter 2. In this chapter, we want to examine two specific areas of development of welfare pluralism which are very closely linked, and define many recent developments in the provision of health and social care services. The first is the shift in the way services are being funded and delivered, in particular the increasing use of market-style mechanisms to organize and deliver health and social care services. The second is the rise of consumerism.

Delivering welfare services: approaches to coordination

The principle of universal provision, was introduced in the post-war welfare state, as a means of ensuring a broad equality of entitlement to fundamental social resources, by virtue of citizenship or membership of that society, irrespective of wealth and occupational status. Thus, the health status and educational opportunities of post-war British citizens, were no longer dependent upon their ability to pay for services. This system was based upon principles of social justice, and not egalitarianism however: the persistence of income and wealth inequality was acceptable and socially just, once the principle of merit was preserved and citizens could be genuinely said to have equal life chances (see Chapters 1 and 2).

Welfare services and benefits were to be funded and provided collectively by the state. The rapid development of public services was, therefore, a feature of the UK welfare state in the post-war period. These services were managed by public servants accountable to local or central political masters (local government or Parliament), and were hierarchical in nature, with policies planned by politicians and senior public servants, and implemented by those lower down the organization. This view of public organizations as bureaucracies with principles of fairness and equal access by service users, is perhaps one that is most familiar (see also Chapter 2). This approach was also thought to be more equitable than that which could be provided through the private market, where access to services would depend on having sufficient resources to pay.

However, to some extent, this system of broad equality in welfare resources really coexisted with a small commercial sector restricted to a minority of very wealthy individuals, without calling into question the legitimacy of the underlying framework (although the compatibility of private education, with equality of educational opportunity, was undoubtedly questioned). The best way to preserve the goals of universalism was not to prevent private provision (which may be interpreted as an unreasonable restriction on individual freedom), but to ensure that the quality of state services was of a sufficiently high level to restrict growth of commercial provision (as in the Swedish system; see Esping-Anderson 1990). This balance was maintained in many services, at least, until the 1980s – although, we have discussed aspects of commercialization in previous chapters, with the introduction of charges in the NHS for prescriptions, dental and optician services which have been increasingly provided privately (see Chapter 3).

It could, of course, be argued that by encouraging those who can afford to pay, for private care, to opt out of state provision and use alternative private providers paid directly for services supplied, it is possible to target state resources more effectively on those in real need. The problem with this approach is that the development of two-tier systems of welfare provision, can lead to socially stigmatized services and the haemorrhaging of highly trained staff into more lucrative and attractive posts in the commercial sector (as has been recently argued in the context of opted-out or Foundation hospitals).

Political developments in the last 20 to 30 years, or so, have resulted in some major policy shifts away from universal statutory provision towards greater reliance on the commercial sector. Such shifts have been brought about by a range of factors, some of which reflect ideological commitments and others matters of expediency. Examples of the former can be seen in the commitment of the New Right to reinforce the 'traditional' role of the family (and of patriarchal social relations) in society, reduce public dependency and promote individualism, and featured in much of the rhetoric of the Conservative governments between 1979 and 1997. On the other hand, demographic pressures and changes in family structure have led to concerns about the fiscal sustainability of the post-war Beveridgean welfare state, founded on principles of universalism and social citizenship. The key concern here is often said to be the need to contain public expenditure, but linked to this is a particular view of the market and the price mechanism, as the superior means of allocating social goods and facilitating consumer choice. These issues have been actively debated by the current Labour government, which has espoused the need for increased individual and family responsibility and also supported a greater role for private organizations and market mechanisms for the delivery of health and social care services.

The impact of New Right ideology appears to have brought about a shift from a tolerance of parallel private provision, to a view of private provision, as inherently better and morally superior to statutory provision. It has been argued that the introduction of financial incentives and subsidies to both employers and individual 'consumers' has led to the expansion of the commercial sector ideal, to the point of undermining the solidaristic foundations of the welfare state itself (Pollock 2005). In addition to the impact of the New Right on domestic politics, Taylor-Gooby (1994) has argued that accession to the European Community increased pressure for policy convergence across European welfare systems. These, he argued, are dominated by Bismarckian, insurance-based welfare systems and not by the British 'universal state safety-net model' (p. 26). These systems of welfare provision tie social entitlement much more closely to employment status, with benefits closely linked to insurance-based contributions by both employees and employers. These ties can be seen in Labour policy on entitlement through employment, increased use of Tax Credits and an emphasis on making personal provision, such as in pensions.

The commercial sector is seen by the government as being more efficient, better managed and more responsive to the needs of the consumer than the public sector, which is seen as insulated from competition, dominated by the trade unions, bureaucratic in nature, unable to respond quickly to changing needs of service users and therefore inefficient, wasteful and unresponsive to patients. In the late 1980s and early 1990s, the Conservative government sought to reduce the public cost of health care by introducing greater efficiency into the NHS by 'managed' competition – arguing that competition among providers would not only reduce costs but also increase effectiveness and responsiveness (DoH 1989a). Conservative policy, in relation to health care, covered a range of different elements, including:

- encouragement of the growth of non-NHS provision, including the commercial and voluntary sectors;

- encouragement of employer-provided health care;
- increased charges for NHS services;
- competitive tendering and contracting-out of NHS ancillary services;
- the introduction of private sector management styles and methods into the NHS;
- the introduction of managed markets and the purchaser/provider split in health care;
- an increased emphasis on informal care.

On coming to power, the Labour government sought to dismantle what it saw as the worst aspects of the NHS internal market (see Chapter 3). In reality the government, especially in England, has built upon these developments with an expansion of private sector initiatives in the financing of capital projects through the public-private partnership and PFI schemes, expanding the contracting of services in hospitals, purchasing health care from the private sector, and developing a range of different health and social care providers in the private and voluntary sectors (Pollock 2005).

Such arrangements have not, however, completely displaced publicly delivered health and welfare services, so hierarchal and market approaches to service delivery coexist alongside each other. In fact it is clear that this mix of market and state delivered services has always existed to some extent, and that the introduction of further market-based approaches to health care in the 1990s was not the same as a commercial market and has been described as a 'quasi-market' (Powell and Exworthy 2001). This mix of approaches to organizing and delivering services has also traditionally relied on the building of partnerships or networks. For example, hospitals were funded by the state, run by medical practitioners and administrators, but relied on working relationships with other staff groups and even the development of relationships with general practice and community health services, social services and other hospitals. These relationships were built on non-market and hierarchal structures involving trust, reciprocity and the sharing of values and goals (although not always very well). While the Labour government emphasized the importance of markets and hierarchal approaches (performance targets, national quality standards, inspection regimes etc.), a key element of government policy has also been the emphasis on partnership. Public, private and voluntary sector agencies were to work together more closely.

Partnerships stretch across the health and social care spectrum and are a key part of addressing public health problems to deliver 'joined-up' solutions (see Chapter 5). The drive towards joined-up thinking, generating joined-up solutions, is a response to the need to address what have been described as 'wicked issues' (Audit Commission 1998; Clarence and Painter 1998; Powell and Exworthy 2001; Glendinning et al. 2002). In other words, the issues facing local communities – such as tackling health inequalities and social exclusion, providing seamless care for people with disabilities or for older people and so on – are multi-faceted and require multi-agency and multi-disciplinary attention. This approach was embodied in government policy documents such as Saving Lives: Our Healthier Nation (DoH 1999a) which emphasized the important role of integration and partnership, '*working across Government to attack the breeding ground of poor health – poverty and social exclusion – and we believe in creating partnerships with local authorities, health authorities and other agencies to tackle the root causes of ill health in places where people live.*' (p. 3). Each country within the UK has placed partnership at the centre of service developments so, in England *The NHS Plan* (DoH 2000a), identified the NHS's role in helping to '*develop Local Strategic Partnerships, into which, in the medium term, partnership approaches . . . [such as the health actions zones of the 1990s and other local action zones have been integrated would] . . . strengthen links between health, education, employment and other causes of social exclusion*' (p. 111). More recently, the introduction of Local Area Agreements in England has provided a formal mechanism for developing partnership agreements between the NHS and local government. Northern Ireland sought to build on existing joint structures within the primary and community sector, Scotland has developed interagency partnership groups and most recently the community health partnerships at local level, and in Wales the development of LHBs has emphasized the need for coterminosity and a bringing together of a range of agencies at board level to improve coordination (NHS Scotland 2000; NHS Wales 2001).

In reality the NHS and welfare services, more generally, retain elements of all three approaches (markets, hierarchy and networks) to the coordination and delivery of services. At the same time, it has been argued that, in reality, the welfare state has always incorporated elements of all three approaches. It is suggested that there are quasi-hierarchies, markets and networks rather than actual markets or only networks and partnerships, and that in any given situation a combination of all three can be found (Powell and Exworthy 2000). However, it is clear that the mix of approaches is changing. Greater emphasis is being placed on partnerships and collaboration, at the same time as more market approaches are being developed. The increasing fragmentation of service delivery means that both approaches are more likely to be needed. However, the emphasis on performance targets, nationally defined outcomes and quality standards, means that collaboration and competition have to operate within a system of centrally (or hierarchically) controlled environments.

These changes reflect the shift from the state as a provider of welfare services to what has been described as the 'regulatory state' (Majone 1996). The role of government is to ensure that welfare services are provided and that it achieves this through regulation of a range of different approaches to welfare provision. It is argued that as economic globalization has developed, individual states have had to change their role. In particular, health and welfare services are increasingly being subjected to trade pressures as international firms operate in many different countries (e.g. Pfizer, United Health and BUPA). Health care services pharmaceutical companies, health care providers and health insurers, are all examples of this internationalization. Thus, individual states are increasingly involved in regulatory functions. However, as Moran (2002) has argued, it is not clear whether the adoption of a regulatory approach is more effective than direct provision. One driver for increased fragmentation and marketization, is the idea that society is generally more consumerist and that this applies to health and welfare services as much as to any other goods and services.

We introduced the idea of welfare consumerism in Chapter 2 but it is worth exploring this in more detail in relation to health and social care.

Welfare consumerism

References to consumerism in social welfare services originated in the 1980s, with debates about the individualization of welfare and the introduction of more market-based approaches in health and welfare services. Clarke *et al.* (2005: 167) argued that for New Labour, the citizen consumer is central to its approach to public service reform. In particular, the development of the welfare choice agenda is based on the conceptualization of the service user, as a consumer free to make choices between different welfare services. There is a long history of attempts to increase public participation in health and welfare services, including the establishment of Community Health Councils in 1974, which has provided important contributions to the way we understand the interaction between services and service users (Lupton *et al.* 1998; Taylor 2003; Baggott *et al.* 2005).

These interactions can be seen as an attempt, in the public sector, to introduce approaches to strengthen user voice, in the recognition that they rarely had a choice, as normal consumers in a market-place, to use alternative services. In a market-place, consumers can either choose to change where they shop, for example (exit strategy), stay loyal to a particular shop or brand (loyalty) or complain (voice) (Hirschmann 1970). In the public sector welfare state, there are fewer opportunities for the use of exit and voice strategies, and little is known about the circumstances through which users become loyal to public organizations, express dissatisfaction through complaint or other means, or attempt to exit to another service (Dowding 1992). Equally, however, there is a long history of attempting to get service users to participate in the running of services, in a role more usually identified with that of a citizen through participating in the public sphere (Lister 1997) in the formal organization of services, or in civil society (Deakin 2001) by volunteering or other means of co-production, as a way of improving voice in the recognition that exit options are limited.

As such, participation appears to be characterized as either positioning users as consumers (Baldock 2003; Shaw 2003) or customers (Greener 2005), or a more collective agency-based around citizenship (Marshall 1981). However, it is important to question how far consumerism applies to welfare. Baldock (2003) has argued that consumerism is a result of the regulatory state, but it is not clear that welfare consumers are like other consumers. Services still predominantly remain those defined and provided by professionals, rather than being seen as being stimulated by demand. Entry of new providers is difficult as, in the UK, services predominantly rely on state funding – especially in health – so purchasers retain control over what choices for exit exist. While consumerist concepts of choice appear attractive and seem to provide the consumer with more choice – as in health – in fact choices are limited by the 'choice set': the range of services available to individuals and which are usually agreed by local health and welfare funders. Thus recent policy, introducing patient choice in England may be limited by the ability of the NHS to provide such choices.

In England, the set of options for health care, a range of four or five providers as defined by local commissioners (PCTs or practice-based commissioners) is provided by the GP/practice. In Wales, the system is centralized through the 'second offer commissioning team' and in Scotland, choices are clinically led by the GP. In Northern Ireland a limited choice is being developed along the lines of the 'second offer' system. Clearly availability of information and knowledge about alternative providers is key to how choice is exercised. The differing approaches in each country, place the need for information and knowledge, and the point at which decisions are made about different providers, at different levels in the system and involve the patient in different ways. In England the pattern of local services and the degree of involvement of local patient and public representatives, is structured around local commissioners (PCTs and practice-based commissioners). In Wales (and planned for Northern Ireland) the focus is more on one-off decisions about individual patients made by the central commissioning group. In Scotland, GPs retain the major role in providing choices. The extent to which patients are supported in their choices will therefore differ. Since access to support, including relevant and appropriate information and support in decision-making are crucial, these differences have important implications (Fotaki *et al.* 2005).

Any discussion about choice of health care services, needs to consider the extent to which patients and the public are able to choose, and particularly the range of available services and treatments from which they can make choices. In England, there has been a long debate about public and patient involvement, but policy and the reorganization of public and patient involvement structures has taken place alongside, rather than as part of, policies on patient choice (NHS Executive 1996; Lupton *et al.* 1998; Peckham *et al.* 2005). This contrasts with the situation in Wales, where patient and public involvement is seen as central to the wider choice agenda (Gilbert *et al.* 2001; NHS Wales 2005). In Scotland, NHS boards are legally required to involve members of the public in decisions about service planning and this is monitored by the Scottish Health Council. Thus, in Hirschmann's (1970) terms, choices can be seen as being derived from policies aimed at 'voice', through patient and public involvement and 'exit', through individual patient choice. Reconciling these different aspects of 'voice' and 'exit', is a challenge for health care services (NHS Executive 1996; Lupton *et al.* 1998).

However, current policy emphasizes choice of secondary provider – i.e. the location of treatment. There is some evidence to support the view that patients benefit from being involved in treatment decisions, and from the provision of evidence-based decision support interventions (processes that provide patients with access to health care intervention evidence on the effectiveness of different treatments), but there is also evidence to suggest that it is not necessarily the offering of a choice *per se* that generates the benefit (Fallowfield *et al.* 1990; O'Connor *et al.* 2003; Fotaki *et al.* 2005). Attempts to increase the extent to which patients are offered treatment choices may have negative as well as positive effects, especially if there is a lack of information for patients to base decisions on, and if patients feel inadequately supported by health professionals or, are distressed by the responsibility of being asked to make choices for themselves (Entwistle *et al.* 2006). Policies that aim to increase choice of secondary care providers may increase these problems, by exacerbating the extent to which patients are given inadequate information, for example, about possible treatment effects and side-effects, and receive conflicting advice from different health care professionals (Harrison *et al.* 2002a; Healthcare Commission 2005). There will also be impacts on the volume and capacity of services, producing the possibility of unused spare capacity as well as increased volumes of service use.

Current policies, to develop and support welfare consumerism through choice and by expanding the type and range of providers, will therefore go some way to offering choices of voice, exit and loyalty. However, the type and range of choice is still likely to be determined by policy and expediency. In health care, treatment choices remain limited and raise substantial questions about concepts of patient and professional autonomy (Askham and Chisholm 2006; Entwistle *et al.* 2006). While providing some welfare users with the ability to make direct payments can help assist in giving free choice, many service users are still constrained by the limited range of options from which to purchase support services. The Labour government did introduce nursery vouchers but these were set aside by the introduction of the Child and Working Tax Credit systems. Welfare services are likely to remain centrally funded and thus any development of the choice set (the range of services from which users can choose) will remain shaped by the main funders. Choices will therefore remain limited by what is offered. In addition people's capacity and opportunity to make choices will also be limited by their social and economic circumstances (Fotaki *et al.* 2005). Critical questions remain therefore about the extent to which welfare consumerism is likely to achieve the outcomes envisaged by government and at the time of writing, despite some positive outcomes from pilot schemes, there are many unanswered questions about the effectiveness and implications of choice policies as an approach to achieving welfare consumerism.

Privatization and welfare

The role of the commercial sector in the provision of welfare is by no means new; indeed, it has dominated social provision in some areas. The levels of both political and public support for privatization, indicate a broad consensus in some areas (such as housing) coexisting with fierce debate in others (such as education and health care). This section focuses on developments in commercial welfare, defined as the purchase of social goods in the market-place by consumers. It is important to distinguish between two forms of commercial provision at this stage: that selected and paid for by individuals and that provided and paid for by employers. The latter category was termed 'occupational welfare' in Titmuss' (1955) social division of welfare.

Welfare provision by employers, for their employees, is similar in many respects to commercial provision. Indeed, it is purchased from the commercial sector by the company concerned and has the effect of shifting responsibility away from the state as primary provider. Both forms of commercial provision have also been recipients of state subsidies and both serve the goal of promoting private industry and profit. Occupational welfare does, however, differ in important respects, because membership of any such scheme does not imply a conscious choice, as such, on behalf of consumers. Such occupational benefits, typically, form part of a broader package of employment-related remuneration. Membership of a private health care scheme, for example, may 'come with the job', and may not otherwise have been selected by the employee concerned. The employer may either offer such benefits as a form of paternalism, as a 'perk' or incentive to their employees, or they may receive fiscal benefits from the state as an incentive to provide such benefits – perhaps even as a substitute for increased remuneration.

In addition to the purchase of alternative or additional welfare services in the commercial sector by individual consumers and employers, privatization has brought about broader changes in the way statutory bodies and the voluntary sector work. The introduction of commercial sector management techniques, case management and contracting-out of functions in these sectors, has changed the ways in which many public services operate. For example, the introduction by the Education Reform Act 1988 of local management of schools and procedures, enabled individual schools to opt out of local government control and become budget-holding bodies funded directly by central government. In addition, the recent introduction of Academy Schools, supported by private finance for buildings and facilities, illustrates the broader impact of privatization within the public sector. The development of what have been termed 'quasi-markets' as a means of increasing efficiency and effectiveness, by introducing the discipline of the market into former public monopolies has, therefore, become widespread. The implementation of the community care reforms in 1993, created a social market in domiciliary and day care, with local authority social services departments being required to purchase services from the commercial and voluntary sectors (see Chapter 7). This provided the basis for current developments in a pluralist health and welfare market for the delivery of services (Means et al. 2002). The establishment of semi-autonomous agencies to administer social security and deal with Civil Service purchasing and estates, and the selling off of specialist agencies, such as the government laboratory service, have all been part of the same process.

Clarke (2004) has argued that there are different routes to the market in terms of service and organizational design including:

- *direct provision:* the transfer of services, organizations and resources to the commercial sector;
- *public-private partnerships:* public agencies working in partnership with private agencies to provide services, or support services through the provision of premises (e.g. through PFI);
- *outsourcing:* public agencies contracting out aspects of their services, such as cleaning and maintenance;
- *creating new markets:* developing markets for particular services, such as

with the arrangements for community care in 1993, and current approaches to developing private health care services with independent treatment centres or orthopaedic surgery;

• *making internal markets:* separating purchasers from providers within a health or social care organization, such as the NHS, housing etc.;

• *creating new conditions for competitive success:* contracts based on per person allocation of resources, such as in school recruitment or patient treatment (linked to payment by results and patient choice), bidding processes for additional resources, additional resources associated with performance assessment.

The development of these approaches does not mean that there will be privatization of services, but rather that market methods of coordination are being used in preference to more hierarchal or bureaucratic approaches, in the belief that this will better serve users and provide benefits in terms of improved performance.

The development of private and commercial health care

The underlying philosophy of the NHS was that health care should not be a commodity provided and consumed in a market. The main principle informing the funding of the service, was that only public provision of health care could deliver an acceptable level of equity in access to, and use of resources, as well as making the most effective use of the resources available.

However, private and commercial health care were not completely eliminated when the NHS was introduced in 1948. When the NHS was founded, about 270 hospitals remained outside it, but they often treated NHS patients on a contractual basis. Apart from the commercial sector, consultants employed by the NHS were also permitted to undertake private practice, and there were private (pay) beds in NHS hospitals. The NHS has nevertheless played the dominant role in the supply, control and financing of health services in Britain, and until the Labour government began the phasing out of pay beds in NHS hospitals in the mid-1970s, the majority of private patients were treated in NHS facilities. One consequence of the reduction in NHS facilities for treating private patients was an increase in privately-run facilities.

The Conservative administration elected in 1979 was ideologically committed to the expansion of private health care, although there has been a marked reluctance on behalf of the British people to move even to a partial, let alone a total, reliance on private care. Governments have had to step back from any radical reforms, that change the basic right to free treatment based on need and funded out of general taxation. Any attempt to change the nature of the NHS has met with strong opposition, and administrations have been forced, on a number of occasions, to reiterate a commitment to retaining the NHS. It was clearly an intention of the Conservatives, for example, to encourage more people to take out private health insurance, and although there has been an increase it has not reached the 25 per cent coverage rate that government had once hoped to achieve. A perception that there has been a reduction in services has not resulted in people turning to commercial treatment, but in demands for improvements to health services provided by the state. Opinion surveys have consistently demonstrated that there is considerable support for increased taxation specifically designed to increase health care spending. This does not mean that some people are not paying privately for some health care needs, when conventional medical care provided by the NHS proves ineffective or is unavailable (e.g. IVF and pregnancy termination services). In addition, changes in the way some services are provided (e.g. dental, optician and pharmacy services), have also led to distinct changes in the patterns of service delivery that have expanded private sector involvement.

In the last 15 years in particular, dentistry has shifted from the NHS to private treatment and concerns about access to NHS dentists have prompted the development of a new type of contract for dentists that sets target activity with fixed levels of reimbursement. This places an emphasis on developing community dentist services, although these changes have not led to a significant increase in the availability of NHS dentists (Hancock *et al.* 1999; Newsome 2003). As a result patients are increasingly paying more towards dental fees, either through NHS co-payments or privately, amounting for example, to some 55 per cent of the total fees of £3 billion earned from dentistry in 2001/2. Alongside this increase in co-payments, the number of adults treated by an NHS dentist, in the last 10 years has fallen by 23 per cent with the corresponding fall in the number of children treated being 5 per cent (DoH 2004b). In England, the government has devolved funding decisions to local levels, and developed access centres which should start to impact on the traditional pattern of dentistry provision, through small dental practices (DoH 2003a). As will the increasing incursion of corporate bodies, registered with the General Dental Council, who in 1999 employed about 4 per cent of all dentists (Newsome 2003). The new dental contract, introduced in 2006, does not appear to have altered these trends or provided additional access to NHS dentistry, and concerns remain about the future of the NHS dental service. Optician and pharmacy services have also rapidly expanded in the commercial sector, with larger chains dominating the market (52 per cent of all pharmacies are in chains of five or more) (*Guardian* 2004). There has also been an increasing emphasis on developing pharmacy services and the role of the pharmacist (Ottewill and Magirr 1999; Hassell *et al.* 2000). Over the last 10 years, there has also been a growth in private walk-in centres, GP services and screening services (House of Commons Health Select Committee 1999), although these have, as yet, only been marginal to mainstream NHS primary care services. In addition, the enormous growth in the range and availability of CAM practitioners has been a key feature of the private sector (see Chapter 3).

The NHS also funds consultations with practitioners and many health care professionals, particularly in primary care, practise complementary therapies. It is estimated that nearly 40 per cent of all general practices offer some form of complementary medicine, with about 20 per cent providing direct provision, and a further 20 per cent referring patients to practitioners without conventional health care backgrounds working in general practices (Zollman and Vickers 1999). In a survey of GPs in 1995, 40 per cent had recommended or endorsed the use of CAM and 21 per cent had made a direct referral. While 10 per cent had directly treated a patient (Thomas and Fitter 1997). Based on an assumption that non-responders to this survey were 'non-providers', Thomas *et al.* (2003) suggest slightly lower figures of 17.5 per cent for provision by health care practitioners, 18.1 per cent referred within the NHS and 4.9 per cent provision in the practice by an 'independent' complementary therapist. The average expenditure on CAM visits was estimated at £108 per user, with total out-of-pocket expenditure for the eight main CAM therapies totalling around £580 million (Thomas *et al.* 2001), and the total value including over-the-counter use in the region of £1.5 billion (Ernst and White 2000). Ong and Banks (2003) estimate that the NHS accounts for 10 per cent of consultations, at an annual cost in 2001 of £50–55 million. This represents just over 1 per cent of general medical services (GMS) expenditure (£4695 million in 1999/2000).

The percentage of the population relying totally on private health care remains small. The majority have an NHS GP. Indeed, access to private hospital (consultant) health care is most frequently obtained through a GP, as is access to NHS consultant health care.

The commercial sector benefits in a number of ways from the existence of the NHS. The NHS is forced to accept all patients who seek help; the commercial sector can select whom they choose to treat, leaving the state to provide for chronically ill people and those needing expensive treatments. Private health insurance premiums increase with age, making it difficult for older people with an increased risk of ill health and developing chronic medical conditions, to afford to continue paying premiums or indeed to take over the cost from their employers on retirement. Health insurers limit the amount available to cover the cost of treatment and the length of time over which they will cover treatment. Health checks to screen out those with pre-existing conditions, and premium rates based on actuarially calculated risk factors designed to keep claims low and prevent premiums from rising unduly, mean that private health insurance tends to be held mainly by middle-class people in employment (Higgins 1988). The commercial sector also benefits from the fact that the NHS trains medical and nursing staff and the allied health professionals, and makes little contribution to the training of staff. The services of NHS GPs are also an important element in supporting private health care. The commercial sector also benefits from the state, because health and local authorities purchase services from it, especially beds for older people in nursing homes. Finally, the commercial sector benefits from being able to use NHS facilities – especially 'high-tech' ones – that the sector could not afford to purchase. The main concern, however, has been that the existence of private health care not only enables the purchase of treatment superior to what is available on the NHS, but also breaches the principle of equity. Being able to pay for treatment enables people to obtain it earlier than they would on the NHS, and in some cases this increases the waiting time for those who cannot afford to pay by encouraging greater private practice by NHS consultants. (Iversen 1997).

Commercialization and the NHS

As discussed previously, from the earliest years, charging has been a feature of the NHS. The principle of free treatment was first breached in 1949, when it was decided to levy charges on visitors and subsequently on people not ordinarily resident in Britain. The latter provision was not widely used until 1982, when the government introduced complex rules for charging overseas visitors. These rules were seen as racist and in particular as linked to immigration controls, and concerns over the levying of charges and visitors accessing free NHS care remain. The use of charges also introduces a commercial element to health care provision.

In 1951, the Labour government introduced charges for spectacles, dentures and NHS prescriptions. These remained modest until 1979, accounting for less than 2 per cent of NHS income. Since 1979, charges for NHS treatment have increased dramatically and, income from this source has risen to over 4 per cent of total expenditure. Dental, optician and prescription charges have all increased. Those not exempt from payment (children and young people in full-time education and those on low incomes), now frequently have to pay the full cost of dental treatment and of spectacles, while the cost of an NHS prescription can actually be greater than the cost of the medication prescribed. Indeed, changes to the payments made to dentists, for treating NHS patients, mean that many are prepared to take on new patients, only if they are 'private'. This makes it especially difficult for those who cannot afford to pay to get dental treatment, if they have to leave the list of a dentist who has been treating them, or have not been registered with a dentist in the past. However, commercialization of the NHS is more than just the setting of charges, or, most recently the privitization of health care and health care support services. GPs have always been independent contractors and London hospitals have enjoyed a range of freedoms (Klein 2001).

The introduction of commercial sector management styles and methods

Responding to concerns about inefficiency in the NHS (see Chapter 3), the Conservative government, elected to power in 1979, was convinced that the problems of funding in the NHS were at least in part due to inefficient management, that the NHS was over-administered and under-managed (Hunter 1980). As Hunter (1994: 2) has indicated: *'Strengthening management, raising its profile and status, developing management skills and competencies, investing in management information systems and so on are seen as crucial to the success of policies directed towards securing value for money and improved quality of care for a given budget, while holding individuals and organizations accountable for what they do'.* The concern was that the NHS was bureaucratic, paternalistic, unresponsive to the needs of patients and organized to meet the needs of doctors; that is, it was a service dominated by administrative hierarchies and professionalization. A need was perceived for general managers to be introduced to manage the NHS.

Following a review by Griffiths (1983), general managers were introduced in 1983, with the intention of bringing about a cultural change in the NHS with the introduction of commercial sector management practices. These included planning, target setting, monitoring performance against preset targets, stricter control over the professional and manual labour force costs and performance, ensuring greater consumer satisfaction, and rewarding good performance. General managers were introduced at all levels of the NHS, appointed on short-term contracts with performance-related pay.

The new managerialism, that underpinned the creation of the new management structures, emphasized excellence and leadership rather than technical expertise in management science – or, indeed, knowledge of health or the NHS. The government had intended that a significant number of general managers should be recruited, from the commercial sector, to infuse the NHS with industrial and commercial managerial talent. However, a majority of those appointed in the first round were former NHS administrators, nurses, community physicians, consultants and former officers from the armed forces. Indeed, Pettigrew *et al.* (1992) suggest that the most effective management occurred when the managers understood the health service, and that the 'best' managers were former NHS administrators.

Cox (1991), summing up the impact of the introduction of general management, prior to the implementation of the National Health Service and Community Care Act 1990, argued that there was little evidence to indicate that greater control than previously was exercised over medical decision-making. However, at ward level, nurses had felt an increased managerial pressure on productivity and on the skill mix. The most radical change (discussed above) was the contracting-out of services, and this tended to create a more marked feeling of an 'us' and a 'them' among ancillary workers.

The new general managers were encouraged by the government to develop income-generation schemes to help fund NHS activity. The Health and Medicines Act 1988 facilitated this development and, in 1989, the DoH issued guidelines on the scope of income-generation schemes. As a consequence, schemes such as renting shop space in hospitals, renting advertising space in casualty departments and the selling of land for car parks, developed rapidly. The income from such schemes is, however, very modest compared with the overall cost of the NHS.

There was also a growth in the internal NHS market in the late 1980s, advocated by Enthoven (1985). By 1987, some London teaching hospitals were charging directly for services for out-of-district patients, rather than waiting to be compensated two years in arrears, through adjustment to their district financial allocation. By 1988 in East Anglia, such an internal market, within the national health system, had been established (Timmins 1988).

In 1987 and early 1988, there was a funding crisis in the NHS and considerable concern that people, especially young children, were not getting the emergency treatment they needed. The Conservative government argued that this was a result not of under-funding but of inefficient use of resources and poor management. Following a review, a White Paper – *Working for Patients* (Department of Health 1989a) – was published, to be followed by the National Health Service and Community Care Act 1990. The major objectives of these reforms were that doctors would be held accountable for their actions, that there would be a real shift in power from doctors to managers and that a consumer-oriented service would result. Hunter (1994) has indicated that the 'new public management', introduced into the NHS in the 1980s and early 1990s, had eight distinct features:

1 An emphasis on patients as customers.
2 Commercial sector management styles.
3 Competition 'created' through the use of managed markets and contracting.
4 Explicit standards and measures of performance.
5 A greater emphasis on outputs and results.
6 Disaggregation of public bureaucracies into agencies operating on a user-pay basis.
7 Stress on performance indicators for managers.
8 Stress on discipline in resource use and unit improvement.

Cox (1991) suggested that policies designed to introduce good management and limit the power of the medical profession were welcome but, he argued that the government did not always give NHS managers the independence to manage and, did not provide an adequate funding base. Furthermore, he suggested that some reforms were motivated more by an ideological commitment to a 'small business' approach, than by the aim of securing a planned and rationalized corporate provision. This, he indicated, had, on the one hand, lowered the income and morale of ancillary staff and, on the other, prevented general managers from taking the control over standards they felt could have been achieved if they had employed their own staff.

In the 1990s, the Conservatives carried out the first major reform of the NHS since its introduction in 1948. The National Health and Community Care Act 1990 legislated for internal/managed markets, with a split between the purchasers of health care on the one hand, and the providers on the other. There seems to have been a general acceptance that changing the basic principles, on which the NHS had been founded, would be extremely unpopular. Nevertheless, the government were intent on making the NHS more effective and less inefficient. They maintained that it was wasteful of public money, that too much was spent on administration and not patient care, and that the NHS was not responsive to the needs of customers. They argued that this was because it was not subject to the discipline of the market – that is, to competition. The 1989 White Paper, the recommendations of which were implemented in the 1990 legislation, was heavily influenced by reforms that had been introduced in the USA, which had proved effective in reducing spiralling costs there, but the main source of finance for health care in Britain continued to be general taxation. However, while drawing on US models, it was recognized that the US health system was not equitable in terms of coverage, as many people do not have health care insurance and access, with poorer people having much worse access than those in higher income groups. The NHS was also to remain the main provider of health care for the vast majority of the population, with commercial provision acting as a supplement to the NHS rather than a substitute.

There were five key elements contained in the legislation, in relation to health care:

1 A separation of purchasers and providers of health care.
2 NHS trusts were to be established which were to be responsible for providing services.
3 District health authorities were to be responsible for the purchase of services from providers on behalf of their populations.
4 Larger GP practices were to have the opportunity to become fund-holders and purchase health services on behalf of their patients.
5 The use of contracts/service agreements to link purchasers and providers.

The intention was that the reforms would establish competition among providers of health care services. As the finance would follow the patients, it was assumed that providers would become responsive to the demands of patients and those purchasing services on their behalf. Research evidence on the impact of these market reforms has been mixed (Le Grand *et al.* 1998). For example, GP fundholders (see Chapter 3) were able to attain advantages for their patients in terms of shorter waiting times, especially in specialities where the longest waits were experienced (orthopaedics, oph-thalmology and gynaecology). In addition GP fundholders reduced their rates of elective hospital admissions, compared with non-fundholders, and held down prescribing costs. These advantages were linked to clinical engagement.

However, fundholders' transaction costs were high – costs of £232 mil-lion in the first three years, compared to savings of £206 million (Audit Commission 1996). Fundholders may also have received a higher than equitable share of resources in some areas (Dixon *et al.* 1994). One reason for some practices to go into fundholding was precisely the access to additional management, administration and IT resources that would be available to the practice. In this sense, purchasing was seen as a route to develop the practice (Glennerster *et al.* 1994). Primary care purchasing rapidly evolved in the 1990s with new models, such as total purchasing, being introduced (Peckham and Exworthy 2003). Total purchasing pilots tended to be selective purchasers and achieved most gains this way, the majority achieving reductions in admissions and occupied bed days, through direct clinical engagement in patient pathways and the develop-ment of alternative approaches to care, use of discharge services etc. However, accountability of total purchasing pilots (both to the health authority and to the patient) was weak. In addition, single practice pilots achieved fuller clinical engagement than multi-practice ones, with the researchers concluding that the *'integration of clinical and financial roles is more likely to happen within single-practice than in multi-practice organisations'* (Baxter *et al.* 2000: 60). The evaluation of total purchasing found that there was a positive association between a pilot's ability to achieve its commis-sioning objectives and its *per capita* management costs (Mays *et al.* 2001: 85). Much of this evidence has direct relevance to current developments in health care markets being introduced by the Labour government in England (see Chapter 3).

Current developments are marked by an increasing emphasis on plurality of provision in all areas of health care. Since the mid-1990s, the increasing use of private finance for capital projects through public-private partnerships, LIFT (for primary care) and the PFI for major hospital projects, have been both widespread and controversial (Pollock 2005). While private financing of primary care has been well established for a number of years, hospital construction projects in the PFI scheme have been dogged by controversy around both the benefits of the method of financing and also impacts on the shape of local services, criticisms of poor design and impact on health agencies who are locked into long-term repayment terms (Pollock 2005). Reports of capitalization of assets by private contractors extracting substantial profit from PFI schemes, have also served to tarnish their image. Fundamentally, however, a key concern has been the way PFI schemes limit local health policy development, as developments lock health agencies into 30-year plus agreements for hospital provision, despite current moves to shift care from hospital to the community and reduce bed numbers.

Use of the private sector has also increased in terms of treatment and provision of services in the community. In England *Commissioning a Patient-Led NHS* (DoH 2005b) stated the government's intention to develop private and not-for-profit provision of health care services, indicating that some 15 per cent of NHS activity could be delivered in these sectors. National contracts, to develop specialized private sector involvement in surgery (e.g. orthopaedics and cataract surgery), and the development of independent sector diagnostic and treatment centres, are key features of current policy. In addition the government has signalled its intention to develop a market for primary and community care services, including encouraging private providers and the establishment of social enterprise companies by NHS staff (GPs in Southampton, East London and community nurses in Surrey). This represents a radical departure from traditional service delivery structures in the NHS.

Contracting-out of NHS services

The contracting-out or purchasing of services from commercial companies, as opposed to providing them 'in house', has always been possible within the NHS. However, until the return of the Conservative government in 1979, the norm was for services to be provided by NHS employees. In 1979, 2 per cent of NHS domestic cleaning, 14 per cent of laundry and far less than 1 per cent of catering was provided by the commercial sector. Since 1979, there has been a push to privatize ancillary services, the government arguing that the commercial sector can provide more efficient and effective services than those provided by employees. On the one hand, the government was concerned about the power of trade unions among ancillary workers and the way in which they disrupted hospital services in 1978–9, and on the other they argued that the commercial sector could provide the services more cheaply. Competitive tendering, in particular, was seen as a way of ensuring that an adequate service was provided at the lowest cost. However, Ascher (1987) has argued that the need to economize played only a small part in the decision to introduce compulsory contracting-out of services, and it is not clear that the claimed savings of £1000 million per annum (*Independent*, 15 June 1988: p. 6) have been put back into patient care.

The government instituted *compulsory* competitive tendering for NHS services in 1983: health authorities were required to put hospital cleaning, catering and laundry out to tender. The full implementation of the requirement was delayed, and the process was also undermined by resistance from health authorities and ancillary workers' trade unions. In the first round of competitive tendering, only a small percentage of contracts went to private firms, and the DoH put pressure on health authorities to award more. Health authorities were also forced to remove 'fair wage' clauses from service contracts (they had already been prevented from tying contracts to the minimum terms and conditions of employment of NHS staff; see Ascher 1987).

By December 1985, 40 per cent of contracts had been awarded to the commercial sector (Ascher 1987); however, this percentage had declined to 23 per cent by 1990 (MacGregor 1990). One in four private contracts had not been adequately fulfilled, and 5 per cent of private contracts had been withdrawn. By the late 1980s, health authorities were awarding fewer contracts to the commercial sector and renewing fewer of those already held there. However, between 1981 and 1988, the number of NHS ancillary staff fell by 33.5 per cent and the pay and conditions of employment of those remaining also fell. Pollock and Whitty (1990) have argued that poor conditions of work, poor wages and inadequate staffing levels are likely to have adverse consequences for patient care, whether the services are provided by commercial contractors or 'in house'. Contracting-out remains, however, a significant feature of health care and while recent concerns, over hospital cleaning services and the rise in MRSA, have reignited debates about the use of private contractors, this market continues to grow and may in the future include clinical services (Pollock 2005).

Employer-provided health care

The extent of employer-provided health care is difficult to determine, as it has not been the subject of research in Britain (May and Brunsden 1994). Titmuss (1955) has pointed to the 'hidden' welfare benefits received by those in employment. We do know, for example, that some 45 per cent of private health care insurance is paid for by employers (Higgins 1988). May and Brunsden (1994) argue that within an individualistic, risk-minimization, self-help and lifestyle modification framework, there has been an increase in corporate health care. They suggest that the major aim is to increase work performance, with an emphasis on individuals taking responsibility for their own health and regulating their own behaviour. Balcombe *et al.* (1993) estimate that 75 per cent of British employers provide some form of 'wellness intervention', such as single-factor screening and/or specialist responses to health issues, such as alcohol abuse, substance abuse and HIV/AIDS. An increasing number of employers are providing specialist screening for female employees, and health promotion measures, such as 'healthy eating', 'no smoking' or 'no alcohol' policies. Many employers provide sport and recreational facilities for employees. However, apart from paying for the premiums for private health insurance, few employers provide direct health care, although an increasing number are providing counselling, including personal counselling.

Pluralism: the third sector

Following the introduction of community care reforms in the 1990s, there has been a steady increase in the use of voluntary sector agencies to deliver social care services. This sector has developed alongside increased private sector involvement and is characterized by increases in direct service provision (see Chapter 7). This growth has been stimulated by health and social care funding at a local level, in areas such as care services in the home, residential and nursing home provision, hospice care and housing. More recently moves by the government, in England, have seen discussion about the development of independent and voluntary sector agencies to deliver health care services (DoH 2000a, 2005b, 2005d, 2006). Voluntary agencies operate within the health and social care market-place competing for contracts with private sector agencies. The nature of services provided by voluntary organizations has changed rapidly in the last 15 to 20 years (see Chapters 7, 8 and 9). Many of the national welfare voluntary agencies (e.g. Age Concern, MIND) have substantial service delivery sections at a national and local level (Baggott *et al.* 2005). This has presented challenges for many organizations, that also retain an advocacy and support function, which may conflict with the provision of services.

Conclusion

We have seen that the role of commercial provision has increased in many areas of social policy. Public support for the commercial sector varies depending upon the service in question, with private housing – and, to a lesser extent, pensions – receiving public support, while the expansion of private health care receives little support. Even where there is public support for the growth of private 'options', these are seen principally as a means of supplementing state provision and not as a replacement.

One of the key arguments, used to support the growth of the commercial sector, has been the perceived need to contain public expenditure on universal state provision during a period of demographic change and escalating costs. While this remains an important factor, the evidence suggests that it is only one consideration and broader, ideologically-motivated considerations often assume priority. In practice, privatization or the introduction of commercial sector management practises often increases the overall costs of service provision (Pollock 2005). In addition, the shifting balance also implies a stronger role for central government in the regulation and financing of provision, coupled with important restrictions on local autonomy (and the role of local government) in some areas.

Summary

- The election of the Conservative government in 1979, led to a renewed emphasis on the role of the commercial sector in welfare provision.
- The proportionate contribution of the private sector varies depending on the type of service. In the field of housing, for example, the private sector has long dominated provision, while in the area of health care it has, until recently, played a very limited role.
- Public support for privatization similarly varies with strong support for owner-occupation and private pensions but much weaker support for the erosion of public sector health and education services.
- The privatization of welfare has taken a number of forms including the encouragement of alternative, parallel, private provision, the contracting-out of certain services and the introduction of fees and private sector management techniques within the state sector.
- The growth in privatization policies both within the NHS, and welfare services more generally, may lead to increased levels of social inequality and polarization.
- Progressive privatization in some areas has not resulted in the anticipated reduction in public expenditure, but simply a transfer of resources from the state to the private sector or not-for-profit sector.
- Despite the concerted push in England towards private sector involvement in capital projects and services, this remains a controversial area of health policy.
- Commitment to developing non-public sector provision varies across the UK, with Wales and Northern Ireland having virtually universal public provision, Scotland incorporating limited non-NHS provision and England moving towards greater plurality of provision.

Further reading

Pollock, A. (2005) *NHS Plc: The Privatization of Our Health Care*. London: Virgo.

Powell, M. and Hewitt, M. (1998) The end of the welfare state? Social Policy and Administration, 32(1): 1–13.

THE MIXED ECONOMY OF COMMUNITY CARE

- Introduction
- The development of community care
- Reforms in the 1990s
- Older people and community care
- The mixed economy of care for older people
- Residential care
- The management of long-term conditions
- Conclusion
- Summary
- Further reading

Introduction

In Chapter 1, we indicated that there is a mixed economy of care in Britain: provision by the state, the commercial sector, the voluntary sector and informal carers. In this chapter, we look at this mix, briefly examining wider concepts such as social inclusion (see Box 7.1), before going on to focus particularly on services for older people and, recent policy development for people with long-term conditions. As in other chapters in this book, readers may find that some of the policy language used historically is outdated and stigmatizing.

The development of schemes to promote 'care in the community' exemplifies how the mixed economy of welfare works in practice. We have argued in previous chapters that all dimensions of social policy interact, but this interrelationship is nowhere as explicitly acknowledged as in the development of community care. Indeed, the success or failure of care in the community depends on the careful balance of responsibilities and partnerships, both within the statutory sector itself (between different agencies, such as social services, PCTs and local authorities) and between the range of non-statutory providers. In particular, the need for better coordination between health and social care bodies has been urged (they are, after all, both under the same government department in England, the DoH). Despite this, however, Lewis (2001) argues that the funding of care for people with 'intermediate' needs has not been properly planned nor funded since the inception of the NHS, nor has that gap been generally acknowledged.

Thus, if we apply the principles of equity referred to in Chapters 3 and 5, community care does not carry a universal entitlement, there is no pooled financial risk and it is not free at the point of delivery, and neither access nor care are equal. Selection on the basis of need, and an ethos of science, can be problematic as 'need' in community care can be a slippery concept, and it depends on assumptions about whether the family or other informal carers have a role. Our ambivalence about some forms of community care, such as care homes, means that the 'feel-good factor' of national approval does not exist.

Community care is most easily understood as the alternative to institutional care. It consists of a wide range of welfare services which provide care for dependent groups (e.g. older people, children, people who are physically disabled, people with learning disabilities, or those who are mentally ill) within the community, rather than within institutions such as long-stay hospitals or large residential homes. A community care policy may embrace one or more of the following:

- services are provided by the state in the community;
- decarceration (literally, removal from prison), i.e. dependent people are no longer cared for in long-stay hospitals;
- care is provided by informal carers, especially families;
- the lives of dependent people are 'normalized' and their contribution to society is valued.

Michael Bayley (1973) made a distinction between 'care in the community' and 'community care'. The former concerns geographical location, in that people are cared for not in large hospitals but, instead reside in small local hospitals or hostels or with their families. The latter suggests that people are cared for by both formal and informal agencies, and relatives, in the community. Community care has been supported and promoted by successive governments since the 1960s, not least because it has been seen as a cheaper and more humanitarian alternative to residential care. However, in practice, community care may mean either community neglect (especially in the case of mentally ill people transferred from hospital to boarding houses) or care by relatives, especially women. Historically, local authorities have been slow to provide community care services, and individuals with relatives to care for them have been less likely to receive services than those who live alone. This has been accentuated by the greater targeting of services by local authorities for those in greatest need. Government policies have tended to emphasize the responsibility of families to care for their dependent members. As Martin Bulmer (1987: x) has pointed out: ' *"Community" as a concept invokes images of the family to convey the warmth and intimacy which its bonds are supposed to foster ... The term "community care" appeals to sentiment and postulates a range of supportive ties which may not actually exist in practice, thus putting the burden of care upon particular family members'*.

This chapter begins by documenting the development of community care strategies in the post-war period. It considers some of the explanations for the increasing attractiveness of this type of policy, including concerns about public expenditure, issues about the 'quality of care' and ideological pressures to shift 'responsibility' further on to individuals and families, and away from the state. In particular, the changing policy on care homes is discussed and recent policy development in the care of people with long-term conditions. This focus on community care illustrates the changing role of the state in contemporary Britain, from one of direct provider (of residential homes and domiciliary services for older people, mentally ill people and children) to one of financier, regulator and coordinator of a broad range of inputs, where the state withdraws from funding some elements of care, and users are encouraged to coordinate their own care. The debate on funding, and the Royal Commission on Long-Term Care, will be discussed further in this chapter.

Recent policy developments have led to better coordination of services. Such developments include the creation of NSFs, for example, for older people and for mental health. The user movement has also grown, particularly in mental health services, and the rights of users are now underpinned by legislation, including the Human Rights Act 1998 and the Disability Discrimination Act 1995. There is also a Disability Rights Commission (although it is about to be subsumed into the Commission for Equality and Human Rights) which has disabled commissioners, including people with learning disabilities. The literature on social policy has also evolved; the early feminist writing envisaged care largely as a burden for women, whereas later disabled feminist writers contested this and provided a different viewpoint, arguing that disability is a social construct.

The development of community care

As a social policy, community care is relatively new in Britain. There is also a considerable overlap with the term social care. Tizard (1964) was unable to trace the origins of the idea of community care as a policy objective. However, Scull (1977) indicated that the policy was considered in the late nineteenth century, but could not be implemented for lack of community services. The 1904–8 Royal Commission on the Care of the Feeble-Minded, although mostly concerned with institutional care, did advocate guardianship and supervision in 'the community'. The 1929 Wood Committee recommended greater use of all forms of community supervision, and by the late 1930s experts were suggesting that, given favourable conditions, people with learning disabilities could be supervised at home. The term itself was first used in the *Report of the Royal Commission on the Law Relating to Mental Illness and Mental Deficiency* (Royal Commission 1958). This report recommended a shift of policy from hospital to community care and emphasized the desirability of supported family care.

Certainly, psychological and sociological research in the 1950s and 1960s strongly suggested that children developed better, both cognitively and emotionally, if cared for in a family environment (Bowlby 1954; Lyle 1958, 1959a, 1959b; Tizard 1964) and that hospitals and other large institutions were dehumanizing (Barton 1959; Goffman 1961; King *et al.* 1971; Wing and Brown 1971). The policies also fitted in with the ideology of welfare and equality of opportunity that was developing in Britain (Scull 1977). In the case of mentally ill people, the development of psychotropic drugs, which could 'control' the 'unacceptable' behaviour of many, was a key factor, as was the critique of orthodox treatment by writers such as Laing (1964). An important selling point at the time seems to have been that policies of community care appeared to be cheap as well as humanitarian alternatives to residential care. As Scull indicated, the general welfare services, which had been introduced in the 1940s, were available to meet the needs of dependent groups – specific services did not have to be provided.

Scull (1977) has pointed out that while the rejection of institutional care in asylums and other long-stay institutions was based on research findings that demonstrated the dehumanizing nature of such care, the advocacy of community care was not based on research demonstrating its efficacy. Furthermore, what community care means has never been fully clarified. In general, it seems just to mean care outside large-scale institutions – remote, impersonal asylums or other long-stay institutions. Community care can mean living in a small local hospital, a hostel, a group home, in lodgings, independently or with a family. It can mean that a range of services are provided, such as sheltered workshops, community nursing, home care, social work support, respite care, day care and so on, or that families are left entirely to fend for themselves.

Lewis (2001) argues that in the UK, there is a history of particularly sharp divisions between the centrally funded NHS and locally run social services, which has led to a constant battle between the two, largely to avoid expenditure on their own budget. This divide was created at the founding of the welfare state, when the 1946 NHS Act made the health service responsible for both acute and continuing care, whereas Part III of the 1948 National Assistance Act left local authorities with the responsibility for providing residential accommodation, together with a range of domiciliary services, including home helps and home nursing (the latter of which became part of the health service in 1974). Hospital doctors, were, however, largely resistant to providing continuing care. Complaints about 'bed blocking' emerged by the late 1960s, and while there was a 14 per cent rise in the population of older people between 1961 and 1971, the overall number of assigned hospital beds remained static.

Despite this division between health and social care, which exists elsewhere but is most pronounced in the UK, in the last 40 years community care for dependent people has become a policy objective in most western countries. As discussed above, in Britain by the 1950s, residential care, especially in large institutions, was being criticized for children deprived of a normal home life, as well as people with learning disabilities, mentally ill people and older people (National Council for Civil Liberties 1951; Townsend 1962). Subsequently, a number of academic studies of long-stay residential institutions suggested that they were dehumanizing, and official inquiry reports indicated that residents were ill-treated. King *et al.* (1971) argued that organizational factors were a key to the problems faced in providing adequate, personalized care in institutional settings. The Report of the Royal Commission suggested community care as an alternative to hospitalization, and the Mental Health Act 1959 advocated community care for mentally ill people and people with learning disabilities. A DHSS report in 1964, *The Development of Community Care*, recommended the development of a family-oriented service and an expansion of non-institutional day care and domiciliary services, staffed by professional workers, in expanding local authority health and welfare departments, while recognizing that some residential care might still be necessary. The Seebohm Committee (1968) argued that the existence of community care remained an illusion. Despite this, government policy throughout the 1970s was to implement community care, but the extent to which community services did actually develop has been questioned. A number of welfare benefits were also introduced to assist dependent people with the costs of living in the community. These included benefits which were not means tested, such as mobility allowance and attendance allowance paid to disabled people themselves, as well as means tested income maintenance benefits, including invalidity benefit and the invalidity care allowance paid to carers (but withheld from married women until 1986).

Box 7.1   Normalization and social inclusion

By the late 1970s, besides community care, 'normalization' was being advocated – the idea that dependent people should lead as normal a life as possible in the community (see Jay Report 1979). Community care has continued to be advocated by governments as a major policy objective. However, the emphasis switched from the provision of services by health and social services departments to informal care with support as necessary: *'Whatever level of public expenditure proves practicable, and however it is distributed, the primary sources of support and care for elderly people are informal and voluntary ... It is the role of public authorities to sustain and where necessary develop but never displace such support and care ... Care in the community must increasingly mean care by the community'* (DHSS 1981: 3).

It was argued that services should be targeted at those most in need and directed at maintaining people in the community with, wherever possible, informal carers playing a major role (DSS 1989).

An important development under the current government has been an emphasis on inclusion and citizenship. For example, the White Paper *Valuing People: A New Strategy for Learning Disability for the 21st Century* (DoH 2001f) refers to the key principles of rights, independence, choice and inclusion, and states that *'People with learning disabilities have the right to a decent education, to grow up to vote, to marry and to have a family, and to express their opinions'* (para. 2.2).

Social exclusion is also an important theme in mental health. The Social Exclusion Unit's (SEU) report *Mental Health and Social Exclusion* (2004a) states that about 900,000 people claim incapacity benefit for a mental health problem, and that care costs, economic losses and premature deaths cost over £77 billion a year. There are plans for stronger links between mental health services, Job Centres and benefits agencies.

Bainbridge and Ricketts (2003), reviewing older people's services for the Social Services Inspectorate, conclude that a fundamental cultural shift has begun, in which the principle of person-centred, needs-led planning is beginning to offer empowerment and choice. More recently, a review of the literature on the effectiveness of policies aimed at limiting social exclusion in old age (Phillipson and Scharf 2004), found that the number of older people in relative poverty had decreased and that support for people with high levels of dependency had increased, but that social exclusion due to cumulative disadvantage (such as poor education) was difficult to change, and that social exclusion due to community change (e.g. high population turnover and an increase in crime) was also a problem.

Reforms in the 1990s

During the 1970s, Lewis (2001) argues that there were intractable disputes between health and social care about their responsibilities for older people, despite the imposition of joint planning structures. These difficulties 'magically disappeared' in the 1980s due to the massive injection of funds from the social security budget into private residential care, but this was largely inadvertent and could not continue. By the early 1980s, the government came to realize that if more very dependent people were to live in the community rather than in long-stay residential hospitals, then costs would escalate unless much of this care was undertaken by informal carers, or was self-funded. Between 1980 and 1989, social security expenditure on older people in residential care rose from £10 million to £1000 million (Lewis *et al.* 1995: 75). Nearly half of all social security payments in 1993–4 were made to older people (CSO 1995: 135) and nearly 60 per cent of residents in commercial and voluntary homes in 1992 were funded by the Department of Social Security (DSS, now the Department for Work and Pensions) (Wistow *et al.* 1994). This should, however, be set in the context of the economic value of informal care at the time, which the Family Policy Studies Centre estimated to be between £15 billion and £24 billion per year in 1989.

The Audit Commission report *Making a Reality of Community Care* (1986) advocated closing the funding loophole and having a unitary authority to plan and purchase the care of older people, but did not address the role of the NHS. The Griffiths Report (DHSS 1988) was a response to this. It clarified the responsibility of the NHS, which was that hospital care was appropriate only if *both* medical and nursing care were needed round the clock; in other words, hospitals should concentrate on acute care. This clarification, however, was not accepted by the DHSS which did not attempt to define either health or social care in the White Paper.

The provisions in the White Paper, *Caring for People* (DoH 1989b) were enacted in the NHS and Community Care Act 1990, the community care provisions of which were implemented in April 1993. The Act required local authorities to make substantial changes in the way they managed and delivered services, many of them based on research carried out by the Personal Social Services Research Unit; it envisaged that social services departments would become 'enabling authorities', responsible for the stimulation and coordination of 'independent' providers within a mixed economy of care. Local authorities were also required to separate the purchaser and provider functions within social services departments, as a means of reducing direct social service provision and encouraging the buying-in of commercial and voluntary services to support informal care. Through more effective joint planning, social services departments were to oversee the development of a 'seamless service' within a mixed economy of service provision. The intention behind these policies was to reinforce the role of informal care, through the provision of additional domiciliary support in the form of home care, meals on wheels and community nursing, to prevent caring relationships from breaking down as a result of high levels of dependency. In summary, then, the key objectives of the 1990 legislation were:

- to facilitate the development of services in the community, which would enable dependent people to live in their own homes;
- to ensure that the needs of users were prioritized, that is to change from service-led to needs-led provision;
- to ensure that needs were assessed by care managers who were responsible for purchasing packages of care;
- to ensure that the voluntary and independent sectors were major providers of services;
- to ensure better value for the public monies spent on community care;
- to ensure that services were targeted at those most in need.

The key role of social services departments was to be the lead authority, and to purchase and coordinate care within a social care market, which they were responsible for stimulating, in consultation with health authorities. The intention was that there would be a shift in the balance of welfare provision from the state to the voluntary, commercial and informal sectors with the establishment of market forces that would drive down the cost of service provision. Four key concerns were the balance between:

- institutional and community services;
- supply-led and needs-led services;
- the provision of services by the public sector and the commercial/voluntary sectors;
- funding and provision by the NHS and local authority social services.

> **Box 7.2   Promoting user independence**
>
> The move towards community-based care marked an ideologically motivated shift away from direct public provision in favour of a 'mixed economy of care', and from provider/professional-led services to needs-led services. The introduction of new procedures for assessment, which emphasized 'needs-led' care, may be interpreted as a positive initiative aimed at reducing bureaucracy and the power of welfare professionals, and genuinely empowering service users. Although the rhetoric of user empowerment may mean little more than a shift from being clients to consumers within a managed market (Lewis *et al.* 1995), since the 1990s there has been a shift towards greater user-centredness, pioneered by the disability lobby (Oliver and Barnes 1998). However, policies such as direct payments, which may be welcomed by younger disabled people, may be burdensome to older people and few have taken them up (Phillipson and Scharf 2004). Policies and legislation include:
>
> - The 1995 Carers (Recognition and Services) Act, which provides carers with the right to have their own needs assessed.
> - The 1996 Community Care (Direct Payments) Act, which from April 1997 provided cash instead of social services for disabled people of working age and in 2000 was extended to older disabled people.
> - The 1998 White Paper *Modernising Social Services*, which emphasized the promotion of independence and dignity, and introduced a £647 million partnership grant for health and social services to promote independence, including the provision of 'low-level' support.
> - The 1999 National Strategy for Carers.
> - The 2000 Carers and Disabled Children Act, which included direct payments for carers.
> - The 2001 Promoting Independence grant.
> - The 2005 Green Paper on social care, *Independence, Well-being and Choice*.

Older people and community care

In 2003/4, expenditure on social protection benefits (defined as 'the help given to people who are in need or are at risk of hardship') for old age and for 'survivors' (such as widows) accounted for 45 per cent of the £286 billion total (Babb *et al.* 2006). Wittenberg *et al.* (2001) have modelled projections that long-term care for older people will increase from £9.8 billion in 1996 (including NHS expenditure of £2.2 billion and user fees of £1.5 billion) to £24.3 billion in 2031 (including NHS expenditure of £6.0 billion and user fees of £3.4 billion). A major concern, then, has been the growth in the number of individuals in the population aged 65 years and over, both in absolute terms and as a percentage of the UK population as a whole. PSSRU projections (Comas-Herrera *et al.* 2006) state that in 2002 there were about 2 million disabled older people in the community and about a third of a million in care homes. The numbers overall are projected to increase by about 70 per cent between 2002 and 2031, and by about 98 per cent between 2002 and 2041. Care home places would need to expand by about 115 per cent, and expenditure overall by about 325 per cent in real terms. There is likely to be an increase in spouse carers, but these projections are very sensitive to assumptions about the availability of informal care and expenditure is likely to increase greatly if this becomes less available.

Older people live in many different circumstances, and therefore have a wide variety of needs. The most obvious differences are those between the frail and the fit and healthy, and between those who have adequate economic resources and the poor. (Even over the age of 85, in the 2001 census 26.5 per cent of men and 21.9 per cent of women said they were in good health). Those who have adequate resources are often in a position to purchase their own social care services from the commercial sector; those who do not are dependent on state support.

In 2002, around 900,000 older people were considered to have high levels of need, according to the standard assessment of being unable to carry out one or more of the main activities of daily living (ADLs) (being able to wash, dress, feed, toilet, walk and so on) (Wanless 2006). A further 1.4 million older people had low levels of need. Over the 20 years to 2025, it is projected that there will be a rise in the number of older people who do not require care of 44 per cent, a 53 per cent increase in those with some need and a 54 per cent increase in those with a high level of need. Based on expert analysis commissioned for the Wanless Review, these increases reflect a future where population health improves due to moderate reductions in obesity and other 'lifestyle' conditions, as well as the introduction of effective new treatments or technologies.

The number of older people with mental health problems is growing rapidly; depression affects between 10 and 16 per cent of people over 65 (Audit Commission 2000). There are currently over 700,000 people with dementia in the UK, and this is forecast to reach over 1.2 million by 2040 (Association of the British Pharmaceutical Industry, cited by DoH 2005a). There are gaps in meeting mental health needs, particularly for people with dementia, and for older people from ethnic minorities (Phillipson and Scharf 2004). There is also little research, to date, on the particular needs of this population.

Old age, even *very* old age, is not synonymous with dependency and ill health; nor is it synonymous with financial dependency on the state, and only a minority are extremely dependent. However, there is a close relationship between advancing years on the one hand and the increasing incidence of physical disabilities and mental incapacities on the other, and also a greater use of personal social services. For example, in 2001/2 the General Household Survey found that 10 per cent of people aged 75–79, but 28 per cent of those aged over 85 had a private home help; the figures for district nursing were 5 per cent and 19 per cent. There is also a gender imbalance: the greater life expectancy of women means they form an ever increasing proportion of those surviving into advanced old age. Women are also more likely than men to be dependent on state benefits in old age, being less likely to have a private pension. In addition, the percentage of employers making any pension provision for their employees has declined from 52 per cent in 2003 to 44 per cent in 2005. Hence the urgent need for a reform of the pensions system, including raising the retirement age.

Taylor-Gooby (2004) considers that, in the UK, the greatest increase in risk for vulnerable people was due to the pension reforms of the late 1980s, which substantially cut back the contribution of the social insurance-related pension scheme to retirement incomes and encouraged people to take out private personal pensions. Initially these were not sufficiently regulated; this became part of the remit of the Financial Services Agency, established in 2001. Employers have also cut back occupational pension commitments, such as final salary schemes, and an estimated 85,000 people have lost their pension due to employer bankruptcy.

The Turner Report on pensions (Pensions Commission 2005) showed that nearly 10 million workers are not saving enough, and that there will be 'major and increasing problems' after 2020. The commission included a professor of social policy at the London School of Economics, John Hills, illustrating how academics can have an important role in policy-making. The initial remit of the Turner Commission was to advise on how to encourage private saving, but he widened the scope to include the state system, since it was a major disincentive to saving due to its complex means testing. Lord Turner proposed a combination of higher savings, more tax and raising the pension age to 68 by 2050, which would cost an additional £8 billion a year by 2045. He argued for a simpler, less means tested system than the current one, which consists of the basic state pension, the top-up state pension, and the means tested Pension Credit. He also recommended that the pension should be based on residency rather than National Insurance contributions, thus acknowledging the research by Arber and others (Arber and Ginn 1991), which showed that older women are far more likely to live in poverty due to their employment, and hence their pension contributions, having been interrupted by caring responsibilities; only 14 per cent of women aged 55–59 have a full contribution record, and more than 40 per cent have fewer than ten qualifying years, some of whom may have been in poorly paid jobs which were below the National Insurance Threshold. However, as Turner acknowledged, although life expectancy has been rising, the average masks a range. In the most deprived council wards of Britain (in Manchester, Blackpool, Liverpool and seven in Scotland), life expectancy for men is still only 69, so under the Turner recommendations (and assuming that their life expectancy does not increase) they would have only one year of retirement on a state pension. Employer contributions are also contentious, since many small businesses do not currently contribute, and there has been recent union unrest on proposals to increase the public sector retirement age from 60 to 65. The White Paper on pensions, *Security in Retirement: Towards a New Pensions System* (DWP 2006b), launched in May 2006, accepts many of the Turner recommendations. The link with earnings, rather than prices, will be re-established in the next parliament and there is a proposal for a low cost savings scheme, with automatic enrolment for staff and compulsory employers' contributions. The state pension age for both men and women will increase to 66 in 2024, 67 in 2034 and 68 in 2044. Turner's residency criterion has not been accepted, however.

The need for care in old age, then, and especially the need for care from formal services, is mediated by a number of factors, including the household circumstances of the older person, their socio-economic circumstances, their extended family networks and the type of disability or ill health they suffer. Changes in these other factors suggest that the growth in the numbers of older people will provide a formidable challenge to health and social care agencies. The decline in the numbers of young people in the 1970s, because of low birth rates, means that there will be difficulties recruiting nurses and other care workers, especially to work with older people. The care of older people relies heavily on informal carers, but the increasing number of older people is not matched by a similar increase in potential carers (see Chapter 8). The second report of the Pensions Commission (2005) predicts that once the baby boom generation of the 1940s to 1960s retires, there will be a steady rise in the old-age dependency ratio, which was about 15 per cent in 1941 and will accelerate from about 30 per cent in 2011 to reach 50 per cent in 2031.

Caring for older people

The major source of help for those unable to care for themselves is relatives and other informal carers (see Chapter 9). Government policy, for example, the Green Paper *Independence, Well-being and Choice* (DoH 2005d) also assumes that informal carers will continue to be the main providers of care for older people, and while it is stated that public services should support informal carers, in practice they often receive little, if any, help from statutory services. Although the 1995 Carers (Recognition and Services) Act gives new rights, and the number of carer assessments is increasing (Bauld *et al.* 2000), most carers have little knowledge of their entitlements. Parker (1999: 63) states that '*there is a serious question mark over whether or not the changes have delivered significant, rather than marginal, improvement in access to the core services which support carers best*'.

Table 7.1 People's preferences should they need care

Preference	%
Stay in my own home with care and support from friends and family	62
Stay in my own home but with care and support from trained care workers	56
Move to a smaller home of my own	35
Move to sheltered housing with a warden	27
Move to sheltered housing with a warden and other social care services such as hairdressing and organized social outings	25
Move in with my son or daughter	14
Move to a private residential home	11
Move to a local council residential home	7
Move to a residential home provided by a charitable organization	3
None	1
Don't know	2

Note: Base: all respondents aged 15+ (1,049)
Source: Commission for Social Care Inspection, cited by Wanless (2006)

Analysis of General Household Survey data (Pickard 2002) has also shown that patterns of care are changing. Intergenerational co-resident

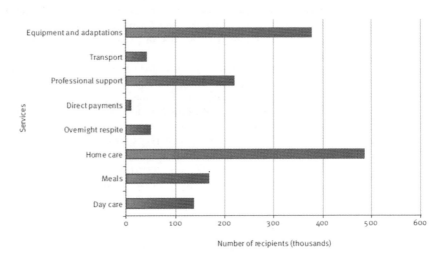

Figure 7.1 Number of recipients of community-based services aged 65+ during the year 2004/5
Note: the figures for the number of clients receiving each different component of service do not necessarily sum to the total of clients receiving community-based services because a client may receive more than one component of service during the year.
Source: DoH (2005d), Wanless (2006)

care has declined, and spouses are now the largest group of co-resident carers, a reflection of couples' greater longevity.

A number of concerns have been raised about the provision and deployment of domiciliary care services, although Phillipson and Scharf (2004) indicate that this may be improving and Bauld *et al.* (2000) have found a general improvement since the Act was implemented in 1993. From April 2003 domiciliary care agencies in England have been regulated, and national minimum standards have been introduced. Councils have also been required to undertake user experience surveys. Overall, the evidence suggests some gains for people with complex needs, but fewer improvements for people with lower levels of dependency, some of whom may not even get an assessment of need. This is particularly important for older women since, as Clark *et al.* (1998) state, their public identities and self-presentation as competent are often based on the standard of their housekeeping. Pressure on resources may also lead to routinized care plans from care workers on the lowest rates of pay. As in other areas of care, older people from ethnic minorities are often unaware of the range of services available; Patel (1999) found that mainstream services were often inadequate, and that minority ethnic organizations continued to act as the primary providers.

The number of home help hours purchased or provided by councils in England has increased over the past decade, from 2.2 million hours per week in 1994 to 3.4 million in 2004 (Babb *et al.* 2006). Whereas 81 per cent of these hours were directly provided in 1994, this had fallen to 31 per cent in 2004, since services are now generally purchased rather than provided by local authorities. 16 per cent of households receiving home help received more than five hours in 1994: this had increased to 46 per cent in

2004, reflecting the policy of focusing on those with greatest need. The 2001 census identified 1.9 million unpaid carers in the UK, who provided at least 20 hours of care a week (4 per cent of women and 3 per cent of men, indicating that the gender gap in care identified by feminist writers may be closing somewhat). However, the pattern of care differs. The likelihood of women providing at least 20 hours was greatest for the 55 to 64 age group, whereas for men it was greatest for the 75 to 84 age group, indicating that whereas women often care for elderly parents, male carers are more likely to care for their own elderly spouse (there were nearly 4000 carers aged over 90 in the 2001 census). Women are also more likely to undertake personal care than men. The areas of England and Wales with the highest levels of unpaid care were mainly poorer areas such as South Wales, Merseyside, and in London, Newham and Tower Hamlets.

There is also debate about whether the home help service can substitute for residential care. Indeed, it is not clear that residential care can be substituted by domiciliary services in any straightforward sense, even when home helps provide social and personal care as well as domestic help. Evaluation of successful experiments indicates that if effective and efficient care is to be provided to those with a high and complex mix of needs, then it requires careful coordination and integration at the level of the individual user. Research suggests that frail elderly people can be maintained in their own homes at a cost lower than that of residential care, but that care management is essential. Challis and Hughes (2002) found that there is marked variability in assessing need and managing access to social care services which needs to be addressed, and there is an increasing need for the involvement of specialist clinicians.

In summary, the great majority of older people, including the very elderly, care for themselves or are cared for by informal carers. Only a minority receive domiciliary services, and home helps/carers and meals on wheels are mainly provided to elderly people living alone. While there is some evidence that residential care can be a positive choice, the vast majority of older people want to remain in the community, with support from their families and statutory services, for as long as possible.

The mixed economy of care for older people

The range of problems with which welfare providers need to deal in order to maintain older people in their own homes is very wide. There are three major areas of concern:

1 *Financial difficulties*: many older people have very low incomes.
2 *Health and personal problems*: not all older people are ill, but as a group they are more likely to suffer from chronic conditions, such as arthritis, or degenerative conditions, such as dementia. Many of the health problems typically associated with older people not only need constant medical attention but also reduce the patient's mobility; for example, many older people are unable to manage stairs easily, if at all. They may also have physical difficulties with shopping, cooking their own meals, keeping the house clean and even washing themselves.

3 *Social problems*: many older people in Britain are isolated either because they have no family or friends or because they do not live near them. Even when family and friends live nearby, older people are sometimes reluctant to leave their homes for fear of crime, because they find public transport inadequate or because of a physical difficulty. The increasing participation of women in the labour market means that daughters now are less likely to be co-resident carers and may have less time than in the past to visit older parents.

The four sectors together (the state, the voluntary sector, the commercial sector, and the informal sector) may deal with these problems as follows. *Financial difficulties* are often alleviated by provisions, such as housing benefit, council tax rebates, pensions (provided by the state, by employers or through commercial insurance schemes) and heating allowances, and/or through financial help from family or friends. Home Improvement Agencies, which receive some funding from the Office of the Deputy Prime Minister (ODPM), can help to fund improvements, such as fitting new locks or installing a downstairs bathroom. *Health and personal problems* may be assisted by a range of services, including packages of care purchased by care managers (social service workers who assess needs), access to or visits from a GP, home visits by a district nurse or community mental health nurse, meals on wheels to provide a cooked meal, occupational therapists to assess the need for aids, such as chair-lifts or bath-hoists, and home helps to perform social and personal care tasks. Finally, many *social problems* can be overcome by providing access to free transport, cheap off-peak cinema and theatre tickets, or drop-in clubs and coffee bars; people who visit in another capacity (home helps, district nurses etc.) also have an important role to play here. This is by no means an exhaustive list, but it shows the range of services required to meet the aims of community care for older people (see Fig.7.2).

Who *pays* for the care is a more complex question:

- the state could provide the services, using its own employees, or it could purchase the required services from the voluntary or commercial sectors or even the informal sector. Whatever the case, the elderly person is likely to be means tested and, on a sliding scale, required to make a contribution to the cost of providing the service, if their income exceeds a bare minimum or savings exceed a certain sum. If the elderly person is sufficiently disabled, they will be entitled to an attendance allowance, which is not means tested and which could be used to purchase the additional services that were needed. If a relative provides considerable care for an elderly person in receipt of the allowance, they might be eligible for a carer's allowance – a weekly, means tested benefit for those not in paid employment providing full-time care;
- the voluntary sector may provide services, paying for them out of donations and/or grants made by the state. Volunteers may give their time free. Recipients of services may or may not pay a charge for the service, and the charge may or may not be means tested;
- the commercial sector could provide services for a fee; they could be paid for by the state, the elderly people themselves or relatives;
- employers may provide services for ex-employees, and the receipt of an

employer private pension will enhance the possibility of an elderly person purchasing services from the state and other sectors;
• relatives may purchase the help elderly relatives need rather than provide it themselves.

As with the question of who provides the care, more than one sector could be paying for it. The needs of older people living in the community can be met by more than one agency, and when more than one service is required, a number of providers may be involved. This may include more than one sector providing care and more than one purchaser – that is, a mixed economy of provision requiring a skill mix. A person's needs may be met by more than one statutory agency, but it is likely that other sectors will also be involved, almost always including the informal sector. The 1990 legislation requires that when a client has complex needs, a care manager should assess their needs and ensure that they receive an appropriate package of care. However, there is currently little evidence of specialist care management for people with complex needs (Challis *et al.* 2001).

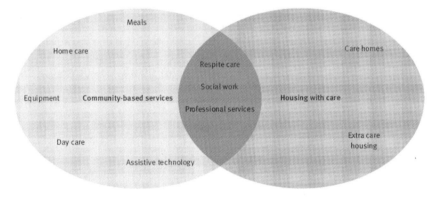

Figure 7.2   Service options within community-based services and housing with care.
Source: Wanless (2006)

There is clearly a need to coordinate packages of care for those whose needs require a complex mix of skills. It is also necessary to ensure that services are being provided by the most appropriate agencies, even when a user is receiving only a single service. Under the legislation, care managers are responsible for assessing needs and purchasing a package of care; the services required can be purchased from the state, the commercial or the voluntary sector. In some cases, under the 1996 Community Care (Direct Payments) Act, the older person may be given the money with which to purchase the necessary services, although the take-up of this has not been great, as older people may not want to take on the responsibilities of an employer and may be worried about finding a suitable person. A remedy for this are 'individual budgets', which allow people to choose the service they want without having to be responsible for the cash to pay for them.

Residential care

Although care homes provide a key role in supporting older people (Wanless 2002), Henwood (2002) considers that:

> The history of long-term care in Britain, as in most other countries, is one that has been punctuated by scandals ... The roots in the poor law and the workhouse have left an enduring legacy that has been hard to shake off ... At root there is a fundamental ambivalence towards long-term care. The existence of care homes disturbs us. Both as individuals and as a society, most people retain a sense of guilt and shame at 'putting away' older people and others needing care.
>
> (Henwood 2002: 24)

Peter Townsend's (1962) indictment of residential care homes argued for alternative provision, whereas an argument could instead have been made for better quality of care, training and regulation. Growth in the residential sector in the 1960s was mostly in the public sector, although a small number of private residential and nursing homes began to emerge. By the mid-1980s, it was recognized that long-term residential facilities were a vital part of the care spectrum, and the Wagner Report (1988) shifted the focus to long-term care as a positive choice rather than a service of last resort. As discussed earlier, changes to the benefit system stimulated growth as large numbers of older people moved into private residential homes. This huge increase in public expenditure was curtailed by the NHS and Community Care Act 1990, under which the money previously allocated to the DSS, to provide income support for those wanting or needing residential care, was transferred to the local authorities, who took on the responsibility for care management and purchasing care. Residential care became used only as a last resort for those who were reliant on local authorities for funding, and there was a requirement that if a person was vacating their home to go into a care home, then the house should be sold and the proceeds (apart from a small reserve) be used to pay for care. Henwood (2002) considers that social services have used their virtual monopsony (a monopoly on purchasing) to drive down, and hold down, prices, and since 1998 they have had a duty to do so, under the government's Performance Assessment Framework and Best Value regime. By 1999, public sector analysts Laing and Buisson claimed that there was a £40 per week gap between the fee paid by local authorities and the sum needed for a reasonable quality of care (Hirst J. 1999). *Future Imperfect* (Kings Fund 2001) stated that the £13 billion social care sector needed a cash injection of at least a third in real terms to 'avoid catastrophe'.

In Henwood's (2002) view, the establishment of the Royal Commission on Long-term Care, under Sir Stewart Sutherland in 1997, could have created a major opportunity to consider fundamental questions about care provision, since in her view neither the government nor the local authorities have tried to actively manage the social care market, and the disappearance of NHS continuing care was by default rather than intention. The Royal Commission was, however, constrained by its terms of reference, which were solely to look at funding. Its recommendation that people should contribute to the housing and living costs of care, but not to the costs of care arising from frailty or disability, was accepted in Scotland, but not in England where a compromise was reached, whereby nursing care by trained nurses is free but not other personal care. This leads to a complex set of categories:

- care organized and paid for in full by individuals who are self-funding;
- means tested provision for those supported by local authorities;
- payment of the registered nursing care contribution for those in nursing homes;
- NHS long-stay hospital provision;
- continuing health care fully funded by the NHS.

More recently, as discussed further below, the Wanless Review of social care (2006) has suggested abolishing the current model whereby older people with assets of over £20,500 are often required to pay the full cost of their care. Rather than recommend free personal care, as in Scotland, the Review proposes a 'partnership model' in which two-thirds of the cost of care is free at the point of delivery, with the balance split equally between the government and the individual. It also recognizes that in order to offer the current level of service, the costs of social care will need to rise from £10.1 billion in 2002 to £24 billion in 2026, due to the expected rise of 54 per cent in the number of old people with high levels of need.

Regulation of care and the effect of the new standards

Prior to the Registered Homes Act 1984, the private and voluntary residential and nursing home sectors were, in effect, unregulated. Under the Act, residential homes were registered and inspected by local authorities, and nursing homes by health authorities. There was no statutory duty to investigate complaints or allegations of abuse, but registration and inspection units were also involved in this work. Although the quality of care improved under this system, there were criticisms that the local and health authorities were purchasers, providers and also regulators, that there were local inconsistencies, and that some authorities were unable to meet their targets or provide adequate training for inspectors. The distinction between social and health needs for registration, as either a residential or nursing home, was also seen as increasingly artificial. The Longcare Enquiry (Burgner 1998) severely criticized Buckinghamshire County Council's registration and inspection unit for its failure to properly investigate reported allegations of abuse, and changes to the regulatory system and a set of national minimum standards were proposed in *Fit for the Future?* (DoH 1999c).

There was considerable disquiet and lobbying from the care homes sector both prior to and after the implementation of the new regulatory body and standards, particularly from residential homes which were generally smaller than nursing homes, not part of large groups, and therefore more at risk. Frank Ursell, chief executive officer of the Registered Nursing Homes Association, considered that there was a 'huge cultural resistance' to accepting that the private sector is the major provider of nursing home care, and has more beds than the NHS for the care of older people (Bunce 2001). The standards also affected charities; for example, the Multiple Sclerosis Society cited them as one of the factors behind a decision to close two holiday homes. Although physical standards, particularly having a single room, are important to residents (Counsel and Care 1992), it was felt that too much emphasis was being put in the draft standards on physical aspects, such as bedroom size (Coldman and Duffy 2000). It was also thought that the enforcement of physical standards would exacerbate the number of home closures, particularly of smaller residential homes (Laing and Buisson 2000) and could not address the wider issues such as chronic underfunding or staff shortages, both of care assistants and of nurses. The staffing problem is particularly acute in areas of high employment and has been exacerbated by the introduction of the minimum wage, which has driven up wages in other, competing sectors (e.g. in West Kent the Blue-water shopping centre effectively competes in the same labour market) and high property values, where the incentives to sell up are higher. The shortage of places in Kent was such, in 2001, that the strategic director of social services, Peter Gilroy, was reported as considering sending older people to homes in France or Belgium, although a DoH spokeswoman said that it would not be allowed (Carvel 2001). As in hospices, additional cost pressures for care homes are created by the pay scales in the NHS, such as the recent Agenda for Change pay reforms. Pressure on costs could lead to lower staffing levels, and the inappropriate use of restraint and psycho-tropic medication. It was also reported (Kingston 2004) that care homes were struggling to meet the standard for training half the staff to NVQ level 2, which was estimated to cost £1,000 per candidate, and found that staff, once qualified, tended to move on.

In 2001, DoH statistics indicated that approximately 700 residential homes (4700 beds) and 200 nursing homes (6500 beds) ceased trading; these figures were disputed by the sector, which claimed that the number of care home places overall fell by 12,300 in 2000, and 12,600 the following year (Laing and Buisson 2001). By 2002, the report *Calculating a Fair Price for Care* (Joseph Rowntree Foundation 2002) found a shortfall in weekly local authority fees of £75 for residential and £85 for nursing homes. Paul Burstow, the Liberal Democrat spokesman for older people, found that charitable care homes were subsidizing half their residents (Burstow 2002). Referring to the situation as a 'meltdown', Burstow claimed that due to the lack of capacity in the financial year 2001/2, 122,881 people over 75 were readmitted to hospital as an emergency within 28 days (an increase of 14 per cent on the previous year) and 24,356 had their discharge delayed (an increase of 13 per cent). The DoH replied that, on the contrary, the government was keeping more people inde-pendent in their own homes, and that households receiving intensive support had increased by 12,500 in the same year (Carvel 2002).

Findings from a survey of 216 residential home owners in Kent (Meer-abeau and Antoncino 2002) supported those from the national study by Netten *et al.* (2003). One respondent, who had closed their home in anticipation of the new standards, commented that '*It seems to me that, like so many other professions, the care industry is becoming more to do with filling in forms, assessments, reports and the like and less to do with looking after the real needs of the elderly'*. Even before the implementation date of April 2002, the DoH compromised on some of the standards rather than addressing how much it would cost to meet them. In January 2002, a report by SPAIN, the Social Policy Ageing Information Network (an alliance of 21 organizations including Help the Aged, Age Concern and the Alzheimer's Society), called for an urgent review of funding and claimed that in the previous year 700,000 older patients had experienced delay in leaving hospital, mainly because of the lack of community and residential care services (Akid 2002).

Box 7.3   Regulatory bodies

The Care Standards Act 2000 created the National Care Standards Commission (NCSC), which started its business in April 2002. (The equivalent bodies are the Scottish Commission for the Regulation of Care and the Care Standards Inspectorate for Wales, although the latter is not independent of government.) The NCSC was intended to regulate the independent sector, both 29,000 care homes and also 11,000 other establishments including acute care and hospices. Previously this work was regulated by 230 bodies. However, in January 2002, before the NCSC had even started to operate, it was announced that the regulation of the latter would be under the Commission for Health Improvement (now the Healthcare Commission) and that care homes would be regulated by the Commission for Social Care Inspection. In 2005 it was then announced that the regulation of adult social services would probably move to the Healthcare Commission, and children's services to the Office for Standards in Education (Ofsted), the education regulator.

As may sometimes happen in policy-making, the regulation of care homes was affected by a single, high profile tragedy. In July 2002, the press highlighted the case of Alice Knight, aged 108, who starved to death in protest after being forced to leave her care home in Norfolk where she had lived for six years, which closed because it was unable to meet the new national standards. Prior to that, in March 2002, 102-year-old Rose Cottle led a protest to Downing Street when she faced eviction from her care home in Hertfordshire. These events led to a 'climb down' by the Secretary of State, and it was announced in July 2002 that the standards would apply only to homes opening after April 2002, and would be good practice guides. This, however, pleased neither the NCSC, which felt that there were mixed messages, Age Concern, which justifiably felt that the standards were being diluted, nor the National Care Homes Association, which considered that the decision had been made much too late, since there had already been many closures. The Secretary of State, Alan Milburn, also announced funding of more than £500 million to increase capacity, including 6000 new care home places.

> **Box 7.4 'Bed blocking'**
>
> As Lewis (2001) states, from the inception of the welfare state there were deep-seated tensions between health and social care providers over intermediate care, i.e. the care of people, particularly older people, who require personal care but do not require medical care and may not require the care of a trained nurse. Although not stated explicitly, NHS hospitals began to reduce their role, and focused on acute care. This trend was encouraged by reimbursing hospitals for finished consultant episodes rather than bed days, so that long stays would result in financial losses. However, although care has not, until recently, been planned as a unified system (Lewis 2001) a reduction in capacity in one part of the system will cause problems elsewhere. This occurred when there was a loss of capacity in the care home sector, leading to delayed discharges from hospital. At the same time, acute hospitals were under pressure because of the star rating system and targets set by the DoH, to increase their throughput, thereby reducing the pressure on accident and emergency and on surgical waiting times, two of the key areas for target-setting. In October 2001 it was announced that an extra £300 million would be committed over two years to provide more places in care homes, and so avoid a 'bed blocking crisis' (Carvel 2001).
>
> Since the mid-1990s, intermediate care has been an important element in the care continuum. It includes hospital at home, rehabilitation and recovery teams, and nurse-led beds in care homes.
>
> From January 2004, under the terms of the Community Care Act, acute trusts are able to charge local authority social services departments for each extra night a patient stays, if the reason is failure by the local authority to find alternative care.

Future proposals for social care

As indicated in Box 7.4, Wanless (2006) comments that the interface between health and social care has become a flashpoint for arguments about inequities in the provision of care. His review of social care for the King's Fund considers that there is a need for clarity about the role of social care in the future. The review's terms of reference are:

- to examine the demographic, economic, social, health and other relevant trends over the next 20 years that are likely to affect the demand for, and nature of social care for older people in England;
- in the light of this, to identify the financial and other resources required to ensure that older people who need social care are able to secure comprehensive, high-quality care that reflects the preferences of individuals receiving care;
- to consider how such social care might be funded, bearing in mind the King's Fund's commitment to social justice.

The Wanless Report (2006) states that there is little information about whether the current investment in social care meets its aims, and that there is some evidence that it is not equitably distributed. The costs are considerable. In 2004/5, local authorities spent £8 billion on personal social care services of which £1.6 billion was recouped through charges. £3.7 billion was paid in non-means tested benefits to help with the cost of care, and private spending on residential and home care by older people is likely to be more than £3.5 billion. There is widespread dissatisfaction, and complaints that means testing penalizes people who have saved for their old age. Between 1981 and 2001, increases in healthy life expectancy did not keep pace with increases in total life expectancy, and so it is likely that the number of frail older people will increase. Disability in later life arises from heart disease and stroke, vision and hearing problems, arthritis, incontinence, dementia and depression. In 2002 around 900,000 older people were considered to have high levels of need, needing help with one or more ADL, and 1.4 million had lower levels of need. It is estimated that both categories will increase by over 50 per cent by 2025. Meeting lower levels of need can delay the need for residential care, but as discussed earlier, the recent policy shift has been towards meeting higher levels of need only and there is evidence of significant unmet need. Housing needs for older people also come too low on the list of strategic housing priorities.

Three scenarios are outlined, the current service model, 'core business' which estimates the services needed for the highest levels of personal care and safety outcomes justifiable in terms of cost, and a scenario which provides improved social inclusion outcomes. The ADLAY (activities of daily living-adjusted year), a measure analogous to the QUALY (quality-adjusted life year) is used to assess the cost-effectiveness of each. In scenario 1, total costs are projected to rise by 139 per cent from 2002 to 2026, to £24 billion. In scenario 2, total costs in 2026 are estimated to be £29.4 billion. In scenario 3, total costs are estimated as £31.3 billion. All these projections rely on assumptions, for example, on the availability of unpaid care and cost inflation. Wanless considers that any additional funding should only be made if the system is reconfigured and made fairer. Funding options are also explored and the best are considered to be:

- a partnership model which provides a level of care free of charge, with additional care above that level funded equally by the individual and the state;
- free care;
- a means tested system for the first three or four years, followed by free care.

Financial modelling shows that most people would be better off under the partnership model, and it is considered that because there is an element of charging, users will feel more able to express their views. The report was well received by the government, and Sir Derek was invited to serve on a group advising the Treasury on the next comprehensive spending review. It therefore seems likely that at least some of the recommendations will be accepted.

The management of long-term conditions

Tackling chronic disease has become one of the key health care issues of the twenty-first century (see Box 7.5). The focus on chronic disease and long-term conditions, arises from successes in acute health care in the post-war pe-riod, improved living conditions leading to an older and frailer population and a recognition that chronic disease is largely poorly supported by health and social care systems yet, consumes substantial amounts of health and social care resources. It is estimated that 17.5 million adults in the UK are living with a chronic disease and that the incidence of long-term conditions among those aged over 65 will double by 2030 (DoH 2004a, 2005d). In a recent survey of 3000 people over the age of 45 (Ellins and Coulter 2005), 72 per cent of the respondents had been diagnosed with, at least, one chronic condition. The most common condition was arthritis or rheumatism, reported by 30 per cent of respondents, followed by high blood pressure (29 per cent), high cholesterol (19 per cent), chronic pain (18 per cent) and angina or heart problems (12 per cent). Chronic health problems affected not only their physical and mental health but also daily social activities. Use of health care services was substantially higher among people with chronic diseases, with 15 per cent having made use of accident and emergency services in the last 12 months. Long-term and chronic conditions therefore have a significant impact on the NHS.

Box 7.5   The NHS and long-term conditions

The increased incidence of long-term conditions presents a major challenge to the NHS:

- in Britain, 17.5 million people may be living with a long-term condition;
- around six in ten adults in the household population report some form of long-term health problem;
- around 80 per cent of GP consultations relate to long-term conditions of which a quarter are minor complaints;
- care of long-term conditions accounts for 60 per cent of bed days in hospitals;
- by 2030, incidence of long-term conditions in those over 65 is estimated to more than double.

Source: DoH (2005e)

As part of the modernization of the NHS, greater attention is being given to how people use the health service, and to managing demand. Research by the company, Dr Foster Intelligence, indicates that so-called 'frequent flyers' – the 439,000 people who are admitted to hospital as emergencies at least three times in one year – cost the health service about £2.3 billion a year (Curtis 2006). Of this £253 million was spent on emergency treatment for people with emphysema-type respiratory illnesses, and £64 million on emergency asthma admissions. Sickle cell anaemia may also be a cause of frequent admissions in black minority ethnic (BME) populations. The people most likely to be frequent flyers are low income families and older people living in council housing in the inner cities, which may partly reflect the historically poorer provision of general practice in these areas. Mental health problems, such as anxiety and depression, also lead to frequent admissions, partly because they can exacerbate respiratory diseases, and partly because admission to hospital can ease loneliness. Research by Creed *et al.* quoted by Cole (2006) found that people with depression or similar mental health problems incurred costs which were 46 per cent greater than people with a comparable physical health problem, who did not also have a mental health problem. Educating people about their illness, and cognitive behavioural therapy can be effective remedies. However, people with chronic conditions are, by virtue of their position, less likely to be able to adopt self-management techniques without support, and to have access to less personal resources to support their own care:

> *Fewer people with chronic conditions had progressed to an advanced level of self-management, in particular those with depression, chronic pain and digestive problems. Of all the groups within the sample, the capacity to self-manage health and healthcare was least evident among people with poor health; only 33% of those with poor health felt able to take and maintain action to improve their health, compared with 60% overall.*
>
> (Ellins and Coulter 2005: 3)

Supporting People with Long-Term Conditions (DoH 2005e) provides a model of care based on the model used by the American health care provider, Kaiser Permanente, which maps the level of need that each patient has. Patients at level 3, the most complex level, constitute about 5 per cent of people over 65; their care costs three to four times as much as the average for their age group. They will be offered case management by a community matron, which includes GP and social care. Another American model which has been used is Evercare, which is reported to have improved care and reduced hospitalization for over 60,000 older people in the USA, although the evaluation of both models in England, to date, has been inconclusive (Hutt *et al.* 2004). The Evercare model of case management has the role of advanced primary nurse as a key feature with an interim evaluation suggesting improvement in some outcomes, such as patient and carer satisfaction, although effectiveness in reducing hospital emergency admissions is less clear (DoH 2003c, 2004c; Boaden *et al.* 2005). The expanded nursing role, such as Evercare or the currently evolving role, and competencies of the community matron, are designed to meet the needs of those most vulnerable with complex morbidities (DoH 2005a). *The NHS Plan* (DoH 2000a) proposed that there should be 3000 community matrons caring for around 250,000 patients by 2008. In addition to their nursing skills, community matrons will need:

- advanced level professional practice, including managing risk, physical examination and history-taking;
- skills in brokerage and inter-agency working;
- skills and knowledge in medicine management;
- skills in health promotion;
- skills in managing care at the end of life.

As is often the case when nurses develop new roles, GPs were initially resistant and thought that community matrons should be under their supervision. *Supporting People with Long-Term Conditions* also endorses self-care, which as discussed above is an important element of managing long-term conditions, as is the use of telemedicine for managing problems, such as hypertension and diabetes. Research by the King's Fund (Corben and Rosen 2005), highlighted the need for the better coordination of care, and the importance of shared decision-making between clinicians and patients, many of whom are expert in managing their own care.

Many pharmacists are also extending their role in long-term care, major drivers being their new contract introduced in April 2005, and the extension of prescribing rights in May 2006. The mixed economy of care has been further promoted by the White Paper *Our Health, Our Care, Our Say* (DoH 2006), which recognizes the centrality of carers and promises to fund a helpline, to provide training and to put more resources into emergency respite cover. However, the current deficits in the NHS, and the amalgamations of PCTs, announced without prior discussion in July 2005, have created turbulence in the system. The document *Commissioning a Patient-led NHS* (DoH 2005b), also stated that PCTs should no longer provide services, although it was not clear which organizations would then become providers. The plans were heavily criticized by the House of Commons Health Select Committee and were partially withdrawn, although it is likely that many PCTs will divest themselves of some of the services they provide. The government is promoting the concept of social enterprise, for which a unit will be set up in the DoH. According to the Department of Trade and Industry (2002), '*Social enterprise is a business with primarily social objectives whose surpluses are principally reinvested for that purpose in the business or in the community, rather than being driven by the need to maximize profit for shareholders and owners*'. They therefore seem to be synonymous with not-for-profit organizations, although there is little evidence, to date, on where they are situated and how successful they have been. Although social enterprises may be more responsive to patient needs, partnership arrangements will become more challenging if primary care fragments, and adds to the more than 28,000 different providers of social care.

Conclusion

In this chapter, using the example of community care and with special reference to older people, we have illustrated the way in which the mixed economy of care works in practice. Until the introduction of the new community care policy in April 1993, the statutory sector was the main provider of formal services, except in the area of residential care, where the commercial and voluntary sectors were significant providers. The 1993 legislation required the local authorities to stimulate a social market, purchasing services from the commercial and voluntary sectors. Provision was to be needs-led – that is, care managers were to assess the needs of elderly people and their informal carers and purchase services to meet those needs.

The current Labour government has continued its predecessor's policy of a mixed economy, but with a greater emphasis on choice and empowerment and a greater recognition of carers' needs, however imperfectly met. Community care is likely to present an increasing challenge for the state as the number of dependent older people increases. It will continue to be provided in the main by the informal sector, with those who have the ability to buy care for themselves, or have relatives prepared to do so, purchasing services from the commercial and voluntary sectors. Poor older people, especially those living alone, and including a disproportionate number of women and people from ethnic minority groups, will continue to be dependent on the state for support, even if the state purchases services for them from the commercial and voluntary sectors.

We have also examined policy developed in the twenty-first century for avoiding hospital admissions, by the better management of long-term conditions. Such services are likely to become increasingly important, if the costs of health care are to be contained.

Summary

- This chapter has focused on the relationship between the different providers within the mixed economy of welfare, using as an example developments in community care policy.
- The development of community care has drawn considerable support from the critique of residential caring institutions. It is, however, important to distinguish between policies supporting 'care *in* the community' (more locally-based community services) and, those supporting 'care *by* the community' (usually meaning informal or family care).
- The 1990 National Health Service and Community Care Act, required local authorities to make substantial changes in the way they managed and delivered services, shifting emphasis away from direct service provision, to one of coordinator/financier/regulator of the mixed economy. However, the reduction of funding led to some instability in the residential care sector.
- Debates continue on the extent to which the state or the individual should meet social care needs.
- Increasing attention is being given to the management of long-term care, since chronic disease is one of the key issues in health care provision.

Further reading

Heywood, F., Oldman, C. and Means, R. (2002) *Housing and Home in Later Life*. Buckingham: Open University Press.

Means, R., Morbey, H. and Smith, R. (2002) *From Community Care to Market Care? The Development of Welfare Services for Older People*. Bristol: Policy Press.

Means, R., Richard, S. and Smith, R. (2003) *Community Care: Policy and Practice*, 3rd edn. Basingstoke: Palgrave.

Roe, B. and Beech, R. (2005) *Intermediate and Continuing Care: Policy and Practice*. Oxford: Blackwell.

Wanless, D. (2006) *Securing Good Care for Older People: Taking a Long-Term View*. London: King's Fund.

THE CHANGING ROLE OF THE VOLUNTARY SECTOR IN THE PROVISION OF SOCIAL WELFARE

Introduction

This chapter considers the changing role of the voluntary sector in the provision of welfare. The emphasis is on the sector that provides welfare, rather than the volunteers who give their time to provide help; a distinction needs to be made between volunteering and the voluntary sector, concepts which tend to get muddled together in the political/moral rhetoric of active citizenship. Volunteer labour is an important element in many voluntary organizations, but volunteers can also work in the state sector and are an important element in the informal sector. Although the role of the voluntary sector predates the welfare state, its contribution within the welfare state has, until recently, been relatively limited. Recent renewal of interest, in the voluntary sector, reflects rapid expansion both in service provision in some key areas of social policy and in political support for the concept of voluntarism as a morally superior form of provision. Strong support for voluntary action comes from across the political spectrum, and in many ways its ideological importance has been as important as its contribution to welfare provision.

What is discussed in this chapter is the role that the sector does, and could, play within the mixed economy of welfare and the welfare state. On the one hand, there are those who see a minimum role for the sector, seeing voluntary aid as patronizing and outdated; on the other, there is the view that the sector should play a central role. Those who hold the former view tend to see the sector as mainly concerned with the giving of charity to others, while those who take the latter view tend to stress the role of mutual aid (or self-help). A rather different, and increasingly prevalent, view is to see the sector as one provider of welfare among others, part of a welfare partnership. These different views relate not only to different political perspectives but also to different understandings of what the sector is and what it can contribute.

The Victorian legacy

For many, especially on the left of the political spectrum, the founding of the welfare state in Britain in 1948 meant that there was no longer a need for a voluntary sector in the provision of welfare. It was assumed that, to the extent that the sector persisted, its role would be minimal and marginal. Welfare state services made philanthropic organizations redundant, and National Insurance and social housing did away with the need for mutual aid. The universal, comprehensive provisions made by the state, it was assumed, would replace the patchy, patronizing and peculiarly selective provision made by the voluntary sector.

In the nineteenth and early twentieth centuries, voluntary organizations had played a central role in meeting welfare needs, often in areas where the state made little or no provision. Davies (1987: 182), for example, has indicated that in the nineteenth century '*most people were involved in an array of voluntary organisations which met the needs of most for education, leisure, assistance or simple conviviality. The common response to any social problem, personal or collective, was mutuality and cooperation*'. Waine (1992), similarly, has pointed out that by the beginning of the twentieth century, the key social services were provided by voluntary organizations, including unemployment benefits, health insurance and beds in the voluntary hospitals.

The voluntary sector was important both in providing services where the state provided none and, in providing services alongside those provided by the Poor Law. In Victorian Britain, the sector was comprised of two main elements: philanthropy and mutual aid. Philanthropy was concerned with charitable giving and the provision of services, mainly by the middle-classes to the working-classes. Volunteering was often seen as a Christian duty, and one goal was the 'civilizing' of the working-class.

Originally the labour was provided by the middle-classes themselves, as in the Visiting Movements, but by the end of the nineteenth century voluntary organizations often employed working-class women to do the actual visiting, while middle-class women gave their voluntary labour to management and fundraising. Services were often patronizing (Lewis 1980). In Chapter 2, we discussed the Charity Organization Society, which was founded in the late nineteenth century to regulate charitable giving 'in the best interests of the poor' and in society's best interests – that is, to

ensure that charity did not destroy the motivation to take paid employment nor encourage the worst habits of the poor, such as excessive
drinking.

Not all voluntary work patronized and regulated the poor in this manner, however. As discussed in Chapter 10, the majority of hospitals founded in the nineteenth century, for treating acute illnesses, were paid for by
subscriptions from the wealthy. The 'child saving movement' of the late
nineteenth century, exemplified by Dr Barnardo's, was influenced by
evangelical Christian values. It played a vital role in bringing to attention
the abuse and neglect some children experienced and, provided homes for
orphaned and abused children. The philanthropic voluntary organizations
of the nineteenth century were often involved as much in campaigning as
in provision; they acted as pressure groups on behalf of the disadvantaged.
Prison reform and health reforms, for example, were heavily influenced by
voluntary organization campaigns.

Mutual aid, which also developed in Victorian Britain, is based on
voluntary collective efforts, which both serve self-interest and support the
interests of others. The most common mutual aid schemes were voluntary
assistance for income maintenance and health care, but other examples
include cooperative associations (both for goods and for labour), self-help
groups, trade unions and building societies. Mutual aid is, therefore, to be
distinguished from philanthropy; mutual benefit associations are not run
by one set of people with the aim of helping another, but as an association
of individuals pledged to help each other (a form of reciprocal altruism).
Assistance was not a result of charity but of entitlement, earned by regular
contributions paid by all members. The Foresters, a leading Friendly
Society, indicated that:

> For certain benefits in sickness ... all the Brethren in common subscribe to
> one fund. That fund is our Bank; and to draw therefrom is the independent
> and manly right of any Member, whenever the contingency for which the
> funds are subscribed may arise, as freely as if the fund was in the hand of
> their own banker; and they had but to issue a cheque for the amount. These
> are not BENEVOLENCES – they are rights.

(quoted by Green 1993: 50)

Modern voluntary organizations can also be divided into philanthropic
institutions and mutual aid associations. Taylor (1991) identified three
phases in the development of the voluntary sector in Britain since the
1940s. During the first phase, in the 1950s and 1960s, she suggests that
voluntary organizations played on the whole a marginal role, many finding it difficult to establish a niche for themselves, though some succeeded
in doing so. The Women's Voluntary Service, for example, played a central
role in supplying meals on wheels, although these were paid for by local
government. Others continued to provide a service alongside state provision, for example, Dr Barnardo's and the National Society for the Prevention of Cruelty to Children; others, such as the voluntary hospitals, had
been nationalized.

The second phase, beginning in the late 1960s, saw the development of
campaigning groups, influenced by the Civil Rights Movement in the USA,
both for and of disadvantaged and marginalized groups. Major voluntary

organizations, such as Help the Aged, the Child Poverty Action Group and Shelter, were founded in this period, as were the disabled rights movement and other self-advocacy groups. The last of these, often regarded as new social movements, are self-help and populist, concerned with mutual aid and political campaigning (Oliver and Barnes 1998).

The most recent phase, beginning in the 1980s, has been the encouragement of voluntary organizations to take a strong role in the mixed economy of welfare. This was encouraged by the New Right on the basis of both economic and moral arguments, and has been further developed by the Labour administration, for example, by major changes in tax incentives for charitable giving (gift aid). Box 8.1 illustrates the evolving role of the voluntary sector in one field, that of mental ill health.

Box 8.1   The role of the voluntary sector in mental ill health

- Pre-eighteenth century: mad viewed as deviant, and not suitable subjects for Christian philanthropy.
- Late eighteenth and early-nineteenth century: moral treatment in asylums, supported philanthropically.
- Late nineteenth to mid-twentieth century: 'warehousing' – some philanthropic donation to asylums.
- Mid-twentieth century: deinstutionalization – increased role for voluntary organizations, such as the National Schizophrenia Fellowship, the Scottish Association for Mental Health.
- 1990 onwards: focus on mixed economy, greater role for voluntary and informal sector.

Source: Milligan (2000)

While New Right commentators often stressed the moral case for voluntary organizations, and especially for mutual aid (Green 1993), it is the economic case that has dominated (Abbott and Wallace 1992). Many on the centre and left of the political spectrum, have also stressed the important values of mutual help and communality that voluntary organizations can engender, stressing the value of communitarianism. However, feminists have been critical of the renewed emphasis on volunteering and voluntary organizations, pointing out that these often rely on the unpaid and often unrecognized labour of women (Finch and Groves 1983).

The voluntary sector in the welfare state

Since the foundation of the welfare state, the 'values and virtues' of the voluntary sector have received support, in particular from a tradition referred to as the 'middle way' in British political thought, encompassing the ideas of conservatives such as Macmillan, Butler and Gilmour, but also 'reformists' such as Keynes and Beveridge (George and Wilding 1994: 46) and more recently, the 'brilliantly vague' (Toynbee and Walker 2001) concept of the Third Way, originated by the sociologist Antony Giddens and adopted by Tony Blair. According to this tradition, the voluntary sector is not competing with the welfare state, as such, in providing welfare; the two are mutually supportive. Beveridge himself saw the health of the voluntary sector as an index of the general health of society (Beveridge 1948 cited in George and Wilding 1994: 56). Within the context of universal income maintenance, the NHS, state education provision and the greatly expanded role of the social services, he saw the voluntary sector as performing a quite specific range of tasks – giving advice, organizing leisure, pioneering and experimentation (Beveridge 1948: 9). The Beveridge model of the relationship between the state and the voluntary sector went virtually unchallenged until the late 1970s, when advocates of welfare pluralism suggested extending the role of the voluntary sector (Gladstone 1979; Hadley and Hatch 1981).

Richard Titmuss (1968), in perhaps the first major study of voluntarism in British social policy in the 1960s, envisaged a symbiotic relationship developing between the voluntary sector and the state, with the growth of the welfare state actually encouraging the voluntary ethic in society. Indeed, Titmuss saw the development of the welfare state itself as a civilizing force, an instrument of social justice that could promote the 'art of giving' in society. Social welfare constituted '*a major force sustaining the social conscience*' (Abel-Smith and Titmuss 1987: 113). Titmuss saw the development of state responsibility in welfare, as a necessary response to increasing levels of complexity and specialization in modern capitalist societies, to the point at which personal bonds of family, kinship and community were no longer able to meet the needs for social welfare. Some form of formally organized system of social support was therefore required, to be administered by strangers and paid for collectively by strangers: '*Altruism by strangers for strangers was and is an attempt to fill a moral void created by applied science*' (Abel-Smith and Titmuss 1987: 115). Titmuss' own research involved a comparison of systems of blood donation in Britain and the USA. In the USA (in the 1960s at least), blood was treated as a consumption good to be traded in the market-place; donors and recipients were 'prisoners of commerce'. This was contrasted with the system in Britain where blood was (and still is) given by volunteers in a 'social services institution' answering the 'conscience of obligation' (Abel-Smith and Titmuss 1987: 191). This case study was used to demonstrate Titmuss' profound belief that state welfare encouraged voluntarism. For Titmuss, voluntary associations and volunteering by individuals should provide only a supplementary role within terms set out by the state and should not provide charity that was in any sense demeaning. He did not believe that anybody should have to rely on voluntary organizations for basic welfare: this should be provided for all, as a right, by state services.

In contrast to this view of social welfare as a civilizing force, the New Right in British politics, which gained ascendancy in the 1980s, presented a view of the welfare state as creating a 'dependency culture' of welfare-reliant individuals which undermined not only the private sector and the family, but also the spirit of voluntarism and collective self-help. They argued that state welfare was demoralizing and contained perverse incentives which encouraged dependency and undermined the voluntary sector. Appealing once again to the concept of altruism (or helping the unknown stranger), but this time as the preserve of Christian values, the Institute of Economic Affairs (1995: 2) argued that *'Christian philanthropy, like the Good Samaritan, stands beside the suffering person, but charitable bodies founded by Christians as an expression of faith now find themselves "crowded out" by universal state welfare, or acting as its agents'*.

Conservative governments from 1979 to 1997 advocated the growth of the voluntary sector. In its second decade, the Conservative government backed up its moral support with a series of policies, including both incentives and pressures, aimed at a significant expansion in the overall contribution of the voluntary sector. The area in which this policy met with most success was in relation to community care, especially with the implementation of the National Health Service and Community Care Act 1990. Here, it has been argued, voluntary organizations are more flexible, closer to the community and hence to need, and more cost-effective because they employ volunteers. Thus a range of opportunities for independent care providers opened up with the introduction of a market in community care. Local authorities were encouraged to reduce their role in service delivery, becoming instead purchasers of services contracted from the commercial and voluntary sectors (and with the use of informal carers). New arrangements for the funding of community care under the National Health Service and Community Care Act 1990, thus involved the transfer of large sums of money from state provision to the voluntary sector. Under the provisions of this Act, local authorities were required to spend 85 per cent of the element of funding transferred from the DSS (£399 million) on the independent sector, defined as any provider organization which was not owned, managed or controlled by a local authority.

Governments have been less concerned with supporting mutual aid associations, which would arguably most encourage self-reliance, than with creating competition in service provision with the aim of reducing costs. However, some New Right commentators, in advocating the encouragement of the voluntary sector, have been concerned to focus not on the economic argument – support for the market economy – but on the self-reliance engendered by mutual aid. They have been critical of large charities and voluntary organizations that are professionalized and exhibit little, or no relationship, between the members/donors and the recipients (Davies 1987), arguing that professionalization has not only reduced individual responsibility and self-reliance, but also community responsibility. A wholesale shift in provision was not favoured by the public, however. The 1994–5 British Social Attitudes Survey found little evidence to suggest that there was public support for the replacement of statutory services by voluntary provision in the core areas of social policy (Jowell *et al.* 1995). On the contrary, Taylor-Gooby (1995: 30) concluded his analysis with the comment that *'our survey suggests that the public is less attached to the voluntary principle in areas where it has traditionally applied than it is to the principle of state responsibility for its traditional core areas, such as health and education. This is hardly a pattern of attitudes which is conducive to a transfer of responsibilities from government to charities'*. The public, it seems, preferred the coexistence of voluntary and statutory provision with the former supplementing, rather than replacing, the latter.

The Labour government, like its predecessors, has embraced the voluntary sector with enthusiasm, not only for economic reasons but as a possible solution to the decline in active citizenship and in political involvement in the UK (Kendall 2000; Fyfe and Milligan 2003). There is, for example, a Civil Renewal Unit at the Home Office. As in many aspects of current policy-making, this thinking has been influenced by the USA (Putnam 2000). In 1998 the government launched the Compact, a framework of principles and values to improve and develop the relationship between the voluntary sector and government. The five codes of practice in the Compact include one specifically for black and minority ethnic groups, reflecting a developing emphasis on inclusiveness in policy-making. The Cabinet Office review of the legal and regulatory framework for charities and the wider not-for-profit sector, *Private Action, Public Benefit* (2002), spoke of the sector being a more active partner with government, and the parliamentary joint committee which examined the Charities Bill said that it would like charities to play a bigger role in contributing to the modernization of public services and the enhancement of civic responsibility (Philpot 2005). In September 2004, the DoH announced a new strategic agreement between the NHS and the voluntary and community sectors. In April 2006, a new quango, Capacity Builders, with over £70 million of funding from the Home Office, was set up; the money will be channelled via the National Council for Voluntary Organizations. The Labour government has also encouraged volunteering; 2005 was designated as 'Year of the Volunteer'. Mahony (2005) claims that half the population participates in some form of voluntary activity, that 11 million more people would do so, and that employee volunteering is preferable to team building activities for staff development.

What is the voluntary sector? Problems of definition

Kendall and Knapp (1995) describe the voluntary sector as a 'loose and baggy monster'. In 2002, the charity and not-for-profit sector comprised around 600,000 organizations, including 188,000 registered charities, and it is to be expected that organizations change over time or may die out. Most commentators distinguish between large organizations, with paid staff, and small mutual or community-based organizations, with few or no paid staff. The essential features of voluntary organizations which set them apart from the other components of welfare provision are that they are non-governmental, non-profit-making and benefit from voluntarism. Common organizing principles include operating on trust, management by values rather than by rules or profit margins, and user involvement. Taylor and Langan's (1996) research in three locations (urban, rural, and outer London) focuses particularly on local organizations. Half of them had been formed since 1980, and nearly a third had incomes of less than £5000 p.a. (figures for England and Wales at that time were that two-thirds of all registered charities had incomes of less than £10,000 p.a. and 55 per cent had charitable status). Taylor and Langan (1996) classified organizations as:

- user-run/self-help;
- 'donor' organizations run by people giving time and/or money to others;
- not-for-profit organizations run by professionals (mainly housing associations in their sample).

Evers (1993) argues that the voluntary sector mediates between the three major sectors of society: the state, the market and the personal, and that this is often reflected in the variety of stakeholders, and can lead to tensions. According to Philpot (2005), most charities are distinctly undemocratic bodies, since only 3 per cent of trustees are recruited by advertising. Taylor and Langan (1996: 30) comment that *'many organisations found themselves treading a fine line between inclusive structures, where everyone had access to decisions, and structurelessness, where everyone went their own way or where, although the language was of participation, it masked the power and influence held by paid staff or the few most active people'*.

The voluntary sector is heterogeneous, varying from local playgroups to large formal organizations such as Dr Barnardo's. It is, therefore, difficult to define or classify them. As in the formation of policy in general, the establishment of a charity may be triggered by a high profile event, or even a fictitious one. For example, homelessness was rediscovered as a social problem and the organization Shelter was established in the mid-1960s through the television drama *Cathy Come Home*. Voluntary organizations can provide services directly (e.g. tea trolleys run by 'Friends of the Hospital'), coordinate the efforts of other voluntary organizations (e.g. the housing corporations) or lobby for change (e.g. the Child Poverty Action Group). There is also the distinction we made above, between philanthropic and mutual aid organizations. Many voluntary organizations, especially the larger ones, carry out more than one of the functions we have identified. Age Concern, for example, is a philanthropic organization which, as well as campaigning on behalf of older people, provides day centres, home helps and other services for the elderly. The Child Poverty Action Group is a philanthropic group that campaigns on behalf of the poor. 'Friends of the Hospital' are philanthropic groups that are mainly concerned with fundraising and providing help to hospitals by buying equipment. Credit unions, by contrast, are mutual aid groups designed to help people save and borrow money. Organizations like MIND are both philanthropic and mutual aid organizations, both campaigning and providing services. A growing role for voluntary organizations has been in developing expertise and campaigning for health treatment, which has in some instances led to conflict with the medical establishment. In the USA in particular, activists developed formidable expertise on AIDS and HIV, and the knowledge base became heavily politicized (Epstein 1996).

Religious bodies also provide voluntary services (e.g. hostels provided by the Salvation Army), and at least this element of their work is part of the voluntary sector. The independence of voluntary organizations from government, distinguishes them from state welfare and the lack of profit-making – or, more specifically, profit distribution – distinguishes them from the commercial market. And, finally, the dominance of a voluntary ethos (and non-remunerated contribution) sets the voluntary sector apart from both statutory and commercial provision. The term 'non-governmental organization' (NGO) is increasingly used in place of 'voluntary organization' in the EU; these are defined as non-governmental, non-profit-distributing and non-private.

There is also a distinction between the voluntary sector and the informal sector, since a voluntary sector organization or group is 'formal'. This definition, however, excludes many informal community groups, which although 'informal' in terms of structure, are still a type of organization or 'group' and can be distinguished from informal care on that basis. Another means of differentiating between the voluntary and informal sectors has been in terms of an individual carer's or volunteer's motive. The concept of voluntarism is often associated with altruism, defined by Ware and Goodin (1990: 187) as *'behaviour that benefits another (unrelated) actor and which imposes some cost on the originator'*. The motive for informal care is not altruism as such, but typically kinship obligation or particular obligations to close friends or neighbours. Voluntarism, then, stems from broader citizenship obligations as opposed to family, kinship or neighbourhood bonds.

In practice, however, as we shall see in the following discussion, it is very difficult to maintain such hard and fast distinctions.

Box 8.2   Charities

- In England and Wales, organizations wishing to be formally recognized as charities have to register with the Charity Commission. The regulatory body for Scotland will be the Office of the Scottish Charity Regulator. Both in Scotland and Northern Ireland, organizations need to apply to the Inland Revenue to be recognized for tax purposes.
- Organizations, such as churches, schools, community groups and hospitals, don't have to register as they are assumed to have a charitable purpose.
- The criteria for charitable activities are defined in the repealed 1601 Statute of Charitable Uses – a Charities Bill to modernize regulation is currently before Parliament.
- In 2004 there were 166,129 charities registered with the Charity Commission, and 17,684 listed in Scotland by the Inland Revenue.
- Total annual income for charities registered with the Charity Commission in 2004 was nearly £35 billion. £9.1 billion of this went to the top ten charities; nearly 90 per cent of the money is raised by just over 7 per cent of the charities.
- The vast majority of charities are small, with an annual income of £10,000 or less.
- The most popular causes are international, and cancer; charities for people with disabilities have declined in popularity, possibly because people are now seen as more empowered.

(*Source:* cafonline, www.cafonline.org)

The voluntary sector and housing: A case study

In this section we focus on the expanding role of the voluntary sector in the provision of housing; this contribution is mainly through the provision of social rented housing by housing associations. In this context, we consider the impact of new liaisons between voluntary sector bodies, the commercial sector, informal care and the state (particularly with increasing reliance on state funding and accompanying regulation) on the independence and character of the voluntary sector and the 'voluntary ethic' itself. In doing so we highlight both the way in which the voluntary sector has become involved in state welfare, for economic and political motives, and the ways in which it can be utilized for mutual aid. It becomes clear that any static notion of the mixed economy of welfare is problematic. In practice, we are witnessing the development of mixed institutional forms; Taylor *et al.* (1994: 129) comment on the *'increasing fuzziness of the boundaries between the public and private sector and the expansion of a "murkier third terrain" that is both public and private'*.

Housing is also important as an element of health policy (Taske *et al.* 2005), thus illustrating the linkage between social policy and health policy. It has long been recognized that homelessness or living in non-decent housing are detrimental to health, and the government has set a target of bringing all social housing into a decent condition (ODPM 2005). Public health partnerships involving housing officers are also being created, although their effectiveness varies (Stewart *et al.* in press).

The policy context

Housing policy over the last 50 years has been dominated by measures aimed at increasing home ownership (commercial provision). Radaelli and Dente (1996) claimed that housing is an example of a high conflict policy area, although that may no longer be the case, since cross-party consensus now supports the growth of a 'property-owning democracy' and home ownership is a key part of the national culture; Humphrey and Bromley (2006) state that owner-occupation is the type of tenure which 82 per cent of the population would choose if they could. What has distinguished policy since 1980, however, has been a shift in strategy from one of providing incentives for home ownership (the 'carrot' approach) to the deliberate policy of residualization in the public sector (the 'stick').

The 1980 public expenditure paper greatly reduced public spending on housing and the Conservative Party sought to extend owner-occupation to lower income groups through the introduction of a statutory 'Right to Buy' for council tenants (in the 1980 Housing Act). Sales of council properties were encouraged by a generous system of discounts, which were extended by the Housing and Building Control Act 1984 to a maximum of 60 per cent of market value, increased to 70 per cent for flats in January 1987. This policy, accompanied by the imposition of a moratorium on new council house building and tight controls on local government expenditure, resulted in the transfer of a large proportion of public stock into the private sector. Council house sales reduced considerably the ability of housing authorities to house people on their waiting lists; as a result, many people who would have preferred to rent a council house were forced to buy in the commercial sector. This twin policy of incentives and residualization resulted in substantial 'successes' in terms of shifts in patterns of housing tenure in favour of the commercial sector. Economic recession in the 1980s, however, resulted both in a record number of mortgage repossessions as a result of mortgage arrears, which Nettleton (1998) identified as an important public health issue, and a substantial decline in investment in new commercial house building as house prices plummeted.

The 1988 Housing Act was introduced after it became evident, as figures declined after 1992, that sales of council houses alone were not going to achieve the long-term objective of removing general needs housing from the responsibility of local government; the Act provided further 'legislation for demunicipalisation' (Malpass and Murie 1994: 105). The 'Tenant's Choice' provisions gave tenants (other than those in sheltered housing or others excluded from the Right to Buy) the right to 'choose' an alternative landlord. At the time, the response by tenants and prospective landlords was negligible, but local authorities did use the provisions of the Housing and Planning Act 1986 to transfer their housing stock to housing associations voluntarily. Cole and Furbey (1994: 173) explain that *'Initially, the proportion of transfers blocked by tenants was very high. It was only after the financial implications of the Local Government and Housing Act 1989 became apparent, with their indications of a further erosion in the relative quality of public housing, that more ballots produced majorities in favour of block transfers'.*

A new direction was taken to further reduce the stock of public sector housing, but this time the transfer was to be directly from the state to the voluntary sector. The largest transfer took place in 1992 when over 12,000 dwellings were transferred by the London Borough of Bromley (CSO 1995: 175). However, Treasury concern about the costs to the housing benefit bill, of the higher rents charged by housing associations compared with local authorities, inhibited the progress of further transfers (Murie 1993). In addition, over the 1980s, 83,800 houses were sold off from the non-charitable housing association sector; 1992 legislation to extend this was defeated in the House of Lords, due to concern that this would distort the aims of many charities and would greatly reduce the availability of housing for the most needy (Balchin and Rhoden 2002). Overall, housing policy from 1979 to 1997 was one of the main factors in creating a divided society (Balchin and Rhoden 2002).

Although housing policy in the other three countries has diverged since devolution (Balchin and Rhoden 2002), even Scotland, which had a markedly different pattern of tenure, went down the route of transferring housing stock from the local authority, and by 1999, 5.7 per cent of all dwellings were rented from housing associations (a similar figure to England). In Greater Glasgow this entailed 100,000 dwellings, and about 30 per cent of housing association stock in Scotland, is in Glasgow. In Wales, the sector increased from 11,000 dwellings in 1981 to 77,000 in 1999 (4.1 per cent of total stock) although this growth has been slowed by cuts in the social housing budget in the 1990s. The National Assembly for Wales has taken over the regulatory function previously held by Tai Cymru (the Welsh equivalent of the Housing Corporation). Northern Ireland has a much smaller housing association sector (2.6 per cent) and does not have a history of the large scale transfer of housing stock.

The housing association movement

A housing association is a non-profit-making organization which provides and manages homes for people who cannot afford to buy a suitable home on the open market; it may be a charity, a registered industrial provident society, or both. Although associations increasingly obtain funding from private sources and charitable trusts, the majority provide housing with public money from the Housing Corporation. Housing associations provide housing both for rent and for ownership, with some schemes promoting low-income owner-occupation (e.g. including homes for key workers). In 2004–5, the total gross expenditure of the Housing Corporation was £1597.7 million on its Approved Development Programme, with expenditure of £66.7 million on two programmes inherited from local authorities, and £18.4 million on three programmes for the ODPM (Rough Sleepers, Women Fleeing Domestic Violence, and the Homelessness Initiative Leasehold Scheme). These ODPM programmes are a good illustration of the importance of housing in providing welfare. In 2004–5, grants of £15 million were made to ten registered social landlords specializing in homes for BME groups, who have often been poorly served by public sector housing.

The first housing association was the 1830 Labourer's Friendly Society, although it could afford to build few houses; charitable trusts, such as Guinness, Peabody, Rowntree and Bournville were established later in the nineteenth century. Government support for voluntary housing can be traced back to the Labouring Classes Dwelling Houses Act of 1866. The Housing Corporation was set up by Parliament, under the 1964 Housing Act, to fund housing construction by registered housing associations using central government finance in Great Britain (subsequently restricted to England by the Housing Act 1988). The sector had, however, remained very small, accounting for a tiny proportion of housing stock, although the role of voluntary housing was extended by legislation under the Conservative government of the 1950s. The growth of the housing association movement, since 1974, has come about as a result of increased state intervention, mainly in the form of subsidy. The Conservative government, especially in its second decade, recognized the need for rented housing and for subsidized housing for the less well off. Housing associations were seen as the major agency for supplying these, both because borrowing by housing associations was not counted as part of public sector borrowing, and because the Conservatives sought to reduce the role of local government. The Conservatives were especially critical of local authority housing departments, seeing them as being unresponsive to the needs of tenants and encouraging passivity; that is, tenants not being prepared to take on responsibility for the upkeep of their houses and neighbourhoods, because they felt no sense of ownership.

Housing association stock

In terms of the overall proportion of housing stock, housing association properties constitute only about 2 million, compared to about 3 million each rented from local authorities and private landlords, and about 18 million owner-occupied (Social Trends 2006). The housing association sector, however, experienced expansion during a period of overall retrenchment, and has maintained that expansion, although it is still small compared to private enterprise. Local authority building is now virtually zero (see Fig 8.1). The Housing Corporation investment programme for 2004–6 of £3.3 billion is its largest ever, and will include funding to the private sector, illustrating the further intertwining of the public, private and voluntary sectors.

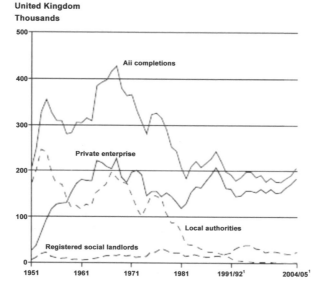

Figure 8.1 Housebuilding completions by sector
Source: Social Trends (2006)

Although the overall size of the sector has increased, the number of housing associations registered with the Housing Corporation, as registered social landlords (RSLs), has decreased from 2165 in 1993 to 1984 in 2005. Their size varies considerably, with a few major players, such as Anchor, controlling most of the units, whereas most associations are small and lack expertise; in 1997 under 20 per cent employed full-time staff (Balchin and Rhoden 2002). There is, therefore, a trade-off between the expertise created by large size, and the closeness to tenants which can be the benefit of small size. The Housing Corporation is also a regulator, and can deregister a failing RSL or place it under supervision.

Balchin and Rhoden (2002) comment on the backlog of repairs which had built up during the underfunding period of the 1990s, and query whether the housing association role is sustainable given the difficulty of

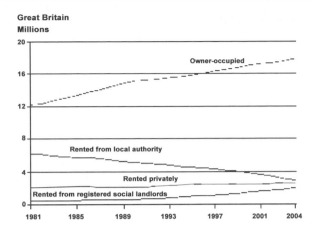

Figure 8.2 Stock of dwellings by tenure
Source: Social Trends (2006)

balancing their role in providing housing to the most needy (up to 50 per cent of tenants in new housing association dwellings were previously homeless, and up to two-thirds overall are on benefit), with the investment needed to build reasonable quality housing. They are concerned at the risk of developing cramped, poor quality 'welfare ghettos', although the issues have been recognized and are being remedied, by proposals in the Housing Green Paper (DETR/DSS 2000).

Housing associations as voluntary organizations

We have already noted that three characteristics of voluntary organizations are that they are independent, non-profit distributing and rely on volunteers. The advantages of voluntary organizations are also said to stem from their relatively smaller size, their ability to identify and respond to local needs in a flexible and non-bureaucratic fashion. The overwhelming majority of housing association stock, however, is provided by very large organizations with a regional, as opposed to local, base. Indeed, many cover substantially larger geographical areas than local authority housing departments and are unlikely to provide a sensitive, local or uncomplicated service (Balchin and Rhoden 2002). National figures also tend to mask large regional variations in housing association provision. The 2004–5 building programme (Housing Corporation 2005) shows that in England most development is in the South East where land is most expensive, with little in the North East (see Table 8.1).

Taylor and Langan (1996) comment that housing associations increasingly see themselves as part of the business world rather than as voluntary organizations. The role of volunteers in this sector is also restricted. As with many voluntary organizations, in practice the label 'voluntary' applies only to the management committees and not to service delivery. In relation to housing associations, even fundraising, which forms the major

Table 8.1 Housing Corporation building programme 2004–5

North East	703
Yorkshire and the Humber	942
East Midlands	1672
North West	1885
West Midlands	2144
South West	2625
East of England	2917
South East	7101
London	8767

Source: Housing Corporation (2005)

occupation of all volunteers, is insignificant. The administration of associations is, therefore, likely to mirror that of statutory agencies.

Housing associations' reliance upon central and local government finance raises important questions. Other changes have further modified the financial position of housing associations, with implications for their autonomy and independence. For example, in order to encourage new partnerships between the commercial and voluntary sectors and to reduce the reliance on public expenditure, the government introduced 'challenge' funding initiatives in the 1980s, which offered additional funds to those associations initiating projects involving an element of commercial finance. These projects were set up to demonstrate that commercial finance could be raised for social housing schemes. Whitehead (1993), however, argues that many of the initial schemes involved elements of additional state subsidy, such as land provided at below-market rates by local authorities. Furthermore, *'if the system were to work for social housing overall, grant rates would have to be significantly higher'* (p. 88). The system also appeared to favour larger asset-rich housing associations, which found it easier to raise loans in the commercial market. The 1988 Housing Act laid down the financial framework, by which commercial finance was to be introduced into all new housing association developments.

The replacement of fair rents with assured tenancies enabled housing associations to set rents at market levels, thus increasing their attractiveness to commercial financiers. What this implies, in effect, is a transfer of state financial responsibility from capital funding via Housing Corporation grant to means tested housing benefit. Although the proportion of state finance via the Housing Corporation has declined with the introduction of 'mixed funding', the majority of funds still come from central government through the Housing Corporation. Associations are still subject to heavy state regulation, exemplifying a shift from state provision to state regulation, which has occurred in other sectors such as health. Balchin and Rhoden (2002: 234) are highly critical of this regulation, stating that over the last 25 years the government has 'meddled' in the work of the Housing Corporation, which has in turn interfered in the work of housing associations, risking distorting the missions of charitable organizations.

While housing policy since 1979 has been led by considerations of public expenditure and a drive to promote the commercial sector, both as provider and financier of housing, this policy has not resulted in the withdrawal of government from housing; rather, we have witnessed a shift in the nature and complexity of state intervention. An important component of this shift has been the increase in control by central government and the declining autonomy of local authorities in the housing field. The rate of growth and development of policy in the housing association movement is highly dependent upon state policy. Malpass and Murie's (1999: 158) assessment of the changes affecting housing associations sums this up well: *'The voluntary and private sectors have become increasingly important elements in housing policy. The financial dependency of a large group of the active housing association movement has left them more clearly as agents of the state – manipulated through the Housing Corporation and its equivalents'.*

The hospice movement

This case study shows that policy-making may be the outcome of a sustained process of campaigning and debate, and the recognition of a previously unexamined problem (Levin 1997). It also demonstrates the importance of a charismatic figure – in this instance Dame Cicely Saunders – in mobilizing networks of influential figures, and in reframing the issues. Clark (1999) identifies four innovations in the founding of the hospice movement; the development of a systematic knowledge base, a greater recognition of the meaning of death, a more active approach to care and a growing recognition of the interrelatedness of mental and physical distress.

Although the NHS was established to provide care 'from the cradle to the grave', in its initial years, as it addressed the problems of acute and chronic care in the context of post-war reconstruction, little attention was paid to care at the end of life. Clark (1999) claims that the ethic of the new NHS was 'intensely modernizing' with a deep ideological suspicion of charity and an emphasis on cure and rehabilitation. Bevan, in fact, had surmised that patients would rather be kept alive in the 'efficient if cold altruism' of a large hospital than expire 'in a gush of sympathy' in a small one (Abel-Smith 1964). Two inquiries into cancer care took place in the 1950s. One, the report of the Joint National Cancer Survey Committee organized by the Marie Curie Memorial (MCM) (established in 1948) and the Queen's Institute of District Nursing, showed that many older cancer patients were dying at home, often in pain, and in squalid conditions. Although MCM responded by extending its nursing service and had begun to open residential homes, there was no evidence of a systematic response from the rest of the health service. The other inquiry, chaired by the surgeon Glyn Hughes, estimated that 270,000 people needing skilled terminal care died outside NHS hospitals each year, and that although 'voluntary and profit-making establishments' would continue to be needed, neither currently had satisfactory staffing or skills. Both reports also concluded that families' readiness to care had been eroded, with changes in attitudes and greater geographical mobility. Medical treatment, according to a 1948 paper in *The Practitioner* cited by Clark (1999) consisted mainly of morphine for the patient, and 'a good dose of barbiturate with a cup of tea' for the 'ringleaders' of the relatives; Clark comments that the medical literature of the period is based mainly on personal experience, with little sense of an accumulated body of knowledge.

The first modern hospice was founded in 1967 by Cicely Saunders (who unusually, was qualified in social work and nursing before she went into medicine) at St Christopher's in south-east London. She put forward a tripartite model, of total care for the person, teaching and research and was a key figure in establishing a coherent knowledge base. St Christopher's built on an older tradition of hospice care. Four existed in London in the 1950s, and Cicely Saunders worked at two of them, St Luke's and St Joseph's. Few existed elsewhere, and they did not form a coherent network. Care was often given by nuns and untrained assistants. Nevertheless, they provided 'an enduring quality of self-help and voluntarism' (Clark 1999). The funding for the hospices, once established, resembled that of the voluntary hospitals which had preceded the NHS, in that it came from public subscription. The hospices involved prominent local doctors, and had religious and philanthropic associations. Recent experience, however, has shown the vulnerability of this model.

Dean (2005), reflecting on the recent death of Dame Cicely Saunders, states that although there are now over 230 British hospices, 80 per cent of them independent of the NHS, they have never received proper funding from the NHS. They raise additional funding of £300 million p.a. through shops and sponsored events, and have recruited over 100,000 volunteers, estimated to be equivalent to another £100 million p.a. However, they have been hit by stock market problems, shrinking legacies and rising costs, including the pressures created by the reforms to the NHS pay system. Mulholland (2002) states that although inpatient services have not grown recently (and it can be argued that the essence of hospice care should be provided in other settings as well), the demand for day and community care is increasing (an example being lymphoedema clinics, for patients who have had lymph nodes removed due to breast cancer). The underfunding of inpatient services slows the development of these other services. Hospices may have also been inadvertently affected by government legislation, namely the Community Care (Delayed Discharges) Act 2003, since they are not currently covered and other patients may therefore be given priority (House of Commons Health Committee 2004). This is an illustration of how changes in one part of the health care system may impact on another in an unanticipated way.

In 1997 when the Labour government was elected, 35 per cent of voluntary hospices' costs were covered by the NHS, but by 2002 it had reduced to 28 per cent (although since restored to 34 per cent). Some of the additional funding announced by the DoH had been siphoned off for other services, and in 2003, 26 per cent of units had been forced to cut beds. Although £120 million had been set aside for capacity-building in the voluntary sector (Futurebuilders), applications by hospices had been turned down as they would not be able to repay the loans. In 2002, the Treasury's cost-cutting review on the voluntary sector recommended that all government departments should ensure that contracts reflected the full price of a service, from April 2006. Dean (2005) doubted that this would happen (a view probably confirmed by the current financial crisis in the

NHS, which has been reported as hitting other voluntary health care providers such as the MS Society). Haffinden (2006) states that the National Council for Voluntary Organizations had, in April 2006, warned that hundreds of charities would have to axe services, unless the financial problems in the NHS were addressed. Not only hospices caring for cancer patients (who represent 95 per cent of current patients), but also those caring for patients with AIDS, have been affected by uncertainties in funding. In April 2006 it was reported (Gould 2006) that the Mildmay Mission Hospital in north London, a centre of excellence for complex HIV/AIDS management and rehabilitation, was at risk of closure. Voluntary income had virtually halted due to people giving instead to large-scale disasters, such as the 2004/5 tsunami appeal, and financial problems in the London PCTs were resulting in fewer referrals. These hospices have also been affected by advances in the clinical management of AIDS, since it is now in many ways a long-term rather than a terminal illness; this illustrates how an organization set up for a specific purpose may be affected when needs change in an unanticipated way, for example, due to advances in treatment.

The future of the voluntary sector

In Taylor and Langan's (1996) research, concern was expressed by voluntary organizations about increased regulation, competition and constraints in funding. Flynn (1996) quotes Gutch's research in the USA, which found that short-term contracts made voluntary organizations less secure, smaller organizations were being squeezed out, and bureaucracy had increased. Although Flynn did not find evidence that the aims of organizations were being distorted by the increased use of contracts, there was some evidence that organizations which dealt with unpopular causes were being squeezed, that organizations were more vulnerable to changes in demand, and that the recruitment and retention of staff could be affected by less stable career patterns. Milligan (1998) concluded from her research on the effects of contracting on mental health voluntary organizations in Scotland, that service provision was favoured over other types of activity, such as advocacy and campaigning, and that if this erosion continues it could be detrimental to individuals who are not able to speak for themselves. Reading (1994) comments that black communities in particular should keep their concentration on rights, politics and social action, rather than being sucked into merely service provision. Flynn and Hurley (1993) concluded that there was an inherent contradiction between the purchaser's desire for flexibility and the provider's need for stability (as there is in any market). Taylor and Lewis (1997) raise similar issues, and found that local organizations were likely to be squeezed by national ones with a better infrastructure for contracting. Important roles such as advocacy, which lay outside the core services, were largely ignored by commissioners. Perri 6 (1997) thought that very large not-for-profit organizations were likely to emerge, which would compete with voluntary organizations.

A report for ACEVO (Brookes and Copps 2004) found that contracts were often short-term, and that contracting procedures were often inefficient and bureaucratic. Voluntary organizations often bore the risks of service development, and were not always able to recover their full costs. Eighty-one per cent said that funding regimes hindered their ability to plan for the future, and 58 per cent said it caused difficulty recruiting staff; Marie Curie Cancer Care stated that lack of up-front funding made them reliant on agency staff, and that although in theory multiple sources of funding can protect organizations, they spent time negotiating 300 separate contracts with PCTs. Generally, relationships were thought to be more advanced in mental health, where some organizations such as Turning Point had ten-year contracts. More recently, it has been reported (O'Hara 2006) that statutory funding for both social services and charities had been delayed or withdrawn in order to ease NHS budgetary problems, in what Stephen Bubb, the chief executive of ACEVO, termed 'the reverse Robin Hood principle' of the rich robbing the poor. This example illustrates the vulnerability of both the voluntary sector and also its clients, many of whom are not politically high profile.

The discussion now moves away from the future of voluntary organizations to consider the issue of volunteering in more detail and, in particular, to address some recent debates about voluntarism. These issues concern the potential exploitation of unpaid work and its impact on paid workers, the development of paid volunteering and the relationship between voluntarism and informal care (the subject of the next chapter).

Voluntarism, altruism and 'paid volunteering'

The term 'voluntarism' and its close association with notions of altruism, implies that time and effort is freely given, without the need for remuneration. Since the 1980s, a new form of relationship has developed, further blurring the boundaries between the voluntary sector and the state. The phenomenon known as 'paid volunteering', which involves cash payments to individual volunteers, raises interesting questions about the future compatibility of altruism or 'active citizenship' in the face of an increasingly market-oriented welfare system. Paid volunteering has been associated typically with innovative and experimental schemes aimed at providing care 'in the community'. Such schemes include good neighbour schemes, where a neighbour is paid to care for a dependent person living in their own home, and respite schemes, where a volunteer is paid to relieve a carer for a given period of time (see Fig 8.3). The greater tendency of local authorities to contract-out work to large voluntary organizations, resulting in considerably larger budgets combined with contractual pressure to guarantee service delivery, has increased the use of paid volunteer workers. This may have resulted from the need to increase the sheer numbers of volunteers (as a form of incentive), to secure continuity of service and, where necessary, to pay for the higher levels of skill required.

The introduction of more market-oriented criteria in both the financing of voluntary organizations, like housing associations and hospices, and in providing incentives and financial rewards for volunteers, raises interesting questions about the future character of this sector and the distinctiveness

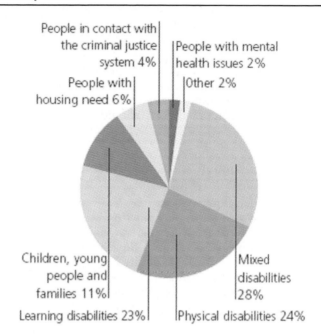

People in contact with the criminal justice system 4%

People with mental health issues 2%

People with housing need 6%

Other 2%

Children, young people and families 11%

Mixed disabilities 28%

Learning disabilities 23%

Physical disabilities 24%

Figure 8.3 Areas of service by community service full-time volunteers
Source: CSV (2005)

of its contribution. Individualism associated with free market philosophy leads to the pursuit of narrow self-interest and a cost-benefit mentality which eventually undermines altruism – giving to an unknown stranger and expecting nothing back in return. In this context, Ware (1990) argues that only altruism practised within a wider reciprocating group as a form of social insurance can survive, and concludes that the general effect of the expansion of the market system has been to corrode altruism.

While the idealism, associated with voluntarism, supports the notion of 'employing' volunteers in care-giving (and in advocacy schemes), there are concerns over the level of training of volunteers and their reliability, although clients are now safeguarded through the requirement for Criminal Records Bureau clearance. There are also concerns about the exploitation of volunteers as a source of 'cheap' labour, which may undermine the jobs of paid workers – not only by volunteers substituting for paid workers, but by voluntary organizations being able to undercut the charges of state and commercial organizations and thereby win contracts to provide services. Hedley and Davis Smith (1992: 33) document the uneasy relationship between the voluntary movement and the British Labour movement, which traditionally associated voluntarism with nineteenth-century charity, philanthropy and dependency, and as a threat to paid jobs. Particular concern has arisen in the past over the use of volunteers during strikes. Hedley and Davis Smith conclude that tensions have eased in recent years, partly as a result of a shift in thinking on the left, away from the notion of state welfare and in favour of the mixed economy of welfare. Caton Hughes' (2005) study of volunteering in hospitals found no

evidence that it undermined employment opportunities, and some organizations had local agreements with the unions. Concerns remain, however, over the implications of the use of volunteers in 'contracted-out'
services which are already low-paid areas of work. The introduction of paid
volunteering schemes similarly raises issues concerning the boundaries
between paid and unpaid work, and fears that such developments herald a
new form of exploitation.

Voluntary activity, obligation and informal care

The voluntary sector provides an important source of support for the
millions of people involved in caring – on an unpaid basis and usually in
the home – for dependent relatives and friends. Voluntary organizations
that provide services for dependent groups of people have, however, been
criticized for offering inappropriate services or working in an oppressive
way, as have the statutory services, and this critique has grown (Oliver and
Barnes 1998). They have, however, been important in raising awareness of
informal care and applying pressure on central and local government to
provide increased levels of support, both in terms of services, such as day
care or respite care and cash benefits for carers. Schemes such as sitting
services for elderly people suffering from dementia, transport schemes and
carers' support groups have provided important sources of support for
isolated and exhausted carers. It is in this area that the voluntary sector has
demonstrated its ability to come up with new and innovative forms of
service, some of which subsequently become incorporated within statutory
schemes (e.g. sitting services have been taken on in some local authorities).
Although there is clearly an important relationship between the voluntary
sector and informal care and, in many ways, recent policy initiatives in
community care have further blurred the boundaries between these sectors, the act of caring for a dependent relative, friend or neighbour must be
distinguished from voluntary work. In one sense, people do volunteer to
undertake these caring tasks, but an act can be considered to be truly
voluntary only when the person has freedom of choice.

Many people providing services in the informal sector have little or no
genuine choice, either because of the lack of alternative services or because
of their sense of duty or obligation. We shall see in the next chapter how
statutory services themselves can be organized around certain assumptions
about the role of the family, and the apportionment of roles within the
family, with implications for the degree of 'choice' available to carers.
Despite changes in family circumstances, such as higher levels of women's
employment, the system of care is predicated on a major role for informal
care. The Green Paper on social care reform (DoH 2005e) states in the
preface by Tony Blair that '*It is family and friends, of course, who still take
most of the caring responsibilities*'. Heginbotham (1990) argues that evidence
of the disproportionate pressure brought to bear on women to undertake
informal care prevents such a role being defined as 'truly voluntary',
although as discussed in Chapter 9, this is now changing and elderly men
are increasingly taking on a caring role.

The sexism inherent in these decisions is reinforced by social attitudes, which bring further pressure to bear on men and women to comply with assigned gender roles. Fielding *et al.* (1991: 98) conclude their book on active citizenship with a 'word of warning': '*The pure theory of volunteering is easily confused by its entanglement with the dilemma of women today which sets them free to move in the world outside the family without releasing them from the bonds of domestic tradition. We have a long way to go before we can talk of volunteering as a universal experience, freely available to all*'.

Conclusion

This chapter has raised some general points about the viability of increased reliance upon the voluntary sector in the provision of welfare. It has noted the enormous diversity of provision and the problems of definition and measurement of the voluntary contribution. Focusing on two aspects of voluntary sector provision, those of social housing and hospice care, it has demonstrated the nature of the voluntary sector and the pressure it is under. The voluntary sector faces a dilemma: in order to become a major player in the delivery of social welfare, it cannot rely on philanthropic donations but must demand substantial financial support from both the state and the commercial sector. While such support greatly increases the potential for development, it also increases dependency, which may pose a threat to the sector's independence and diversity. Voluntary organizations are under pressure to become larger, and more bureaucratically organized. Even the supply of voluntary effort is under question, as organizations are forced to consider the possibility of offering financial incentives to bolster the supply of volunteers. More broadly, researchers such as Wolch (1989: 201) are concerned that these developments constitute a 'shadow state', in which voluntary organizations take on service responsibilities from the public sector, *administered outside traditional democratic politics, but controlled in both formal and informal ways by the state*.

Summary

- The voluntary sector dominated formal welfare provision in Britain until the 1940s.
- There is no universally accepted definition of the voluntary sector. The type of organizations involved vary greatly in size, structure, legal and financial status, their use of paid and unpaid staff and the geographical scope of their work.
- Voluntary organizations can be loosely grouped into two categories; those based on philanthropy and those based on mutual aid and self-help.
- Since the 1980s, the government in Britain has sought to encourage the development of this sector and increase reliance on voluntary provision within the mixed economy of welfare.

- The development of housing associations is used to illustrate the growth of this sector and the increasingly complex interactions and alliances between the state and other providers of welfare, which may be termed a 'shadow state'.
- The hospice movement is used to illustrate the recognition of a social problem, and the development of a voluntary sector service which arguably might have been part of the NHS. This service is now under financial pressure.

Further reading

Balchin, P. and Rhoden, M. (2002) *Housing Policy*, 4th edn. London: Routledge.

Milligan, C. and Conradson, D. (2006) *Geographies of Voluntarism: New Spaces of Health, Welfare and Governance*. Bristol: Policy Press.

LAY PERSPECTIVES AND THE ROLE OF INFORMAL CARE

Introduction

Over the last 20 to 30 years, there has been an increasing awareness of the importance of lay involvement in health. Health is not seen as simply the remit of health professionals, and the delivery of health care is not simply the remit of the health care system. The involvement of patients and the public in the planning, management and delivery of health services is an important feature of health care systems and, is increasingly recognized as being essential for achieving good quality services that meet people's needs. It is also important to see developments in health care as part of a change in focus for the welfare state, with New Labour advocating citizen-centred government, as central to its drive to modernize public services (Martin and Boaz 2000). The aim has been to shift the way services are delivered, so that they meet the needs of citizens, rather than being organized for the convenience of service providers.

These changes reflect a third theme, central to the discussion in this chapter, which is the recognition that health is not something produced by health care professionals and systems but relates to individuals, families and communities. Thus, lay perspectives of health and health care,

including the important role of families and carers in providing and producing health, need to be understood by health care professionals. This
chapter explores the development of lay involvement in health through
the growth of the user movement. It will also examine the role of carers,
addressing who they are, the contribution they make and examining what
is meant by informal care. The chapter will then examine how the state
and professions have responded to these developments, through a growing
recognition of the relationship between informal and formal care, and
acceptance of incorporating lay perspectives in health care with an
increasing emphasis on the service user – for example, individual responsibility, patient partnership and patient-centred care. This will include
examining support given to carers and users, the development of policies
for carers and users, public and patient involvement and outlining organizational and service developments. Finally the chapter examines the
current debates relating to self-care and why supporting self-care has
become of particular policy interest.

The discussion of involvement is also commonly related to two broad
conceptual frameworks. The first was developed by Arnstein (1969), who
envisaged a ladder of participation ranging from manipulation and therapy – where participation is only aimed for as a 'feel-good' factor to citizen
control where people are in control. Arnstein provides us with a way of
thinking about the participation process, and the way that power is exercised within it. Participation has been widely used in the NHS and user
movement to frame discussions of patient and public involvement. It sees
involvement as progressing through a number of stages, like rungs on a
ladder, providing a way of assessing the extent to which any involvement
really engages and empowers users. The other useful concept is that suggested by Hirschmann (1970), already discussed in Chapter 6, who set out
options for the public in terms of 'exit', 'voice' and 'loyalty'. Hirschmann
was looking at consumers in a market-place, but his framework is useful in
that it highlights the limited power of welfare service users, as there are
often few options than to be loyal, and increasing user power involves
thinking about how users can voice their concerns and views about services and, as increasingly being developed in UK policy on choice, providing opportunities to express dissatisfaction with services or employ
choice by switching from one service to another.

Two other approaches are that of consumerist and democratic or citizen
involvement, which characterizes debates about the relationship of the
public to health care services and, more recently, the concept of patient-
centred care. These conceptual approaches are discussed fully elsewhere
(Lupton *et al.* 1998; Peckham and Exworthy 2003). Here, they may help to
provide a useful backdrop to thinking about patient and public involvement. The role of lay people in health care and patient-centred care, in
particular, has important consequences for the role of health care
professionals.

A lay perspective

Over the last 40 years there has been a growing recognition that the views of lay people are important in the provision of health and welfare services. Users of services themselves have gradually organized to articulate their views and ideas, professionals have recognized that involving service users produces better outcomes, and there has been a general dissatisfaction with the paternalism of the apparatus of the welfare state itself, in that it has been over-bureaucratic, unable to respond to needs, limited in the range of services and how they are delivered. In addition, in relation to health care, there has been a concern that services have not been locally accountable. This period has seen the growth of the service users movement, an enormous increase in the number and range of voluntary sector organizations, both representing and providing services to service users, and increasing concerns about the accountability and governance structures of the NHS in particular (Lupton *et al.* 1998; Wood 2000; Taylor 2003).

There has, however, been little recognition of the role of the community in promoting its own health through community-based action and community health initiatives (Petersen and Lupton 1996; Taylor *et al.* 1998). It is clear that individuals, families and communities, provide significant amounts of self-care and health prevention, as illustrated in Table 9.1 (WHO/UNICEF 1978; Zakus and Lysack 1998; Wilson *et al.* 2005). But, as discussed in Chapter 5, despite the continued importance of environmental health, housing, transport and education, public health has become dominated by the medical model and public health medicine promulgated by medical practitioners (Macdonald 1992; Baggott 2000). This has led to an emphasis on disease control and monitoring, epidemiological studies, individual health promotion and support to medical practitioners – most recently in relation to evidence-based medicine.

Patient and public involvement is essential to the delivery of good health care, and while the relationships may be complex, the rewards for professionals and health care service users are clear. The relationship of the patient with the medical practitioner is widely discussed in the sociological and medical literature and, has been viewed both in a structuralist way with the concept of the sick role, where patients are defined as passive recipients of care provided by professionals (Parsons 1951), and in Foucauldian terms, where the relationship is based on power, with professionals dominating the relationship (Foucault 1975). The power imbalance between health professionals and patients can, however, be viewed in four ways. Pendleton *et al.* (1984) suggested that doctors' power is based on three key foundations – knowledge, moral authority and charismatic authority. Silverman (1987) has also added a further view which is based on the passing of responsibility for decision-making from the patient or carer to a health professional, where difficult and risky medical procedures are being undertaken. For nurses the patient/practitioner relationship has always been viewed as different. Since the Nightingale reforms, nursing has been characterized as patient-centred or focused, taking an holistic approach to care. In practice there have been concerns that nursing has

Table 9.1 Patient and community

Who	Act as	How	Who with	Comments
Individuals	Patients, health providers	Self-care, shared care, user involvement, complaints	Themselves, health professionals, other users	Predominantly a medical model operating Example: individual practitioner consultations
Families	Patients, health providers, carers/ parents, supporters, advocates		Themselves, health professionals	Represents a family orientation usually within primary medical care Example: UK general practice
Informal networks	Supporters, health providers	Friend and kinship networks, self-help groups	Themselves, health professionals	May work collaboratively with specific health professionals but main emphasis is on mutual support Example: Carers support groups
Formal networks	Health providers, supporters, advocates	Community associations, patient groups	Members	May provide a range of information and support services to members. This may involve specialist and professional health providers. Example: Patient participation group, tenants association
Community/ voluntary organizations	Providers of services, supporters, advocates	Campaigning, delivering services, participating in working groups	Members, users, health professionals, health agencies	More formalized than networks and may have specific aims to provide services as well as support users Example: MIND, SCOPE, RNID
Geographical communities	Polity, electors, providers, advocates	Voting, campaigning, developing networks between other groups	Health agencies, local authorities, government	Example: neighbourhood

Source: Peckham (2004: 35)

been as dominated by the medical care model as are other aspects of health care delivery. This raises important questions about the autonomy of the patient and thus, challenges professional autonomy and knowledge (Askham and Chisholm 2006).

There is growing evidence to demonstrate that patient involvement is likely to lead to an improved clinical outcome (Coulter 1997), and clearly an informed user of services may gain more than simply improved health. There are also important issues in terms of addressing the health care needs of the community that require partnerships between local people and professionals (Lupton *et al.* 1998).

The wider context for much of the development of shared decision-making and patient involvement in health care is the concept of patient-centred care (Stewart *et al.* 1995). The pressure for patient-centred care comes from developments in clinical practice and patient pressure. In a study on patient preference for patient-centred care Little *et al.* (2001) suggested that patients want patient-centred care which:

- explores the patient's main reason for the visit, their concerns and need for information;
- seeks an integrated understanding of the patients' world;
- finds common ground on what the problem is and mutually agrees on management;
- enhances prevention and health promotion;
- enhances the continuing relationship between the patient and doctor.

The approach places the patient at the centre of care, where decision-making is undertaken in partnership. It does not mean that the patient will always want all of the information, or be responsible for taking a decision. The key point here is that the patient is involved in making the decision about how much information they may require at any time (Elwyn *et al.* 1999; Gwyn and Elwyn 1999). Pursuing shared decision-making within a patient-centred approach requires substantial changes in the role of the practitioner, creating challenges for all health care professionals. Recent research suggests that nearly a third of primary care patients, and nearly 50 per cent of inpatients, want more involvement in decisions about their care, and studies suggest that doctors tend to focus on technical issues rather than discussing issues more important to the patient, including treatment options (Farrell 2004; Healthcare Commission 2005). While not an explicit element of choice policy, in England, the DoH has been promoting the concept of patient partnership for a number of years, and there is a clear policy focus on patient-centred care, supporting patient involvement and increasing patient autonomy and responsibility for their own care (NHS Executive 1996; DoH 2000a; Harrison *et al.* 2002b). Similar concepts are promoted in Scotland, Wales and Northern Ireland (NHS Scotland 2001; NHS Wales 2005). The medical profession has also recognized the need to develop a more patient-centred approach, and has examined this both in relation to clinical practice (Gillam and Pencheon 1998; Toop 1998; Coulter and Florin 2001; Fisher and Gilbert 2001) and, more recently professional regulation (Irvine 2003).

However, it is not just in the context of the individual patient that changes are occurring, as there is an increasing interest in engaging patient groups or those organizations representing patients' views. Recent emphasis on involving patients in their own care has brought the debate about the nature of the patient/practitioner relationship more into central policy debates. The clear emphasis in *Patient Partnership* (DoH 1996) and *The NHS Plan* (DoH 2000a), underpins the increasing emphasis on ensuring that there are structures and processes for patients to have access to information and organizations, to promote and support their involvement. In addition, the expert patient programme has been promoted by the   NHS (DoH 2000a; DoH 2001d), to support and encourage user-led self-management programmes. This is not a new idea and is aimed at improving the self-esteem and quality of life of those with chronic illness (DoH 1999a; DoH 2006). The rationale, for the programme, is based on the high prevalence of chronic disease and disability, and the self-management programme is being used as the basis for the programme's development in the UK (Lorig *et al.* 1996). A number of programmes have already been developed by health care charities, such as Challenging Arthritis run by Arthritis Care with others run by the Multiple Sclerosis Society and the Manic Depression Fellowship. While such approaches are supported by users and by government policy, there are concerns that the lack of a strategy to challenge professionals' assumptions about people with a chronic illness, may undermine the expert patient programme (Wilson 2001). Such programmes would appear to be set within a more consumerist framework and, are open to being labelled as manipulative. However, proponents of a patient-centred approach would argue that such approaches are based on ensuring real choices and a shift in the power relationship between patients and professionals. There is a clear policy commitment, however, to extend self-care as current levels of support in the NHS have been severely criticized (Wilson *et al.* 2005; Coulter 2006; DoH 2006). In addition, the evaluation of the expert patient programme has identified a number of weaknesses in its approach (Kennedy *et al.* 2005a, 2005b).

Involvement is, however, something that encompasses action beyond the individual. Concerns about a 'democratic deficit' in the NHS are long-standing (Cooper *et al.* 1995; NHSE 1998). These were partially addressed by the creation of Community Health Councils (CHCs) in the 1970s (Klein and Lewis 1976; Moon and Lupton 1995) and by attempts to engage people in local commissioning during the 1980s and 1990s (Lupton *et al.* 1998; Milewa *et al.* 1998). However, in the last 15 years, government health policies have re-emphasized the importance of patient and public involvement in planning and service provision, in addition to the collection of patient satisfaction data (NHS Scotland 2001; Baggott *et al.* 2005; NHS Wales 2005). In England, following *The NHS Plan*, the Labour government introduced a new system of patient and public involvement to replace the CHCs. This involved the creation of the short-lived Commission for Patient and Public Involvement in Health (CPPIH) in 2003, along with local Patient and Public Involvement Forums (PPIFs) based in NHS trusts and PCTs. Patient Advice and Liaison Services (PALS) – to respond quickly to patients' concerns and demands for information – were also introduced and new Independent Complaints Advocacy Services (ICAS) have recently been established. In addition, a general duty on NHS bodies to consult and involve patients and the public, was introduced under Section 11 of the

Health and Social Care Act 2001. Reorganization and rationalization, in 2005, has seen the Commission, become part of the new Healthcare Commission and patient forums have been reorganized around the new PCT structures, as local involvement networks constituted as separate organizations with a staff and budget. New approaches to engaging the public have also been developed with the creation of Foundation Trusts, that have boards elected by a membership of patients, staff, local community and other interest groups (DoH 2003a). The DoH in England also established the post of director for public and patient involvement (Harry Cayton, ex-chief executive of the Alzheimer's Society), to advise on and guide policy in this area. User involvement is also being emphasized in pre-registration training for nurses and other health and social care professionals.

Alongside these policy developments, other informal activities have taken place to address the democratic deficit. Patients, users and carers have long organized themselves, to a considerable extent, independently of government. At national and local level, groups exist for a variety of reasons: to raise funds, to promote self-help and mutual support, to provide information and advice and to influence policy and services (Wood 2000; Baggott *et al.* 2005). These organizations are quite diverse and hence difficult to categorize and analyse, they have been commonly called patient groups, user groups or consumer health groups. Although essentially voluntary bodies, government policy and resources play a vital part in sustaining these organizations by developing their role as policy actors through 'Section 64' funding (DoH funding for non-NHS bodies) and consultation on policy programmes, such as service standards. Moreover, government legislation has prompted them to take a closer interest in policy and service provision issues (Baggott *et al.* 2005).

The number of health consumer groups has grown considerably in the post-war period, with the first being formed in the 1960s (AIMS and Action for Sick Children in Hospital), although some organizations, such as Age Concern, can trace their origins to pre-NHS days (Lupton *et al.* 1998). Wood (2000) found evidence that patients' groups were active at both national and local level, although local organization was often weak and patchy. In their study of health consumer groups at national level, Baggott *et al.* (2005) found that groups such as Carers UK, the Long Term Medical Conditions Alliance and the Patients Forum, became more closely involved in the policy process and in some cases exerted influence over agendas and decisions. This study also found some evidence to suggest that national groups were supporting local action and engaging with local NHS organizations. Specific case studies of HIV/AIDs groups, maternity, physical disability and mental health user groups all found that groups had become engaged in local policy and service issues (Weekes *et al.* 1996; Barnes *et al.* 1999; Taylor 2003). The importance of groups at local level was further underlined by Milewa *et al.* (2002). Their study of Primary Care groups and Trusts found that these organizations, which had a brief to involve the public, viewed patient/advocacy and voluntary organizations as important in promoting patient and public involvement. Indeed attendance at meetings with these groups formed the largest single area of public involvement activity undertaken by NHS primary care organizations (Bond *et al.* 2001; Anderson *et al.* 2002; Harrison *et al.* 2002a).

As discussed in Chapter 8, policy guidance has explicitly identified the local voluntary sector (of which health consumer groups form an important part) as a potential representative. This approach was further bolstered by proposals to create a strategic partnership between voluntary organizations, the DoH and the NHS, based on the principle of the national compact on relations between government and the voluntary sector in England (DoH 1998b; 2003d). It is intended that this partnership will underpin relationships between the NHS and voluntary organizations, including health consumer groups, at local level (Balloch and Taylor 2001). However, despite the above body of research, such investigations have paid relatively little attention to the outcomes of patient and public involvement mechanisms and health consumer group activity (Harrison *et al.* 2002b).

Lay people are also increasingly being involved in the care of others, particularly children with disabilities, people with mental health problems and older people. While informal care has always been provided by family and friends, the increasing need to provide such care and the relationship between informal and formal care (provided by professionals), has raised the profile of informal care in policy and practice. Increasingly the role of the informal carer is becoming more complex and important, and has an enormous impact on the carer, the person being cared for and their families (Pickard *et al.* 2003). This aspect of care, and the significance of the role of the carer have become more important with the increase in chronic disease, an ageing population and the shifts towards more community-based care. More people are being cared for in their own homes, shifting the balance of care from the formal welfare state to less formal and more mixed approaches to providing care. The more recent emphasis on self-care provides a further impetus to this shifting arrangement of health and social care provision.

Formal and informal care

At its simplest, informal care is the regular physical and/or personal assistance given to people (adults or children) with disabilities or illnesses, by people (generally adults, but sometimes children) who are not paid to provide such care. Claire Ungerson (1995: 32) defines informal care as:

> *activities that provide personal services within the domestic domain for people with special needs; most importantly within the British convention, the provision of services is unwaged. The assumption is that the supply of these domestically based caring services is forthcoming, not because it is paid for, but because its provision fulfils certain norms and obligations arising out of the operation of affect, biography and kinship.*

Identifying the nature of the 'task' is important as it is often linked to the relationship of the carer, where wives, mothers and daughters, for example, are more likely to provide personal care.

It is also important to recognize the ambiguous relationship between *formal* and *informal* carers. Assumptions about the roles and responsibilities of informal carers, shape the response of formal service providers to 'the cared-for', and determine the support given by front-line services to informal carers. Graham (1984) has pointed out that formal carers devalue the expertise and experience of informal carers in providing appropriate care, and their knowledge and understanding of the needs of the cared-for person (Abbott and Sapsford 1987). Pickard *et al.* (2003) found that informal carers often had greater insight and knowledge of the condition of the person they cared for than health professionals.

However, Twigg and Atkin (1995) argue that the situation is more complex than this and that the services demanded and received by carers also depend on their own perception of their role. (This may of course be mediated by their understanding of what services are available and the attitudes towards them of service providers.) Twigg and Atkin outline three responses of carers that influence their relationship with formal care providers. First, there are those who are engulfed by their role (mainly women and spouses), see the responsibility of care as theirs and do not ask for services. Others adopt a 'boundary setting' response, detaching themselves from the situation and make a separation between themselves and the person they care for. They define what they see as their responsibility and demand services for tasks they see as lying outside their role. Finally, there are those who adopt a 'symbiotic' approach; they gain in a positive way from their caring role and do not want the responsibility and its consequences to be taken away from them. Their response is typical of parents caring for offspring with mental health problems or learning disabilities, and where the burden of care is not great. Service providers, although not making these distinctions, are aware that services are provided to those carers who are most demanding and assertive.

Service providers also maintain that it is the right of the cared-for person to determine the nature of service provision. This means that the needs or wishes of the carers are frequently marginalized, or ignored, if they are not the same as those of the cared-for person. Furthermore, the relationship between the carer and the cared-for, may influence the provision of formal services – they are less likely to be offered if the carers are spouses or parents than if they are children or more distant relations. Services are also more likely to be offered if the cared-for, person has moved to live with the carer, or vice versa, rather than if they have always been co-resident. Gender, social class, age and race also influence service provision. Men, especially if they are in employment, are more likely to be offered services than non-employed women. Older carers are similarly more likely to be considered as needing formal help than younger carers. Middle-class people are more likely to know their entitlement to services than working-class people and to demand these services. Care-service provision to black people is often unsuitable and inaccessible (see chapter 7).

What is 'informal care'?

These distinctions are important as the role and contribution of informal care in the provision of welfare has, until recently, been largely neglected both by policy-makers and social policy academics – 'hidden from history'. Indeed, when Richard Titmuss (1955) wrote his seminal essay on 'The social division of welfare', he failed to acknowledge the contribution of this sector, despite the fact that *'care by families and within communities has long provided the cornerstone of Britain's welfare system'* (Graham 1993b: 124). The contribution of informal care, to the support of the elderly, disabled people and children, has dominated service provision both before and since the development of the modern welfare systems. It is only in the past two decades, however, that this contribution has begun to be recognized by government and academic research – most importantly feminist research, which has highlighted the unrecognized, unremunerated work that women do in providing informal care. This has become even more evident with the development of explicit policies of community care.

A powerful argument for the expansion of this sector, or at the very least for its continuing role, is that family care is 'quality care' and that it respects the wishes of 'dependants'. Part of this concern reflects a very negative image of residential or 'institutional' care in Britain. Thus, the policy of welfare retrenchment and the development of care in the community gained support from the critique of institutional care. However, the idea of community care, which in reality has generally meant care by the family, has been part of government rhetoric since the 1950s and has always been the dominant mode of care. Much of the government's recent emphasis on community care, and the role of informal carers, must be seen as rhetorical; the evidence available indicates that the majority of people do care for their dependent relatives and want to do so (Abbott and Sapsford 1987; Finch 1990), although with the support of formal services (West *et al.* 1984).

Choosing to care

A major impetus behind the increased visibility of informal care has come from feminist academics concerned to point out the gender implications of this form of care, and the viability and desirability of strategies designed to increase still further reliance on this sector. This concern stems from a recognition that women form the majority of carers and that the concentration of women, in this type of unpaid work, has important implications for their personal autonomy and ability to undertake paid work.

The argument for increasing the range of options available to dependent people is a strong one, and for many dependent people care in their own home, or that of their family, is no doubt a preferred option. There are, however, many dependent people who do not wish to live with their family, not least because this may undermine their independence or they fear becoming a burden to their families. In addition to this, we must also consider the implications of the 'quality of care' and the 'choice' argument from the viewpoint of the carer. It is important to recognize that one person's free choice may mean denial of choice to another. As Twigg and Atkin (1995: 7) noted: *'There is an essential duality of focus involved when addressing the issue of care. Caring takes place in a relationship, and one cannot focus on the interests of either the carer or the cared-for person to the exclusion of the other'.*

Taking on the care of a dependent relative, does change the lives of those who take on the caring role and the lives of other members of the family, not just at the time but for the foreseeable future. There are financial, social and emotional implications. The wages that the female carer earned or may have earned in the future will be lost, other members of the family may have to turn down promotion or overtime, outside contact with other relatives or friends may be severely curtailed or completely foregone, and the carer will have less time and energy to devote to the care – including the 'emotional care' – of the rest of the family. Even when support and other services are available, carers may be reluctant to ask for them or may not even know they exist (Abbott 1982). In research carried out by Abbott and Sapsford (1987a) in a new town, a mother who had to carry her 13-year-old daughter everywhere, had to wait until she fell down the stairs and injured herself, before she was offered a stair lift. The same mother found that respite care had to be booked so long in advance that she could rely on it only when social and physical exhaustion meant that she felt she could no longer cope. It was also evident that parents often did not understand, or know about, the full range of services available to them. Normalizing lives for dependent people may in effect de-normalize the lives of carers.

The tendency to present informal care as the only alternative to large, monolithic and segregative Victorian-styled institutions, rather than seeing the two as polar ends of a continuum of possibilities, may have served a useful ideological function in pricking the conscience of families and reaffirming their 'duty' to care. When feminists have suggested that community care need not mean family care, they are not proposing a return to Victorian standards but the development of new forms of residential care which would enable both carers and the cared-for to lead as independent and 'normal' lives as possible: *'enabling people to maintain links with relatives or friends to whom they are emotionally close, that is, people who care "about" them; but ... removing the compulsion to perform the labour of caring'* (Finch 1990: 55).

Hilary Graham (1993b) acknowledged the emphasis in feminist perspectives on the providers of care, often to the neglect of the experiences of those receiving care – a point picked up by Morris (1993), who was fiercely critical of feminists for failing to consider the needs of disabled people. Morris argued that the focus on carers' needs has sidelined the fundamental question of why dependency arises in the first place (and hence why carers are required). The result has been a failure to challenge the social and economic factors which disabled people have to confront, and an unwitting collusion with the creation of dependency (Morris 1993: 47). For many women in particular, the roles of carer and cared-for cannot easily be separated, as they typically shift between the two and at times women may perform both roles simultaneously (as many disabled or pregnant women do).

In addition to feminist concerns about the desirability of increased reliance on informal care from the viewpoint of carers, there are some concerns about the viability of such policies. Demographic changes, resulting in increased levels of dependency, coupled with changes in family structure, and particularly increased levels of divorce, separation and lone parenting, together result in higher dependency ratios (with fewer women caring for more dependants) and more tenuous kinship links. What obligations will a woman have towards an ex-mother-in-law or a step-daughter, for example?

Caring for and caring about

It is important to distinguish between 'caring for' and 'caring about'. The former refers to the actual tasks of caring, and does not require an affective or emotional bond. Both formal and informal carers may care *for* someone. 'Caring *about*' is to be concerned and can be expressed in a caring relationship and by taking care of someone. It is often assumed that informal carers care about the cared-for person as well as caring for them. This is not always the case; care may be undertaken out of a feeling of obligation or even resignation. Alternatively, someone may be cared *about* but not cared *for* by relatives; there is some evidence that men may, for example, buy in services rather than provide them themselves.

According to Dalley (1988), traditional views about women's roles fuse these two aspects for women so that in order to demonstrate genuine 'care' they have to both care *about* and also care *for* dependent people. Many women (and child carers) are therefore not free to choose 'not to care' for a dependent relative, without either putting that person at risk or damaging their own identity. It is for this reason that Land (1991: 18) refers to women's assigned caring roles as an example of 'compulsory altruism'. Men, on the other hand, are more often able to demonstrate that they 'care about' dependent family members by taking financial responsibility, perhaps by providing the family home or buying in services. They are not expected to 'care for' the personal and domestic needs of the dependent person to the same extent. In other words, a male relative (particularly when he is not an elderly spouse of the dependent person) is not expected to do the 'hands on caring', such as toileting or bathing, nor to give up his work role to care for a dependant on a full-time basis. Men, far more than women, have the choice of whether or not to be involved in informal care and, for men, involvement in such caring roles *translates most visibly and immediately into the loss of male privilege ... the privilege of being uninvolved* (Saraceno 1987: 200).

The costs of informal care

Politicians, and other policy-makers, are well aware of the ways in which community care depends on the work of informal carers, and assume that families should, and will, want to take on these responsibilities. Indeed, it is explicitly recognized that if the care of dependent groups provided by families and other informal carers were to be fully costed, it would be extremely expensive. Recent estimates suggest that carers save the government £34 billion each year (Hirst M. 1999; Pickard *et al.* 2003).

On the whole, government policy continues to assume that much care will be provided by families, but also recognizes that informal carers need support. The community care reforms introduced in 1990 brought the role of informal carers into view:

> *The Government acknowledges that the great bulk of community care is provided by friends, family and neighbours. The decision to take on a caring role is never an easy one. However, many people make the choice and it is right that they should be able to play their part in looking after those close to them. But it must be recognised that carers need help and support if they are to continue to carry out their role.*

> (DoH 1989b)

Similar official recognition can be found in recent statements about self-care and the development of policies to provide greater support to carers (see below). The financial benefits and allowances available to carers have improved since the 1980s, when they were severely criticized as being inadequate (Glendinning 1983; Buckle 1984). However, in addition to the inadequacy of welfare support, carers also suffer additional financial costs in terms of lost earnings. Both female and male care givers are less likely to be in paid employment than similar non-care givers, and when they are in work they earn significantly less, leading to additional financial burdens and greater inequalities (Carmichael and Charles 2003).

However, one may go beyond the simple lack of finance to argue that community care necessarily imposes a special burden on women (Wilkin 1979; Finch and Groves 1983; Abbott and Sapsford 1987; Murphy *et al.* 1997). The actual implementation of the policy means, for example, that the mother of a child with disabilities is expected to take on the main burden of caring for that child. The developments in community care policy have not in practice meant a shift of resources from hospitals to the local community, but a shift in the type of labour employed; paid, trained, professional labour (or, at the very least, paid) is replaced by low paid, poorly trained female formal carers or unpaid, untrained, seemingly cheap labour in the form of informal carers. The burden is much greater than that experienced by the mother caring for a 'normal' young child: the 'disabled child' goes on requiring fairly intensive and regular care, long past the time when 'normal' children have become relatively independent. The mother may in fact become tied to a lifelong 'disabled child'. She will no longer be able to enjoy the normal life experiences of other women – relative independence when the children have grown up, possibly returning to paid employment – and this will affect not only her, but also the rest of the family, including siblings of the child. For example, research (Abbott and Sapsford 1987) has shown that mothering children with severe learning difficulties presents three special kinds of problem which militate against normal employment.

First, depending on the degree of the child's difficulties, more intensive child care may be required than would be the case with a 'normal' child, and this may make it difficult to find babysitters or childminders or, to persuade relatives to share the care. Second, timing has to be very precise as the children must be met from school, or the school bus, and cannot be left to their own devices during the school holidays. In the end, school times come to dominate the lives of such mothers even more tyrannically than is normally the case. Third, the process is protracted long beyond the normal. Many mothers would not leave their 5-year-old children to come home from school to an empty house. Few, however, would still need to be there to receive a 15-year-old, with the prospect of still needing to be there when the they reach 25-years-old.

Thus, while successive governments, since the 1950s, have advocated community care for dependent people, they have not provided adequate facilities for this to become a meaningful way of caring for them. Coupled with community apathy and even hostility, this has meant that care becomes the responsibility of the family (and specifically of the female carer). An apparently progressive and humanitarian policy turns out, in practice, to make little difference to the lives of dependent people. What it does do is to impose additional burdens – both economic and social – on informal carers.

There are significant changes in the demography of caring, demonstrating a rise in spouse care-giving, while underlining the continued importance of intergenerational care-giving by daughters and daughters-in-law. Studies using data from the General Household Surveys in 1985, 1990 and 1995, have highlighted the increasing intensification of caregiving, with carers undertaking more hours of care each week and helping with more personal care and mobility (Hirst 2001).

Approximately 5.7 million people provide informal care with nearly 2 million to someone in the same household. Some 15 per cent of people, over the age of 16, provide care for someone who is sick, disabled or elderly. The care they provide includes personal care, giving medicine, physical help, providing company and 'keeping an eye out'. Nearly a third of carers provide over 20 hours or more of care each week and it is estimated that there are also some 20–50,000 young carers, caring for a parent or other family member (Arksey 2002; Pickard et al. 2003).

Arber and Ginn's (1991) analysis of the 1990 General Household Survey data indicates that, although women provide more informal care than men, men do provide considerably more of it than the literature has until now assumed. In terms of co-residential care, men provide care for spouses and children, and non-married men provide care for parents living in the same household. Married women, as well as providing care for husbands and children, are also the main providers of care to parents and parents-in-law. Women provide considerably more care for dependants living in another household, particularly married women. Twice as many women as men provide personal care, but there is evidence of a strong cross-sex taboo in the provision of personal care except for spouses and children. It is also less acceptable for an informal carer to provide personal care for friends, neighbours and non-close relations.

Children as informal carers

While much attention has been focused on women as carers, more recently concern has been expressed about children caring for disabled parents, though there is little evidence available on the numbers involved or the extent of care undertaken. However, increased awareness of this issue has been prompted by the implementation of both the Children Act 1989, which defines and clarifies the rights of children, and the National Health and Community Care Act 1990, which requires local authorities to take account of the needs of carers. Aldridge and Becker (1993) undertook an ethnographic 'quality of life' study of young carers which sought to reveal the impact of caring on children's educational and psychosocial development and the opportunities available to them. The study found some 300 young carers (defined as carers under the age of 18, providing primary care for a sick or disabled relative in the home) in Nottinghamshire. The findings of the study presented a disturbing picture of children caring for a parent often suffering from a degenerative disease (such as multiple sclerosis or muscular dystrophy), with caring tasks ranging from light cleaning, washing up and preparation of meals to financial transactions, lifting, toileting and dealing with incontinence. The young carers interviewed expressed a need for additional support in three key areas: improved formal services, better information and more emotional support.

Studies on young carers, undertaken by Carers UK and the Children's Society over a ten-year period from 1995, have shown an improvement in support, but over a quarter of secondary school-aged carers are experiencing problems attending school, and only 18 per cent have received an assessment of their needs. Girls are more likely than boys to be carers, and nearly a fifth of young carers provide intimate personal care. Overall, 70 per cent of those needing care in lone parent families are mothers, while in two parent families, 46 per cent of those receiving care are siblings. One third of young carers provide care for between 10 and 20 hours a week, 18 per cent have been caring for between six and ten years, and a fifth of young carers and their families receive no support except that provided by a specialist young carers project (Dearden and Becker 2004).

Carers from ethnic minority communities

The needs of black carers have also been highlighted in research. Atkin and Rollings (1992) indicated the barriers that exist to black people getting the services they need. They argue that not only are black people not offered support services, but those they *are* offered are often inappropriate. They indicate that services need to be made accessible and acceptable to black people. Service provision is often based on stereotyped and ill informed views of what the black community needs. It is often assumed, for example, that elderly Asian people will be cared for by their extended families, although research shows that this is not the case (Katbamna *et al.* 2004). Assumptions about the ability of women to take on unpaid care work may apply even less in black communities – where it is more normal for women to have full-time paid employment – than in white communities. The needs of the black community will grow as its age structure begins to resemble that of the white majority. In particular, poor service support, experienced by carers in general, is exacerbated for carers in ethnic minority communities where services are culturally inappropriate or inflexible and often mired by racism (Askham *et al.* 1995, Katbamna *et al.* 2004).

Informal care and state policy

Over the past 15 years, the nature of 'informal care' and the organizational and policy environment have changed considerably. Supporting carers has become an important policy goal, and there is a greater recognition of the role that carers play in providing essential support to people with a disability, long-term illness or general infirmity. While this reflects, at one level, a concern about the public expenditure implications of an ageing population, it is not just a simple concern to contain public expenditure, but also reflects a broader ideological move to redraw the boundaries between personal and state involvement in welfare. The ensuing debate about the impact of post-war collectivism on personal responsibility and its role in the creation of a 'dependency culture', has led increasingly to a call for a return to individual responsibility. In practice, this has meant arguing for familial responsibility for the care of dependants. Not only was family and informal care seen to be cheaper, it was also promoted as being a morally superior form of care. As the Griffiths Report on community care put it, *'families, friends, neighbours and other local people provide the majority of care ... this is as it should be'* (Griffiths 1988: 5). Baldock and Ungerson (1991: 148) have illustrated the use of moral judgements to justify reliance upon informal care. They argue that the proposed dichotomy – in its crudest form – is that the 'formal' system substitutes skill for tenderness, is contractual, hierarchical, subject to rigid divisions of labour laid down through collective bargaining procedures, with bureaucratically managed resources in scarce supply; in contrast, it is suggested, the 'informal' system is spontaneous, loving, flexible, and untrammelled by ideas of rigid divisions of labour (except, though this is rarely spelt out, the sexual division of labour). To conclude, care in the community is seen as good, care at home better and care by the family, as best.

Government policies, of community care and decarceration, obviously have an impact on the role and nature of informal carers. There has been a policy shift in favour of an explicit recognition of, and commitment, to the promotion of informal care. Community care policy over the last decade has encouraged statutory agencies to support informal carers – this was explicitly embraced in the *National Health Service and Community Care Act 1990*. Government policies have also encouraged a shift in responsibility from the NHS to social services departments, and from institutional to domiciliary care. However, since this shift was not initially accompanied by a growth in community services, this meant that informal carers were expected to take on a greater burden of care (Means and Smith 1998).

Supporting carers has become an increasingly important element of government policy. In 1995 the Conservative government passed the *The Carers (Recognition and Services) Act*, this was followed in 1999 with the Labour Government's *Caring for Carers: A National Strategy for Carers* (DoH 1999d). This recognized the need for primary health care teams to improve communication with carers, provide support to them and, with the consent of the person cared for, work collaboratively with them. Alongside this policy objective, the Labour government also established national guidance requiring primary care and social services to '*Provide carers with the support and services to maintain their health and the person they are caring for . . . [and] ensure that systems are in place to identify patients and service users who are or who have carers*' (DoH 1998c: 24). Initially this requirement was to establish mechanisms for identifying carers by April 2001, but subsequently the timing was amended to April 2002, and then to 2004. The NHS has also been set explicit standards and guidelines for supporting carers and these have, most recently, been incorporated into the NSFs which apply to both primary and secondary care services.

The *National Service Framework for Mental Health* (DoH 1999e) contained a specific standard relating to carers. Standard 6 is '*To ensure health and social services assess the needs of carers who provide regular and substantial care for those with severe mental illness, and provide care to meet their needs*'. The NSF notes that about half of those people suffering with severe mental illness live with family or friends, and emphasizes the vital role that carers play in looking after people with mental health problems. The *National Service Framework for Coronary Heart Disease* (DoH 2000b) also emphasizes the important role carers play '*in tackling the causes of CHD, in supporting people who are suffering from CHD – including those in need of palliative care – and in providing emergency care for people suffering heart attacks*' (para. 1.17). The NSF requires health and social care agencies to involve carers in discharge and service planning arrangements.

Similarly the *National Service Framework for Older People* (DoH 2001e) places great emphasis on the need to support carers of older people. The framework explicitly sets standards of care which include recognizing and supporting the role of carers. Service providers are required to meet certain standards which include '*providing information so the service user and, where appropriate their carer, can be involved in decisions about their own care*' (para. 2.5) and when undertaking assessments:

> *Carers should be identified and offered either the opportunity to be involved in the older person's assessment, or where it appears appropriate, informed of their right as part of a holistic assessment to an assessment in their own right under the Carers and Disabled Children Act 2000. Guidance on carers' assessments is to be found in the practice guidance on the Carers and Disabled Children Act 2000, and the Practitioner's Guide to A Carer's Assessment.*
>
> (para. 2.37)

In relation to the development of intermediate care the NSF makes the following provision:

An integrated multi-professional record should be used by all members of the team. It should set clear goals and timescales for the individual care plan, and a management plan following discharge from the service. The care plan should demonstrate user and carer involvement in decision-making and each user and carers should hold their own copies of the care plan.

(para. 3.28)

The changes provide unprecedented opportunities for health and social care agencies to support carers through a proper assessment of need. The key focus of these relationships will be within primary care, and there is a further requirement in the NSF for older persons, for PCTs to establish systems to explore user and carer experience by April 2004, and in the NSF for mental health, to establish procedures for identifying carers. However, these proposals raise issues about how carers are to be identified and recorded by service providers, and how informed consent can be established to allow the sharing of information (between professionals, the carer and the person being cared for), allowing the involvement of carers in decision-making processes about care plans.

Increasingly, the state has provided financial support for carers. As suggested above, while these financial benefits do not compensate for the full cost of caring, the introduction of new allowances has been an important element of state support for carers. State income support for carers was non-existent until the 1970s; those who were not entitled to a universal benefit (mainly the elderly) were dependent on means tested benefits, to the extent that they met eligibility criteria. In the 1970s, invalid care allowance was introduced, a means tested benefit for people under retirement age who gave up paid employment to care for a dependant. Married women were unable to claim this benefit until 1986, when the European Court ruled that this amounted to sex discrimination, and the British government was forced to include them. The benefit is paid only to full-time carers, the person being cared for has to be claiming attendance allowance/disability living allowance, and the rate is equivalent to that of non-householder income support. Changes, in the 1990s, to benefit payments with the introduction of the carer's allowance have improved the financial status of many carers.

There are still concerns about paying informal carers for their role. While accepting that any distinction between informal and formal care, based on assumptions that the motivations of informal carers are qualitatively different (reflecting kinship obligation and a 'labour of love' as opposed to a contractual agreement), has always been problematic, the development of forms of remuneration for carers further muddies the waters. It becomes increasingly difficult to argue that formal and informal care are substantially and qualitatively different: *'they both contain elements of labour and love'* (Ungerson 1995: 32). In addition to schemes involving direct payment to carers, there is a second, more popular, trend in the provision of cash benefits directly to dependent individuals, in the expectation that they will use the money to purchase their own care (the community care allowance/disability living allowance paid to severely disabled people in Britain is intended to enable the purchase of services). Austria is currently turning over its entire care system to high cash payments to care recipients, so that they can buy in their own care. Both forms of payment have different implications for the autonomy of carers. While both schemes constitute an explicit recognition *'of the work involved in domestic caring labour and provide the basis for carers' autonomy and a modicum of financial independence ... the systems are often gendered in conception and are certainly gendered in consequence'* (Ungerson 1995: 39).

Of course, there is no guarantee that recipients will use the benefits in the way intended (i.e. to buy in care), nor that they will pay appropriate wages. Indeed, Ungerson notes the growing concern in Europe over the development of unregulated 'grey labour' with no guarantees of minimum working conditions, pay levels or workers' rights. Furthermore, the symbolic nature of these payments may be used to encourage carers to remain in the private domain rather than entering paid work. As such, this extra pressure on women to give up paid work may be *'entrapping rather than liberating'* (Ungerson 1995: 48). This is especially true of payments channelled through care recipients, where no minimum wage rates or conditions are specified. Such payments also tend to reinforce reliance on one single carer, as they typically only identify one person to receive the whole benefit.

Schemes involving payment of informal carers, thus, raise similar issues to those discussed in relation to paid voluntarism:

1 How does the payment of informal carers affect the relationship between the supply of formal and informal labour? Will it affect the level of funding for care workers employed in the public and commercial sectors?
2 What are the implications of payment for the rights, citizenship and quality of life of carers and those receiving care? In particular, how does the public funding of informal care affect the quality of carers' working conditions and the quality of care provided? How do different systems of payment affect the autonomy of carers and the recipients of care?

Carers relationships with health and social care services

Research on carers has identified a number of concerns over the relationship between carers and service providers (Henwood 1998), particularly with the primary health care team. There are two distinct elements to this relationship. The first is as a carer supporting the cared-for person. With an increasing emphasis on primary and community care, and a growing trend towards supporting people with chronic illnesses and long-term needs, in their own homes, there has been a blurring of informal and formal care roles. An increasing burden is being placed on carers in that there is a need to improve communication between carers in that professionals (Kirk and Glendinning 1998; Pickard *et al.* 2000; Walker and Dewar 2001). In particular carers want information, support, access to services and coordination of services, but practice staff do not see this as their role (Simon and Kendrick 2001).

The second element of the relationship relates to the health of the carer. Caring for another person with a disability or health care problem has been shown to be harmful to the health of the carer themselves. Henwood (1998) found that 52 per cent of the carers she surveyed had been treated for stress-related illnesses, and 51 per cent reported a physical injury as a result of caring. Simon and Kendrick (2001) report that studies of carers of stroke patients, show that 40 per cent suffer from psychological health problems. One American study suggested that all-cause mortality for carers may be increased by up to 60 per cent (Schultz and Beach 1999). Yet carers often have poor relationships with their general practice. Research has identified a number of problems relating to:

- the non-identification of carers by the health team members and other professionals;
- the fact that carers are seen as low priority by many practices and professionals (Walker and Dewar 2001);
- poor interagency collaboration – especially between general practice and other agencies;
- the fear that if carers' needs are addressed by practices, it will open the floodgates of demand – especially as many of the problems faced by carers do not fit in to the medical model of treatment (Yee and Blunden 1995).

In fact carers' access to health care is complicated by their role as carer. Andersen *et al.* (1983) identified a range of factors which limit people's access to health care services, including socio-economic status, access to transport and travel distance. Carers will be similarly limited but are also further dependent on these limitations as they affect the person they care for as well. Thus carers' 'access-entry' and 'in-system access' (to secondary care and other services) is severely restricted. For example, carers would require services to be delivered to the person they care for if they needed to visit hospital themselves. Carers' access to health care will be further differentiated by their age, location, ethnicity and type of health care problem that they (and the person they are caring for) are suffering from. Therefore, carers, access to health care is uniquely dependent on the NHS response to both themselves and another person. This acts as a 'double jeopardy' for carers.

Therefore, the context of access for carers is more dynamic and reliant on the access to health and social care/support services of another person, and the way their position as a carer further complicates their ability to access health care services. Many carers are physically limited by not being able to leave the person they care for, or require complex care arrangements before they can leave. Some carers were only able to access their GP and other services or activities, in the two out of eight weeks, when the person they cared for was in respite care – this left six-week periods when their ability to leave their home was severely restricted. For many carers, such restrictions are exacerbated by additional caring or family responsibilities. Multiple responsibilities are a particular problem for women who are the majority of carers (Hirst 2001). Assumptions made by service providers about the normal role of caring further exacerbates these problems (see Box 9.1).

Box 9.1   Relevance of caring relationships for service providers

Twigg and Atkin's (1995) study of service support for carers, found that support does not follow simple needs-related criteria (in terms of level of disablement, etc.), but rather socially constructed notions of carers' needs. Here the nature of the kinship relationship, the age and gender of the carer together underpin the attitudes of both service providers and users (including both carers and dependants). In terms of the assumptions of service providers, Twigg and Atkin (1995: 24) found that: *'One of the ways in which gender assumptions were significant was in relation to the visibility of the carer. Actions that were noteworthy in a male carer and resulted in him being recognised as such, were passed over when performed by a female, subsumed under her general domestic role'.* Furthermore, service response varied depending on the relationship in question: *'Service providers would go to more extreme lengths to support the continuance of caring where it was between spouses ... Where the cared-for person is a parent, the assumptions are different. Privacy is less strongly defended, and there is a greater tradition of autonomy and separation'* (Twigg and Atkin 1995: 19).

Many carers still remain critical of the support they receive, and as we have seen for particular groups of carers, such as young people and carers from ethnic minorities, the situation is even worse. Developments in community-based care have thrown the role and position of carers into sharper light and, with more recent moves to promote self-care have placed increased importance on examining the role of informal carers and the role of the welfare state, especially health and social care services, in providing appropriate and adequate support.

Self-care

While there are a number of definitions of self-care the DoH has defined it as:

> *the care taken by individuals towards their own health and well-being, [including] the care extended to their children, family, friends and others in neighbourhoods and local communities. Self care includes the actions individuals and carers take for themselves, their children and their families, to stay fit and maintain good physical and mental health; meet social, emotional and psychological needs; prevent illness or accidents; care for minor ailments and long-term conditions; and maintain health and well-being after an acute illness or discharge from hospital.*
>
> *(DoH 2005a: 1)*

There is a growing recognition of the need to provide greater support to patients with long-term and chronic health conditions, and to help them take care of their conditions more effectively. As suggested at the beginning of this chapter, most care is provided by individuals, families and local communities (see Figure 9.1).

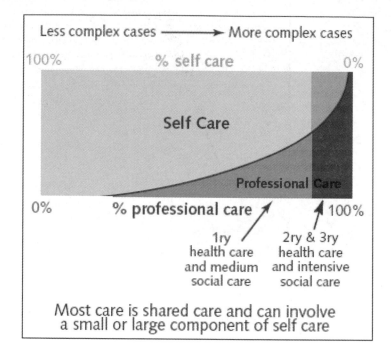

Figure 9.1 Provision of care
Source: DoH 2005a

The British Household Surveys of 2001 and 2002 and the Health Survey for England 2001, suggest that over 50 per cent of the population have some form of chronic health problem. People with chronic disease are more likely to be users of the health system, accounting for some 80 per cent of all GP consultations and 10 per cent of inpatients account for 55 per cent of inpatient days (British Household Panel Survey 2001). Older people are more likely to have multiple chronic problems and be intensive users of health care services, and '*15 per cent of under 5s and 20 per cent of the 5–15 age group, are reported to have a long-term condition*' (Wilson *et al.* 2005: 658). In addition, it is also estimated that as much as 40 per cent of general practice consultations and 70 per cent of accident and emergency visits are for minor ailments that could be taken care of by people themselves (DoH 2005a). The benefits of supporting self-care have been shown to be improved health outcomes, a better quality of life for those with long-term conditions, increased patient satisfaction and effective use of a huge resource to the NHS – patients and the public (DoH 2005a).

The DoH has been developing a stream of policy-related work on self-care for some years, and self-care is identified within a number of NSFs. The DoH is keen to see research, developed in this area, building on existing work particularly relating to how the NHS supports self-care (DoH 2004c, 2005c, 2005f, 2005g). Initial programmes of work in the NHS include NHS Direct, the Expert Patients Programme, work on long-term care and the establishment of the working in partnership projects – the self-care skills training for health care professionals project and the self-care for people project (www.wipp.nhs.uk/). In Scotland, similar proposals are being developed as part of the national framework for service change in the Scottish NHS (NHS Scotland 2005).

There is widespread public demand for increasing support for self-care, though many people already engage in self-care (DoH 2004c, 2005a, 2005h). However, inter-country comparisons suggest that the UK NHS is poor at providing support for self-care, and individuals require the confidence and knowledge to successfully embark on self-care, with different demographic groups, such as older people, requiring more support than others (Ellins and Coulter 2005; Coulter 2006). Existing mechanisms for developing support for self-care are through education, training and commissioning activities. To date, there is little evidence to show that PCTs have utilized the flexibilities offered by primary care contracts to develop greater support for people with long-term conditions (Wilson *et al.* 2005). In a recent survey, PCTs did not have strategic approaches to support self-care, and a major area of work activity tended to be subsumed into a number of work streams with no coordination. Following their analysis of US Managed Care organizations' approaches to organizing care for people with chronic conditions, Dixon *et al.* (2004: 225) concluded that *'More evidence is needed on the best ways to identify high risk patients and the cost and effects of multi-faceted management of high risk patients and disease-specific management programmes for lower risk patients.'*

Recent changes to the GMS contract quality and outcomes framework, provide financial incentives for primary care to support initiatives, such as self-care support interventions to reduce demand in primary care. The DoH is in further discussions with the BMA on focusing the quality outcomes framework (QOF), more on supporting self-care. In addition, the introduction of practice-based commissioning is seen by the government as a key tool in developing NHS approaches to supporting self-care. To date, however, there is no evidence to demonstrate how commissioners are addressing self-care, nor how existing commissioners, the PCTs, are taking a whole systems approach to developing self-care support (Wilson *et al.* 2005; DoH 2005h). Supporting self-care also requires working with social care commissioners, as services will need to be developed across the health and social care spectrum.

Two recent DoH reports (2004d, 2005i), have highlighted the usefulness of support networks, education and skills training for enhancing self-care among people (Wilson *et al.* 2005). In addition the National Primary Care Research and Development Centre has conducted a review of the expert patients programme (Kennedy *et al.* 2005a, 2005b), and Leeds Metropolitan University is currently evaluating the 'working in partnership self-care projects' in a number of PCTs. Other approaches have included specific projects designed to provide support for people with long-term conditions (see Box 9.2).

Box 9.2 Examples of schemes to reduce prescribing in general practice and increase patients' understanding of medicines

Planned face-to-face review of medicines, for people with long-term conditions, can help them care for themselves by understanding their medicines and taking them more effectively.

Recent research has shown that patients suffering adverse reaction to medicines use 4 per cent of hospital beds (Pirmohamed *et al.* 2004), and a review of medicines can help prevent this from occurring, by identifying potential interactions and side-effects and taking action beforehand to resolve them. Medicines Partnership has published *Focus on Your Medicines*, a patient guide to medicine review. This is designed to help patients to get the maximum benefit from a review, by preparing their questions in advance. Some 400,000 copies of the guide have already been distributed via PCTs. In September 2004, a specific version of the guide for people with epilepsy was published, including an epilepsy diary for patients to complete prior to a review.

The guides have been extensively tested with patients, who felt that these would really help them to get more out of a review. Copies are available from the Medicines Partnership website at www.medicines-partnership.org.

Source: DoH (2005a)

Conclusion

Informal care – that is, care by relatives and friends, but predominantly close relatives – is the major form of welfare in Britain and always has been. The family is the major institutional location of care and welfare for the majority of the population. The main providers of care are women, as they meet the welfare and care needs of their husband and children, as well as elderly relatives and adult children with care needs. The British classic welfare state was built on the assumption that the nuclear family of husband, wife and dependent children was not only how people lived their lives but, how they *should* live them. Women, it was assumed, were and would be financially dependent on their husbands and would meet the care needs not only of their partners and their children, but of ageing parents as well (Abbott and Wallace 1992). The subsequent development of policies on community care have built on this foundation and assumed that women are willing and available to take on additional caring roles for dependent relatives, friends and neighbours.

We have also seen that women are not the only carers; men and children also take on the burden of caring. However, there is not the same assumed relationship, as with women, between natural virtues and the caring role, and so not the same moral pressure to care. Women, it is assumed, are natural carers and, therefore, should be able to take on caring roles and should wish to do so. Women who decline to do so are seen as unnatural and uncaring. For women there can be no separation, as there can be for men, between 'caring about' and 'caring for'.

Summary

- Understanding the lay perspective and how patients, users, carers and the public in general, contribute to health and social services is increasingly important.
- Lay people are equally important in terms of producing health and social care outcomes.
- Informal care and the notion of a 'welfare society' has underpinned and determined all other forms of welfare provision throughout British social history.
- 'Informal care' is a concept used to refer to the work done, mainly within the home, in supporting people at various levels of dependency.
- This work is undertaken, primarily by women, on a largely unremunerated basis with important implications for their financial and personal autonomy.
- Recent years have witnessed the growth of fiscal and ideological pressures to further increase the relative contribution of this sector, via policies of welfare retrenchment and the promotion of 'community care'. In spite of the rhetoric, however, there is little evidence of a substantial shift in resources to enable carers to shoulder this additional responsibility.
- Gendered assumptions about caring roles permeate policy in this area, resulting in discrimination in the allocation of services which substantially increases the burden placed upon women.
- The development of forms of remuneration for informal carers raises complex and contradictory questions; on the one hand they represent an acknowledgement of caring as a form of 'work', but on the other they reinforce caring roles and perpetuate labour market discrimination.

Further reading

Baggott, R., Allsop, J. and Jones, K. (2005) *Speaking for Patients and Carers.* Basingstoke: Palgrave/Macmillan.

Balloch, S. and Taylor, M. (2001) *Partnership Working: Policy and Practice.* Bristol: Policy Press.

Coulter, A. (2002) *The Autonomous Patient: Ending Paternalism in Medical Care.* London: The Nuffield Trust.

Wood, B. (2000) *Patient Power? Patients Associations in Britain and America.* Buckingham: Open University Press.

THE ROLE OF HEALTH AND SOCIAL CARE PROFESSIONALS

- Introduction
- Social work
- Nursing
- Health visiting
- Midwifery
- Medicine
- Professional regulation
- Modernization
- Recruitment issues
- Conclusion
- Summary
- Further reading

Introduction

This chapter will outline the occupational histories of three of the health and social care professions, namely nursing, social work and medicine, with a brief mention of midwifery, health visiting and the allied health professions. The period covered is primarily the nineteenth and twentieth centuries, when these occupations either formed or started to organize themselves in a recognizably modern form. Nursing and social work have been termed semi-professions (Etzioni 1969), since they do not have the same autonomy or prestige as the traditional professions, such as law and medicine, and their knowledge base is less well developed (Becher 1994). Henkel (1994) considers that the nature of social work makes it the most open to state intervention. The work of adult and children's nurses may be seen as an extension of women's caring work in the domestic sphere (James 1992; Dominelli 1997), whereas mental health and learning disability nursing have different origins, and a greater proportion of men in the workforce. Readers should note that some of the language used in this chapter (such as 'mental defectives' and 'lunatics') while offensive now, was the language used at the time, including in legislation.

As discussed in Chapter 2, healing work has taken place in England throughout history, mainly in the home, but also in the monasteries before their dissolution by Henry VIII in the sixteenth century. A few royal hospitals, such as St Thomas's and St Bartholomew's (Bart's), were rebuilt in the sixteenth century. Physicians, much of whose knowledge was theoretical and many of whose cures were ineffectual or actually harmful, have existed since the Middle Ages, together with bone-setters and barber-surgeons. The surgeons separated from the barbers in 1745 and many combined surgery with being an apothecary, a dispenser and seller of drugs; they were therefore the precursors of GPs. Most occupations were regulated, since it was illegal to practise without having served an apprenticeship. Until the development of adequate hygiene and the understanding of the control of infection, hospital care was not only ineffective but likely to be fatal, so was largely confined to those who were homeless, mentally ill or otherwise unable to stay in their own homes.

By the eighteenth century, the growth of cities led to greater inequality and social need, but also greater philanthropy and the growth of professions. It was also an important age for the development of science and medicine, which aided by the 1832 Anatomy Act, made the dissection of corpses legal. The five London teaching hospitals: Guy's, the Westminster, St George's, the London and the Middlesex, were founded between 1720 and 1745. Other similar hospitals were built in other cities and county towns, supported by subscriptions from local philanthropists, and so admission was on the recommendation of a subscriber. The doctors had unpaid positions, deriving their income from private practice elsewhere and from teaching students; other staff were few and were mainly servants. Medical students also took on what were later seen as nursing duties, such as bed-making and dressing wounds. Medical teaching was a combination of apprenticeship, with some theory, taught in private medical schools.

Nursing, midwifery, health visiting and social work were transformed from predominantly unpaid philanthropic women's work in the nineteenth century, into paid occupational groups. The nineteenth century saw the establishment of much of the infrastructure we take for granted today, such as public health and local government. Record-keeping, such as the census and registration of births, marriages and deaths, were developed in the UK in the mid-nineteenth century, thus making, apparent for the first time, the great discrepancies in mortality between the classes and between different regions. In the latter half of the nineteenth century, concerns were expressed about the physical deterioration of the population, underpinned by Darwin's recent (1859) theory of natural selection, and fuelled by the anticipation of war with Germany. Rose (1985, 1989) considers that in the twentieth century, psychological regulation added to physical and moral regulation, as well as advances in the social sciences, psychology and biology, provided the knowledge base for these new professions (see Box 10.1).

Box 10.1   Professions and semi-professions

Until the 1970s, the main theory about professions was the attribute or trait approach, which assumes that it is possible to draw up a list of fixed criteria which distinguish between professions and other occupations. Becker (1970) identifies six criteria in this approach, which originated with Flexner:

1 Predominantly intellectual activity with great personal responsibility.
2 Based on great knowledge, rather than routine.
3 Practical, rather than academic or theoretical.
4 Techniques which can be taught.
5 Strong internal organization.
6 Motivated by altruism.

Although this theoretical approach is no longer used in sociology, it underpins the professionalizing strategy in nursing, for example, the creation of theories of nursing, and the move into higher education.

Freidson's (1971) analysis of medicine stated that the only clear criterion of a profession is autonomy, which is conferred by the state. His analysis applies more clearly to medicine in the USA than to either the UK or much of Europe, both of which have greater state involvement.

Dingwall (1977) argues that there is no stable definition of what a profession is – we need to examine how the word is used in practice, how the members of an occupation establish their professional boundaries, and how they define themselves in relation to other, related occupations.

Davies (1995) claims that the traditional concept of a profession is historically specific to the eighteenth and nineteenth century, and that the process of professional formation cannot now be emulated by other occupations (even if they wish to do so, given the social distance from its clients which medicine created). Gender is also an important factor, since many of the semi-professions have been largely populated by women.

Social work

Social work is a creation of modern industrialized societies; however, societies in general require institutions and structures to regulate and care for their most vulnerable members. The caring role has generally been performed by religious institutions and, to a certain extent, by the feudal system in England. By the Tudor period, there existed a range of statutes to control beggars and vagabonds, and the system started to shift towards more secular provision, which drew a distinction between those who were, or were not, deserving of help. The first Poor Law was passed in 1536. In the eighteenth century, as industrialization resulted in the growth of poverty, the number of workhouses increased greatly, supplemented by 'outdoor relief' for the poor in their own homes. The latter was curtailed by the contentious 1834 Poor Law Amendment Act, which confirmed the principle of 'less eligibility', i.e. that assistance from the parish should not be better than the pay of the poorest labourer.

Social work developed in a piecemeal fashion from Victorian voluntary work and was seen as a suitable occupation for women. Middle-class women were just beginning to emerge from the separation of 'the two spheres', in which men had patriarchal authority and a public role, whereas women's role was a private one within the home, where they were responsible for the moral welfare of both their children and their husband. Early social work leaders, in both the USA and the UK, communicated with each other and with colleagues in Canada, Australia and New Zealand, but also with nursing pioneers. Their view of society was that of the white middle classes. Industrial capitalism was equated with progress rather than being seen as a cause of poverty, which was largely attributed to fecklessness and unwillingness to change.

The administration of charitable funds was an important part of the late Georgian and Victorian economy, and the Charity Commissioners were established in 1853 to regulate this sector. Then, as now, there were debates about whether financial help led to greater dependence, and a distinction was drawn between the deserving and the undeserving poor. Bodies, such as Dr Barnardo's (1870) and the National Society for the Prevention of Cruelty to Children (1884), were also set up in the same era; prior to the late nineteenth century, there was no legislation to protect children and, in some instances, the relevant animal legislation was used.

Both in the USA and the UK, casework with individuals and families was accompanied by groupwork and community work in a variety of settings; only the first has survived, however. The probation service had the clearest mandate (the 1907 Probation Offenders Act). The first hospital almoner was appointed in 1895, the original aim being to assess the ability to pay of patients attending voluntary hospitals. The Association of Psychiatric Social Workers was formed in 1929. Most other social workers were employed in voluntary family welfare organizations.

Lock (1906) suggested that just as doctors needed to be trained, so did 'social physicians', i.e. social workers. Lectures were established by the Charity Organization Society and others in 1895. Formal training was set up in 1903 and moved into the LSE in 1912. Gradually social work moved from philanthropy to a paid occupation with specialisms, such as child care, adoption and fostering, and its religious underpinning decreased. Jordan (1984) identifies a gradual move away from Victorian moral certainty and the belief in self-help, to the belief that people were not free agents, but were shaped by social forces.

Social work grew in importance after the Second World War, as part of the welfare state. Children and child protection were a major focus, particularly since wartime evacuation had made it clear that many children lived in deplorable conditions. The furore over the death of a foster child, Dennis O'Neill, in 1945, provided the main impetus for the 1948 Children Act, which established local authority children's departments. Separate services were provided for elderly people and people with disabilities. However, training was patchy (Younghusband 1978). Entrants to probation work had poor educational standards, whereas other training was highly academic, but did not provide sufficient grounding in fieldwork.

The first integrated training for all types of social work was introduced at the LSE in 1954.

By the 1960s, as social inequalities diminished and general prosperity increased, together with a belief in the possibility of social mobility, the cause of 'problem families' was thought to be not poverty as such, but their inability to cope with society; the remedy, therefore, was the skilled use of personal relationships, rather than material help. The late 1960s was a period of optimism in social affairs. The Seebohm Committee Report (1968: para. 2) recommended services which would promote the well-being of whole communities, and which would be locally accountable. The aim was '*to enable the greatest possible number of individuals to act reciprocally, giving and receiving service for the well-being of the whole community*'. Social work, community work and welfare work were all seen as equally valid.

By the mid 1970s there were two types of social worker. Fieldworkers were the more highly qualified, having at minimum a certificate of qualification in social work (CQSW), introduced in 1972; residential social workers were either unqualified or had a certificate in social services (CSS), introduced in 1976. Social work was reorganized into generic departments bringing services for children together with those for adults, with a generic training overseen by the Central Council for the Education and Training of Social Workers (CCETSW).

The optimism of the period was, however, short-lived, and was eroded by the political and financial instability of the 1970s. Social work came under sustained scrutiny after the death of Maria Colwell in 1973, it highlighted shortcomings in social work practice and in communication between social workers, the police and health workers. The Barclay Committee (1982) recognized that expectations of social work had become unrealistically wide, but also that social workers were insufficiently responsive to the needs of their clients. In its minority reports, the Barclay Committee reflected a debate on whether social work should aim to develop local communities, or whether this was misplaced since communities had become too fragmented in complex industrial societies for this aim to be sustainable.

A new political philosophy, associated with Thatcherism and derived from monetarism in the USA, developed after the Conservative victory in 1979. In the 1980s, the contract culture was introduced in the public sector. At the same time that managerialism was taking hold, social work was developing its own professional value-base, in anti-discriminatory or anti-oppressive practice, as new social movements, such as the gay and lesbian movement, black and ethnic minorities, were recognized (CCETSW 1991). In this approach to practice, individuals are seen both as unique, but also part of a broader pattern of social and political factors. A set of techniques is combined with a set of values, an approach which is also seen in learning disability nursing. As part of the development of this value-base, social work has engaged very specifically in debates about whether it should, or should not, be a profession, particularly from the 1960s to the 1980s when it was influenced by Marxism (Hugman 1998). Radical social work argued that social work could not simply confine itself to individual casework, as that would leave the root cause of poverty and disadvantage untouched. However, Braye and Preston-Shoot (2002) argue that the legislative framework for social work does not provide consistent support for this form of practice.

The CQSW and CSS were merged into the DipSW in 1989. There have, however, continued to be doubts raised about the competence of social workers, and the JM Consulting Review (1999) recommended strengthening the knowledge base. Unlike nursing (Meerabeau 2004), there have been no calls for training to move out of higher education, and given the fragmentation of social work provision, that would probably not be feasible. From 2003, the initial qualification in social work has become a degree, bringing it in line with most of the EU, and social work is now regulated.

Like nursing, few social workers are in private practice, but far more work in small providers. Much of social care takes place in the independent sector, since the Conservative government, in the 1980s, had a policy of reducing the scale of state provision which the current government has continued. As in nursing, regulation and managerial goals have become increasingly important, and senior managers are likely to align themselves with the concerns of the organization (such as controlling costs), rather than the concerns of front-line staff or clients (Cree 2002).

Social work also suffers from a critical press, and difficulty in recruiting (Brindle 1998; Hetherington 2003). Most social work practice is with groups who are not highly valued by the rest of society, and who are increasingly at risk of social exclusion as sectors, such as public housing shrink, and with education and employment becoming more and more achievement-oriented.

Nursing

Nursing has its origins in the religious foundations, but by the nineteenth century was largely the preserve of poor, badly-educated women, either in workhouses or in voluntary hospitals. The reform of nursing in England is largely attributed to Florence Nightingale from 1860; another nurse who practised in the Crimean War at the same time as Florence was the Afro-Caribbean nurse Mary Seacole, who has recently been rediscovered as a role model for black and ethnic minority nurses. Nightingale's work, however, also involved many large-scale reforms outside nursing.

Modern nursing was originally established in the voluntary hospitals; the elite nurses produced in these hospitals then spread the reforms to the Poor Law hospitals, where they supervised care given by working-class women and trainees (Carpenter 1977). Pressure for education reform had been developing since the 1830s. However, no London hospital was keen to have a school of nursing, and Nightingale's hopes that the school at St Thomas's would be autonomous, like a medical school were dashed, when the medical director insisted that it should be under the direction of the matron, Mrs Wardroper. Baly (1995) makes the intriguing suggestion that the 'reforms' were not a break with the past and may have happened too early; had they happened after the 1870 Education Act and the opening of universities to women, there may have been a cadre of educated women to act as tutors and to develop the nursing knowledge base. As it was, nursing knowledge was heavily influenced by the sanitary reforms of the late nineteenth century and by medical knowledge. Nurses were responsible for the surveillance of the patient, and for ensuring that they followed 'doctor's orders'. Most of nursing training took place in small schools attached to hospitals, until many schools amalgamated in the 1980s and then became part of universities in the 1990s under Project 2000. Until the early 1990s, the nursing qualification had no academic currency at all. Project 2000 established education at both diploma and degree level. Wales and Scotland have now moved to degree only (comparable with the other health professions such as physiotherapy), and this is the Royal College of Nursing's preference. However, the majority in England remains at diploma level and there are no clear differences in clinical competences between the two.

The foundations of children's nursing were set in Victorian England when Dr Charles West opened the Hospital for Sick Children, Great Ormond Street, in 1852. Prior to this few children were admitted to hospital for medical care; an estimate undertaken at the time showed 3 per cent of under 10s admitted, but deaths in the same age group accounted for 50 per cent of the deaths in London (Franklin 1964). It wasn't until the late 1800s that changing attitudes towards children, and the changing concepts of childhood underpinned by a greater understanding of children's developmental needs, led to the recognition that children required specialist medical care and services. Changes in societal views about children, led to an acknowledgement that children were valuable and in need of protection, and the establishment of foundling hospitals and dispensaries. This was followed by the growth of hospitals in major cities across the world, specifically for the care of sick children together with the development of medical knowledge and expertise (Seidler 1990). As in adult care, all hospitals were founded as charitable institutions; hospital consultants had responsibility for treatment and care with governing the work of staff. Nurses had no freedom to act on their own initiative but were expected to carry out the doctor's orders (Lomax 1996).

In 1870, Dr Charles West persuaded Catherine Wood, a previous visitor and then a ward sister at Great Ormond Street Hospital, to accept the post of lady superintendent at the hospital. There was no systematic training for children's nurses at that time and Miss Wood, firm in her belief that they needed specialist knowledge and skills, established in 1880 the first formal teaching school for nurses in the UK. This was almost ten years before the training of adult nurses (Miles 1986). Nurse training, based on an apprenticeship system, consisted of two levels of probationary nurses learning through some formal teaching, with observation and delivery of care to children. Great emphasis was placed on diet, hygiene, entertainment and safety, in the belief that they were essential requirements for a child to regain health. The Nurses Registration Act (1919) is discussed later in this chapter. Initially it was decided that nurses who had trained only in a children's hospital should not have their names recorded on the register, nor on the supplementary register that was set up to include the names of male nurses, mental and fever nurses. This led to much debate, but when the Bill was finally presented to the House of Lords, it included a supplementary register containing the names of sick children's nurses. Despite progress there are many who do not believe in the importance of specialist pre-registration education, and the status of children's nurses within the profession, often seeing their qualification as unequal to their adult counterparts (Bradley 2003).

Throughout much of its history, nursing has struggled to recruit, and its academic ambitions have been constrained by workforce requirements. For example, the 1943 Nurses Act established the lower grade of state enrolled nurses, who had a two-year practical training, as one of a series of actions to cover the wartime nursing shortage, and the Wood Report (1947) recommended that training be reduced to two years, of which 18 months would cover all branches. The shortage, however, persisted as the NHS expanded, and Baly (1995) considers that this was exacerbated by the reliance on apprentice (i.e. student) labour. Since students under Project 2000 were no longer part of the rostered workforce, increasingly health care assistants have become part of the skill mix.

District nursing

District nursing was established in 1859 by William Rathbone, a wealthy ship-owner, later an MP in Liverpool. Training became available at Liverpool Infirmary from 1862, and Florence Nightingale was involved in its dissemination. Legislation, in the early twentieth century, required local authorities to accept more responsibility for the care of chronically ill people, and during the inter-war period increased use of hospitals for acute illness meant that district nursing increasingly concentrated on those who were chronically ill. Although training was reviewed in 1955 it was seen as being vocational. Greater parity with health visitors was achieved in 1979, when a six-month course was provided in further education. Since 1993, both groups have parity, in that both courses are the same length and have at least one-third shared, along with other community nurses. This structure has proven unwieldy, however, and has been affected by recent policy changes in primary care, such as the creation of community matrons, and the changes in health visitor regulation.

Mental health nursing

Separate provision for mentally ill people, and people with learning disabilities, was also developed in the nineteenth century. At the end of the eighteenth century, mentally ill people had been cared for in the community, in the workhouse or in privately run madhouses. Then (as now) they might also be in prison. Late eighteenth-century reforms were in part spurred by the 'madness' of George III; well known reformers included William Tuke, a wealthy merchant in York. The 1845 Lunatics Act established a network of asylums for 'pauper lunatics'. However, the purpose of these asylums was not clearly established, and they soon became populated by the inmates of the workhouses, together with their attendants, many of them alternated asylum work in the winter months with agricultural labour. Florence Nightingale saw asylum attendants as on par with servants; no training was provided and attendants had simply to supervise inmates at all times and ensure that they were kept occupied.

A handbook for asylum attendants was established in 1885, and a national training scheme under the aegis of the Medico-Psychological Association started in 1891. Since successful completion did not lead to promotion, attendants regarded the scheme with suspicion, and relationships with the medical superintendents deteriorated, leading to a series of strikes. By 1890 the policy emphasis in mental health had shifted from treatment to the prevention of wrongful admission, and the 1890 Lunacy Act put in place a set of legal safeguards which some historians argue were stigmatizing and precluded voluntary admission for less severe illness. Voluntary treatment did not become possible until the Act of 1930, which also replaced the term 'lunatic asylum' with the somewhat less stigmatizing 'mental hospital'. Hospitals were severely stretched by the First World War, particularly since staff had been called up and demand had increased due to the incidence of shell-shock. Patient numbers also increased during the Great Depression, when resources were not available to fund the service; community options began to be explored.

On its establishment in 1919, the General Nursing Council rapidly took control of asylum attendants from the medical profession, by setting up a supplementary register and establishing an alternative training programme. Nolan (1995: 254) comments that *'Little progress was made in the mental nursing profession during the 1930s and 1940s; the best that can be said is that it survived'*. Treatments such as insulin therapy and ECT were generally not very effective, and sometimes controversial. County asylums were brought into the NHS on its inception; 48 per cent of NHS beds were in mental or mental deficiency hospitals. However, staff shortages were often severe and many asylums were both geographically and culturally isolated; this, in fact, was the aim of eugenicists, who had advocated 'extinction of the tribe' of defective people by isolating them.

The 1959 Mental Health Act laid down new definitions of mental disorder, and created the category of informal patient; this was aided by the discovery of effective medication, such as Largactil and Valium in the mid-1950s and early 1960s. However, local authority services were poorly developed and although the length of stay decreased, many patients were 'revolving door' patients. A series of inquiries, in the 1960s and 1970s, into mistreatment in psychiatric hospitals, showed a great difference in ethos and resources between the training wards and the 'back wards' for long-stay patients.

The 1975 White Paper *Better Services for the Mentally Ill* was the first to take a strategic approach. Implementation was slow, however, and it was recognized that health and social services had very different philosophies. A new syllabus was introduced in 1982 to strengthen the skills base and help prepare nurses for community care, but it was rapidly overtaken by the reforms of nursing education known as Project 2000, in which many mental health nurses felt their needs were subsumed in the Common

Foundation Programme by those of the much larger adult (general) nursing. Up to 80 per cent of current direct NHS mental health care is provided by nurses (DoH 2005j). Mental health nursing has now become even more challenging, with higher bed occupancies since the closure of the large psychiatric hospitals, and a growing use of alcohol and drugs complicating mental illness. The policy climate has also become more contested, as high profile killings, by people with personality defects or untreated schizophrenia, have led to a government push for greater intervention. At the time of writing, plans for primary legislation have been abandoned after eight years, but it is likely that some elements will be introduced through other routes.

Learning disability nursing

The Lunatics Act of 1845 distinguished between 'mental defectives and those of unsound mind'. Several private schools were established, and the 1886 Idiots Act empowered local authorities to establish institutions (although this was challenged by the Law Lords). The 1913 Mental Deficiency Act extended provision, but the system of certification and organization led to services, which were separate from the rest of health care, a situation which has been addressed only in the last 20 years. In 1948 the so-called 'colonies' became part of the NHS, but even in the 1950s, huge 1000-bedded institutions were being built. Reform occurred gradually from the 1970s onwards. The 1971 Education Act (Handicapped Children) placed a duty on local authorities to provide special schools, and the 1971 Social Services Act introduced new arrangements for adult training centres. The Jay Report (DHSS 1979) suggested that mental handicap nurses were inappropriately named, and should be part of social services. This caused considerable unrest, which was not assuaged until the mid-1990s when the chief nursing officer confirmed that learning disability nursing (as it was by now titled) should remain within the 'family of nursing'.

Community services, including housing, were developed in the 1980s, and the transfer of services from the NHS was strengthened by the NHS and Community Care Act 1990. It is now recognized that although many people with complex learning disabilities also have complex physical disabilities, people with milder disabilities have the same needs for mainstream health services, health promotion and screening services as the rest of the population (DoH 1998d, 2001f).

Health visiting

As outlined in Chapter 2, sanitary associations had grown up as part of the great public health movement of the mid-nineteenth century, sparked by the cholera outbreaks. Health visiting originated in the Manchester Ladies' Sanitary Association (1861), which employed health missioners, later called health visitors. In 1892, this development was picked up by Florence Nightingale, who advocated training; county councils had been given the power to fund this under the Local Government Act. It was seen as a separate profession from nursing, although growing concerns about high infant mortality then led to a requirement for a medical, nursing or midwifery background. Child life protection was added to the role by the 1908 Children's Act. The 1962 Health Visitor and Social Work Training Act set up the Council for the Education and Training of Health Visitors, and abolished the alternative training route which did not require a nursing background.

Health visiting has had an uneasy history since it came under the aegis of the NHS in 1974, and in the recent changes in professional regulation, health visiting has lost the legal protection of its title, becoming part of 'specialist community public health nursing'. The more market-driven model of primary care, in the mid-1990s, raised the question of whether population-based health promotion would be squeezed out by the demand for services to the defined GP practice population. Although, since 1997, there has been a greater government emphasis on social disadvantage and on public health, at times of financial stringency acute services take priority.

Midwifery

Midwifery is an ancient occupation, although midwives in the UK have had their dominant role in childbirth challenged since the 1660s, when forceps started to be used by 'man midwives'. This was opposed initially by the general public, by midwives and also by the Royal College of Physicians who did not regard it as part of medicine, since it involved manual activity. Obstetrics did not become part of medical training until the mid-nineteenth century. Although doctors were able to claim superior anatomical knowledge, women were more at risk from puerperal fever from doctors, since they might, for example, be attending childbirth having come, without hand-washing, from an autopsy. The 1902 Midwives Act, which required certification shortly followed by the requirement for a register, put midwifery training under the control of medicine, and midwives were required to summon medical help if a problem occurred during the delivery. Many midwives struggled to make ends meet, since their fee-paying clients were often poor themselves; the 1936 Midwives Act established a salaried service provided by the local authority, which then became part of the NHS in 1948.

In the UK today, most deliveries take place in hospital, since there was a strong policy drive in the 1970s to establish this on the grounds of safety (although the statistical basis for this is disputed, most notably by Tew 1990). The contested nature of midwifery practice continues to this day, as midwives seek to define childbirth as a natural process which does not generally require medical intervention. Midwifery also seeks to distinguish itself from nursing, and since the early 1990s it has been increasingly common for entrants to come directly into midwifery, rather than through nursing. Choice in childbirth is an important element of DoH policy (DoH 1993), although it is limited by midwifery shortages, and has recently taken an unexpected turn with debates on whether women are entitled to ask for caesarean sections.

Medicine

In the eighteenth century many doctors pieced together their earnings from patrons, Poor Law, friendly society and prison work; wealth and prestige generally depended on attracting rich patrons. Many also served in either the army or the navy, as Britain was at war for much of the century. The growth of local medical societies in the early nineteenth century helped to create professional cohesion, although medicine at that time had less status than either the law or the church. The BMA was established in the mid-nineteenth century from one such local society.

The Royal College of Physicians was founded in 1518; the Royal College of Surgeons in 1800. Whereas physicians had a university education, reflected in their title of 'doctor', surgeons served an apprenticeship and have retained a pride in their origins by still titling themselves 'Mr' (or less commonly 'Miss' or 'Mrs') on attaining consultant status. Surgery began to develop in the mid-nineteenth century, with the discovery of chloroform anaesthesia and techniques for asepsis, and the invention of the artery clamp. By the end of the century, hospital-based operating theatres were the norm. There was a dramatic rise in hospital attendances, in the late nineteenth century, and specialist hospitals began to be established, laying the foundation for the further creation of specialisms and corresponding Royal Colleges, and the establishment of greater social distance between doctors and their patients. The mid-nineteenth century also saw the discovery of effective pharmaceuticals, such as aspirin (1899), and the professionalization of pharmacists, of whom the most famous was Jesse Boot in Nottingham.

The 1911 Insurance Act provided access to medical care for working men earning less than £160 p.a., many of whom had previously paid subscriptions to friendly societies. Middle-class patients continued to pay fees. The number of GPs doubled between 1860 and 1914 (although of course the population was also increasing). General practice has, since its inception, been organized as a collection of small businesses, and although the 1920 Dawson Report recommended the creation of health centres with a wider range of services, these were successfully resisted. GPs were the most forceful group in asserting their independence in negotiations with Aneurin Bevan prior to the creation of the NHS, and at the time the (later Royal) College of General Practitioners (RCGP) was formed in 1952. About half of GPs were still single-handed, often without secretarial help. Loudon *et al.* (1998) estimate that about 25 per cent of practices were unsatisfactory, and that the RCGP was an important element in improving professional development. There were, however, few mechanisms, until the creation of the internal market and the growth of audit and evidence-based practice in the 1990s, by which to change poor or expensive prescribing habits.

General practice has not had the status of hospital-based medicine (although there are wide differences in status between the latter special-isms, from cardiac surgery and neurosurgery at one end of the spectrum, to geriatrics and psychiatry at the other). Webster (2002) considers that hospital consultants had their highest status at the end of the nineteenth century, prior to the development of the major specialisms. In part, their development was accelerated by the two world wars. For example, ortho-paedic surgery developed in response to the heavily infected wounds from the Flanders front, and mental illness was reappraised due to the high incidence of shell-shock, first named in 1915. Anaesthetics and plastic surgery both developed as specialisms in the Second World War, the latter due to the use of aircraft in warfare, and the much greater incidence of severe burns from aviation fuel. Other occupations, such as occupational therapy, also developed as a response to the rehabilitation of war-injured patients.

Paradoxically perhaps, although the effectiveness of medicine has developed greatly, public expectation has outstripped its achievements, and modern attitudes towards doctors reflect the general decline in deference. In many developed countries medical power has also been eroded by that of managers, as health care systems struggle to control their budgets (Davies and Harrison 2003). In the UK, medicine is becoming more of a women's occupation; in 2001, 60 per cent of entrants to medical school were women (Carvel 2002) although men dominate in the higher echelons. Both male and female doctors plan to retire at an earlier age than their predecessors. This, together with the reduced availability of junior doctors, due to reductions in their working week, and more structured training programmes, has implications for workforce planning. One solu-tion, discussed briefly below, is to expand the roles of other health pro-fessions; in addition the number of medical school places has increased by nearly 60 per cent since 1997, and four new medical schools have been created.

Professional regulation

The minimalist state leaves people free to pursue their own welfare goals through the working of the market; the interventionist state protects collective interests. In the former, regulation has only a small role to play, and it is left to the individual to use the law to enforce their rights. In the latter, regulation is centralized, and enforced by the state; Parliament, government departments, professional associations and the judicial system are all sources of regulation. In practice, most, if not all, developed socie-ties are somewhere on a continuum.

There is a tension between the state and the occupation, and between service providers and users. Regulation in the UK has increased as medical interventions have become more complex, and consumer groups have become more insistent in their expectations of safe, high quality care and generally more risk averse. Allsop and Mulcahy (1996) observe that health care is highly regulated both by formal rules and regulations but also by norms of behaviour. They also make a distinction between the 'bad apples' approach, which emphasizes individual responsibility, and the theory of continuous improvement which focuses on the organization. The two approaches may sometimes conflict; if for example individual members of staff are punished for drug errors, they will be tempted to cover them up, which may put the patient at risk and reduce the opportunity for organizational learning.

Membership of the EU has also had several effects on regulation, since training should be comparable if a professional group is to have freedom of movement in member states. In particular, European requirements have led to the training of junior doctors being made more structured, under the Calman reforms of the mid-1990s, and initial nursing education (although not that of the other health professions) is governed by a very strict requirement on hours due to European requirements. New legislation will be required in 2007, prompted by the New Professional Qualifications Directive which became European law in September 2005.

Self-regulation

The four core functions of self-regulation are to:

- keep a register of members admitted to the profession;
- determine standards of education and training;
- give advice on standards of conduct (e.g. a code of conduct) and performance;
- administer procedures relating to misconduct, fitness to practice and similar matters, including removal from the register.

Historically, the emphasis has been on misconduct rather than lack of competence, but this is changing. Procedures for maintaining competence after registration, coupled with periodic re-registration, are now widespread.

Self-regulation is thought to be more effective because:

- it allows insider (i.e. expert) knowledge to be used, particularly in occupations which have a very specialist knowledge base;
- it encourages compliance because practitioners consider that the regime is reasonable;
- it is relatively low cost because detailed monitoring of practice is not required;
- it is flexible and responsive in new areas of practice.

Pure self-regulation by occupations is rare, and Allsop and Mulcahy (1996) consider that regulation is generally 'state sanctioned', with the threat to intervene if the occupation proves to be unable to regulate itself. The arguments against self-regulation are that it may be seen as protectionist and lacking accountability. Baggott (2002) notes that in the past self-regulation has been a privilege granted to the elite. Loss of public trust, however, as has happened in medicine in the last few years, may have affected the other health and social care occupations and may lead to a more intrusive system. The DoH is currently reviewing professional regulation, and may propose an outside body to undertake conduct cases for all

Table 10.1 The health and social care regulatory bodies

	Fees (£)	Number of Registrants 2002/3	Year established	Size of council
General Chiropractic Council	1250 registration 1000 annual	2019	1998	20
General Dental Council (also regulates hygienists/ therapists) From 2006 all dental groups, including dental nurses, will be included	40 registration 40–300 annual 10 registration 25 annual	31,827 dentists 4027 hygienists 429 therapists	1956	29 + 4 CDOs
General Medical Council	290 annual (complex range of fees)	203,398	1858	35
General Optical Council	115 Annual	9284 optometrists 5014 dispensing opticians	1958	28
General Osteopathic Council	350–750 annual	3225	1996	22
Health Professions Council	120 biennially	144,141 (12 groups)	2001	24 + president
Nursing and Midwifery Council	129 triennially (changed to 43 annually in 2006)	645,580	2002	23
Royal Pharmaceutical Society of Great Britain (Northern Ireland has own body)	81 registration 21–195 annual	45,641	1941	24
General Social Care Council Unlike other bodies, one per country	30 registration 30 annual	70,000 in late 2005 – will eventually be over 1 million	2001	12

the health regulators; such a move is likely to be hotly resisted. A key debate is the extent to which employers can, or should, take on the first stages of regulating competence. This may become more of an issue if the NHS fragments into more independent providers, particularly in primary care.

Increased regulation

Baggott considers that during the 1980s and 1990s, media and parliamentary pressures, together with public concern and government hostility to the public sector, produced a powerful assault on self-regulation. This has been continued by the Labour government, but underpinned by an ideology of active citizenship and 'modernization'. The 1999 Health Reform Act gave the government the potential to achieve further changes in regulation without the need for legislation, leading to the proposals for the NMC and the HPC, and changes in the powers of the GMC. For the first time, it was explicitly stated that the primary purpose of the new professional bodies was the protection of the public. The Act also created the Council for the Regulation of Healthcare Professions (CHRP) (now called the Council for Health Care Regulatory Excellence). The CHRE reviews the work of the nine health care regulatory bodies, and can refer decisions made by their practice committees to the high court, if it feels that they are too lenient.

Any practitioner employed by the NHS is also subject to other regulatory regimes, such as clinical governance; this is not the case for solo practitioners in private practice. Rosenthal (1995) considers that gossip and rumour are important sources of information about poorly performing doctors, although it is difficult to judge the accuracy of the information, or what to do about it, and there is a 'tacit norm' in medicine of non-criticism. The Bristol Royal Infirmary Enquiry of 2001 and the Shipman case highlighted that such information may be widely known locally, but that other practitioners may fail to act upon it. In addition, the therapeutic discretion of the more autonomous occupations, such as medicine, now has limits established, for example, through the greater specificity of the new GP contract and its quality and outcomes framework, and the job plans which consultants are required to have. In particular, recommendations were made for the appraisal, disciplinary and reporting arrangements for clinical academics, since deficiencies in these were a major feature of the failures at Alder Hey (Follett and Paulson-Ellis 2001).

Managers are not currently regulated, although the Institute of Healthcare Management has been pressing for a compulsory code of conduct and fitness to practice certificates for its members, on the grounds that managers should not demand accountability without themselves being accountable. Both health and social care organizations are also more subject to inspection and regulation, although the structures for doing this alter with confusing frequency (Walshe 2003). Currently health care is overseen by the Healthcare Commission, which took over from the Commission for Health Improvement in 2004. The Commission for Social Care Inspection was set up in 2004, but already it seems likely that it will be disbanded and its work split between the Healthcare Commission and Ofsted, the schools inspectorate.

As discussed further below, in the section on the regulation of nursing, the growth of new roles and new occupations, together with a greater emphasis on risk management, is leading to the growth of regulation. For example, it is likely that 'aesthetic nurses', who undertake treatment such as Botox, will shortly have additional regulation. Both operating department practitioners and applied psychologists applied for regulation by the HPC in 2003, and the DoH is discussing regulation with psychotherapists, counsellors and other practitioners of 'talking therapies'.

Box 10.2 The regulation of complementary and alternative medicine

Almost a third of the UK population uses CAM, and most would like it to be provided by the NHS (Foundation for Integrated Medicine 1997). Figures obtained by Mintel for the House of Lords (2000) showed an annual expenditure of £20 million on essential oils for aromatherapy. There is, however, a balance to be struck between consumer choice and consumer protection. The majority of complementary therapists in the UK work as independent practitioners (Sharma 1994). Medicine has in the past been suspicious of CAM. Siahpush (1999) states that as doctors adopt alternative therapies, they are likely to argue that alternative practitioners should be excluded from practice, or should at least be regulated.

In 1998, Graham *et al.* found that of 105 NHS trusts, 61 per cent allowed the use of complementary therapies, mainly aromatherapy, reflexology, acupuncture and massage.

The House of Lords Select Committee on Science and Technology report on CAM (2000) divided it into three categories:

- The professionally organized disciplines of acupuncture, chiropractic, herbal medicine, homeopathy and osteopathy, for which there is evidence of effectiveness and a recognized system of training.
- Aromatherapy, reflexology and massage, which were seen by the Committee as unregulated and without a firm scientific base; it was accepted that they could relieve stress.
- Alternative disciplines which claim diagnostic powers, such as traditional Chinese medicine, Ayurvedic medicine, crystal therapy, dowsing and iridology, which were seen as scientifically unproven and unregulated, and it was agreed that they should not be available on the NHS.

Budd and Mills (2000) surveyed the CAM professional associations for the DoH, and found a wide range of professional associations. For example, 12 organizations registered aromatherapists, and there were concerns that if a practitioner was struck off by one, they could simply join another.

Nursing

The Nursing Register was established in 1919 after several abortive Registration Bills and about 30 years of campaigning (Baly 1995). The 1919 Act was a compromise between those who believed that nursing was a vocation, in which personal characteristics were more important than technical knowledge, and those who believed it should be a profession. The Ministry of Health had overall control over the standard of entry and the requirements of basic training. Although the title 'registered nurse' was protected, the title 'nurse' was not, and nursing did not have the same control over entry to the profession or over education as medicine had gained. The legislation provided for a register containing a general part, a supplementary part, containing the names of male nurses (men have been able to become general nurses only since 1943), and supplementary parts for the care of persons suffering from mental diseases, and the nursing of sick children. Infectious diseases and the care of mental defectives were added later.

The General Nursing Council and other bodies, such as the Council for the Education and Training of Health Visitors (CETHV) and Central Midwives Board (CMB), were superseded by the United Kingdom Central Council for Nursing, Midwifery and Health Visiting (UKCC) and the four national boards in 1983. It was, however, a rather cumbersome structure with overlapping functions. Nine separate bodies had been brought together and many practitioners, regulated by these, felt that they were not understood by general nursing, which has tended to dominate because of its size (Davies 2002).

Davies and Beach (2000) note a growing media interest in the regulation of nurses from the late 1980s, when there were several controversial cases, where nurses were restored to the register despite serious criminal convictions (in one instance, for rape). In the mid-1990s there was growing concern about the number of complaints against nurses (DoH 1999f); part of the remedy was perceived to lie with employers, for example, in drawing up clear employment policies on personal involvement with patients. The National Consumer Council (1999) had also expressed concerns about regulation in general, arguing for more transparency, more lay representation including lay chairs, and more consistency between the various regulatory bodies.

Both the UKCC and the English National Board also called for the regulation of health and social care assistants, since currently a nurse who is struck off the register could return to work as a health care assistant. A DoH consultation document *Regulation of Health Care Staff in England and Wales* (DoH 2004e), issued in March 2004, proposed that regulation should be extended to about 50,000 additional qualified staff, such as health care scientists, and about 200,000 support staff, such as health care assistants, suggesting that the HPC might be a suitable body. This resulted in claims from the NMC that they should be the main regulatory body since many HCAs work primarily with nurses. The issue of the regulation of support workers then became part of the remit of a wide-ranging review of medical and non-medical regulation resulting from the Shipman Enquiry, chaired by Andrew Foster, the DoH human resources director. At the time of writing, the regulation of assistant roles is unresolved.

The UKCC was replaced by the NMC in 2002, following the review by JM Consulting (1998). The government proposals included a smaller council, a streamlined register reduced from 15 to 3 parts and a broader definition of unfitness to practise, to include deficient competence. Ryan (2000) considered that the replacement of the UKCC was influenced by medical scandals; nursing was seen as much easier to challenge than medicine, even though the GMC had greater shortcomings.

Medicine

Doctors' monopoly over medical expertise was recognized by the 1858 Medical Act which established the forerunner of the GMC, with powers to maintain a register and to determine entry qualifications. As in nursing, many previous Bills had failed to become law, due to rivalries within the profession. Entry to the register gave protection of title; removal from the register was generally due to adultery or disparagement of another medical practitioner, rather than due to issues of actual competence. However, qualifications continued to be awarded by a range of bodies, as they still are, since the Royal Colleges control postgraduate education.

The medical regulatory body was set up at a time when 'gentlemen' were expected to behave well and were not subject to criticism by the 'lower orders'; self-regulation was seen as the most effective safeguard (Merrison Report 1975). Commentators have remarked that this attitude persisted until recently; the eminent sociologist Meg Stacey's experience as a member of the 'white gentleman's club' of the GMC (Stacey 1992), was that she felt marginal both as a woman and as a lay member. In her view the GMC had an ethos of rightness and superiority, a remoteness even from its own rank and file, and exuded a strong sense of difference which excluded and subordinated other health professions. It also had a very light touch in its approach to practitioners, and has been subject to mounting criticism for not addressing serious patient complaints and medical malpractice, the most notorious being the case of the serial killer Harold Shipman, now the subject of a series of inquiry reports chaired by Dame Janet Smith (Shipman Inquiry 2002–5). Many changes have been introduced, including a huge reduction in the size of the GMC from 104 to 35 members with a better balance of lay members, revalidation every five years in order for doctors to remain on the medical register, and the introduction of procedures to address competence as well as conduct. Some of these reforms were won in the teeth of opposition from consultants in the BMA. Other changes introduced by the government include a new contract for consultants, with increased managerial control over medical work, a formal appraisal system and a new body, the National Clinical Assessment Authority, to which poorly performing doctors can be referred.

A comparison between the GMC and the UKCC (Montgomery 1998) showed that the former used its powers to respect and protect the autonomy of doctors, whereas the UKCC sought to impose its values on the professions it regulated. The UKCC was, in Montgomery's view, more prescriptive in its standard-setting and more punitive in its sanctions than the GMC, although a greater convergence was noted. An important structural difference is that the medical schools predated the formation of the GMC, in some instances by several hundred years, and the latter did not seek to prescribe the curriculum. Both also predated the formation of the Ministry of Health in 1919. Nursing, by contrast, entered higher education largely as the result of a regulatory body initiative (Project 2000), and its first regulatory body, the GNC, was established at the same time as the Ministry of Health. Nursing education in England is also purchased by NHS contracts and is thus subject to purchaser power (Meerabeau 2001). Davies (2002) argues that because medicine and nursing are positioned differently, their regulatory bodies cannot be equivalent; the council of a subordinated profession (i.e. nursing) is positioned in a disadvantaged way.

The allied health professions

The Council for Professions Supplementary to Medicine (established in 1960), and its 12 uni-professional boards, were replaced in 2001 by the Health Professions Council (HPC), which owing to its wide remit and title can undertake the regulation of many new health-related occupations; for example, operating department practitioners and applied psychologists both applied for regulation in 2003. The detail in the 2000 proposals for the HPC was very similar to that for the NMC, and the 1996 review of the Professions Supplementary to Medicine Act had been undertaken by the same firm (JM Consulting), addressing the point made by the National Consumer Council (1999) that there should be more consistency in how the health professions are regulated, since it was difficult for the general public to understand the various systems. There was concern expressed from some of the professions regulated by the CPSM that the 'streamlining' would not give sufficient space to recognize the differences between the different occupations regulated by the HPC, and might make it easier for universities to get approval for poor quality courses. These fears appear to have been largely unfounded, although there are tensions as some of the professional bodies, which had a powerful role with the CPSM, negotiate their place in the new arrangements.

Social care

Although social work education was previously overseen by the Central Council for the Education and Training of Social Workers, social workers were not registered on qualification. Social worker is now a protected title, and social workers, like other regulated occupations, have a code of practice. In social care there are a range of new organizations; the General Social Care Council, the Social Care Institute for Excellence (SCIE), the Training Organization for Personal Social Services (one of the Sector Skills Councils now renamed Skills force), and the Commission for Social Care Inspection. These aim to regulate the service, staff and training. SCIE's function is to review knowledge about social care and disseminate best practice, in consultation with users. Social care is also subject to the government's doctrine of Best Value (Thompson 2002), which has replaced compulsory competitive tendering and entails challenging why and how a service is provided, comparing performance with others, competition, and consultation with users.

Modernization

Modernization of services has been a key element of government policy since 1997, and for several years, until its merger into the NHS Institute in 2005, a Modernization Agency existed to introduce techniques, such as process analysis into the NHS, with the aim of improving the patient experience. It was briefly complemented by the NHSU (see Box 10.3), which aimed to provide training throughout the NHS, for example, in customer care and infection control.

Box 10.3   The NHSU

In its 2001 manifesto, the Labour Party promised a university for the NHS. The idea was said to have originated with Jenny Simpson, the chief executive of the British Association of Medical Managers, who had been impressed by the training of Disney employees. The NHSU was launched with great fanfare in December 2003, but ceased to exist as an independent body in July 2005, in the review of 'arm's length bodies', being merged with the Modernization Agency and reducing from 1500 posts between the two, to 300. As in the case of some of the regulatory bodies, which were also affected by the arm's length review, it is an example of the remarkably short life of some institutions under the current administration.

It was a key part of the modernization agenda in the NHS, and its budget for its first year was £50 million. Its main mission was to offer training to more than 25,000 NHS employees, particularly people who did not have formal qualifications and who had, in the view of its chief executive, Professor Bob Fryer, been failed by the education system. It also developed programmes for several new roles, for example, for 'first contact' nurses in primary care.

The size of the task was enormous, and as a result the quality of training was patchy. The NHS has 1.3 million employees, of whom 60,000 work in maintenance, 80,000 in scientific services and 20,000 are ambulance staff. In 2005 it was planned to offer 90,000 staff literacy and numeracy skills.

However, the NHSU encountered problems from the start. First, problems with its title surfaced as early as October 2001. Although it was originally called the NHS University, it could not use that title as it had not been approved by the Privy Council and had too high a proportion of non-higher education work. University governance also stipulates that the government should have no say in the appointment of the governing body of any UK university. Second, there was confusion and overlap between its roles and those of the Modernization Agency. Third, there was some indication of mission drift, since although its original mission appeared to be to meet the needs of staff who had previously had little or no educational provision, it also had ambitions to manage research.

> Universities were also uneasy that the NHSU might make inroads into
> pre-registration education, particularly in nursing.
>   The public sector union, UNISON was a great supporter of the NHSU,
> and claimed that the universities had a considerable part in its demise. It
> is equally likely that the SHAs were involved, since it was claimed that
> much of the NHSU's budget was not new money, but was top-sliced
> from the SHAs.
>   The NHS has now been hit by another wave of reorganization, as SHAs
> have been combined and the education commissioning is likely to move
> to another body. At present, although some former NHSU programmes
> are handled by the core learning unit, it is not clear who might take an
> overview of the education needs of the NHS, as the NHSU planned to do.
> *Main source:* Flood (2005, 2006)

Addressing interprofessional boundaries has also been a key element in
modernization, and it has also been argued that organizational failures,
such as those in paediatric cardiac care in Bristol, can be partly attributed
to poor interprofessional communication (Humphris and Macleod Clark
2002). Hargadon and Staniforth (2000: 1.3) state that: '*It [modernization] is
about looking at the workforce in a different way, as teams of people rather than
as different professional tribes. For too long we have planned and trained staff in
a uni-professional/uni-disciplinary way without a clear and comprehensive look
at the future*'. The DoH (2001g) made a commitment that all pre-registration
programmes would have 'common learning' by 2004, although whether
this has been achieved has not been evaluated. The leading institution is
the University of Southampton with its 'New Generation' project, established in 1999, which involves ten pre-registration programmes (Humphris
and Macleod Clark 2002).

The shifts in interprofessional boundaries began in the early 1990s,
when some nurses began to take on medical tasks, enabled by the UKCC's
1992 Scope of Practice document. This was accelerated by the European
Working Time Directive, which required junior doctors' hours to be
reduced from a norm of about 70 per week. Roles, such as nurse practitioners, were created, although this is not a protected title nor is the range
of skills standardized. Watson *et al.* (1996) also point out that the conditions in the USA, which led to the creation of these roles, may not apply in
the UK. Nursing time was thereby put under pressure, since nursing
education commissions had been reduced in the early 1990s to save
government expenditure, so by using so-called 'skill mix', increasing
numbers of health care assistants were employed to undertake caring work,
such as bathing and feeding. Although this was viewed with suspicion by
some nurses who feared that the quality of care would be damaged, the
research evidence for this was not compelling. There has, however, been
little rigorous evaluation (Masterson 2000; Carr Hill *et al.* 2003).

Since then, it has become the norm that health care occupations develop
extended roles (such as radiographers rather than radiologists reading
some images) and that helper grades are developed. This principle applies,
for example, in dentistry, where better dental health has resulted in less

'drilling and filling' or basic dentistry, and more need for hygienists undertaking preventive work leaving dentists able to undertake skilled restorative work. Comparability between different health care occupations has been aided by the development of an NHS careers structure, and the Knowledge and Skills Framework attached to the recent pay reforms (Agenda for Change), although it is notable that ambitions to include medicine in the latter were abandoned at an early stage.

In nursing, midwifery and the allied health professions, consultant posts have been created, with some positive effects on health care (Guest *et al.* 2004) although it is too early to form a definitive view. Nurse prescribing was introduced cautiously, in the mid-1990s, for health visitors and district nurses for a very limited formulary, in a few pilot sites in England. Since then it has gradually been extended, and since May 2006 experienced nurses and pharmacists have been able to prescribe most of the British national formulary, despite the earlier opposition of the BMA on the grounds of patient safety (Carvel 2005a).

Buchanan and Calman (2004a) examine the evidence on role change and delegation from doctors to advanced practice nurses. They support the view that nurses can provide care at least equivalent to doctors in certain settings, although data is not sufficient for full cost-benefit analysis. Eight of the countries reviewed reported these roles, and three were piloting or considering them. In the UK, the numbers of advanced practice nurses are not large; in 1999 there were about 3500, and the title of nurse practitioner is not protected by law so there is a wide range of seniority and experience. The constraints in the UK are primarily lack of funding, lack of qualified applicants and regulatory issues; it is not clear yet whether *Agenda for Change*, the reform of the pay system, has been beneficial in facilitating new roles.

There has also been discussion since the early 1990s on developing new registered roles which transcend the current divisions or 'silos'. Greater convergence of the various regulatory bodies, outlined earlier, may make this more feasible, as may a greater use of competency-based education and the fact that the great majority of health care education is now university-based. There are current pilots of medical care practitioners prepared at master's level (Carvel 2005b), although these are aimed at either nurses or AHPs. Legislation, and a separate regulatory framework, will be required. The issue may be more problematic for intermediate roles, since they do not recruit from existing registrants. Humphris and Macleod Clark (2002) state that there may be a need for licensing arrangements, and that the government should address this as a matter of urgency.

Recruitment issues

Lastly, modernization of the health service takes place in the context of needing to address skill mix, not only in order to manage costs, but also in order to manage the shortage of trained personnel which affects nearly all countries. In particular, the UK, like many developed economies, relies heavily on nursing and medical personnel who have trained overseas, and it is increasingly recognized that there is a moral issue, since this exacerbates the severe shortages of personnel in much of the developing world, particularly sub-Saharan Africa, which has been greatly affected by HIV/AIDS (see Figure 10.1).

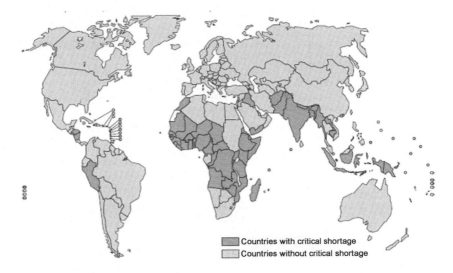

Figure 10.1 Countries with a critical shortage of health service providers (doctors, nurses and midwives)
Source: WHO (2006)

Clarke-Jones (2006) quotes a 2005 survey by Medact/Save the Children, which estimates that the loss of health professionals from Ghana (which has a per capita health spend of £6 per year) had cost it £35 million in training investment, and saved the UK (per capita spend £927) £65 million. The DoH proscribes active recruitment from all non-OECD countries, except certain parts of India and the Phillipines; the latter in fact trains an excess of nurses, since they boost the economy by sending money home. It is unlikely that staffing will stabilize, however, since a quarter of the nurses in the UK are due to retire in the next decade, and the USA, a prime recruiter of UK nurses, is heading for a shortfall of 800,000 nurses in the next decade.

Nursing has an ageing profile; Buchanan and Sellcombe (2004) report that in 1991 one in four nurses on the register were under 30, whereas by 2002/3 this had fallen to one in eight (although the NHS has a somewhat younger profile than the register as a whole). The proportion of nurses over 55 had increased from 9 per cent to 15 per cent. Apart from retirement, only 54 per cent of nurses over 50 work full-time. As Buchanan and Sellcombe (2004) note, the UK cannot ignore that it is part of a broader international labour market for nurses, several of which are English speaking. The USA, Canada and Australia all have ageing nursing populations; the NMC has reported an increase in the number of verifications it is asked to provide to US employers, a reflection of a major recruitment drive. Buchanan and Calman (2004b) conclude that the root of nursing shortages is that in many countries it is undervalued as 'women's work', and that nurses need to be given more access to resources. Nursing shortages are often portrayed as a problem only for nursing, whereas a whole system approach needs to be taken.

Conclusion

This chapter has briefly explored the history of nursing, medicine and social work since the mid-nineteenth century. In recent years, there have been pressures for greater coordination of services and a greater user focus, which have resulted in greater regulation, the development of new roles, and some moves towards shared education, as part of the modernization of the NHS. There is a pressing need to address serious staffing issues which affect most health care systems.

Summary

- The occupations discussed in this chapter took recognizable shape in the mid-nineteenth century, as part of the growth of institutions, followed by a shift to more community-based care.
- There is a gradual shift towards shared working and learning within and between health and social care, although this is patchy.
- The social distance between the occupations and patients/users has reduced, although again this is patchy.
- Skill mix and competency-based education have grown in the last 15 years, and are now amplified by the 'modernization agenda'.
- Professional regulation is increasing, as is the regulation of the delivery of care.
- The NHS is now undergoing continuous modernization, and it is recognized that if costs are to be controlled, and it is to be properly staffed, then the skill mix will need to change.

Further reading

Abbott, P. and Meerabeau, E. (1998) *The Sociology of the Caring Professions.* London: UCL Press.

Adams, R., Dominelli, L. and Payne, M. (eds) (2002) *Social Work Themes, Issues and Critical Debates*, 2nd edn. Basingstoke: Palgrave.

Allsop, J. and Saks, M. (2003) *Regulating the Health Professions.* London: Sage.

Baly, M. (1995) *Nursing and Social Change*, 3rd edn. London: Routledge.

Barrett G., Sellman D. and Thomas, J. (2005) *Interprofessional Working in Health and Social Care: Professional Perspectives.* London: Palgrave Macmillan.

Leathard, A. (2003) *Interprofessional Collaboration*. Hove: Brunner-Routledge.

Walshe, K. (2003) *Regulating Healthcare: A Prescription for Improvement?* Buckingham: Open University Press.

SOCIAL POLICY AND HEALTH IN THE TWENTY-FIRST CENTURY

- Introduction
- Why a social policy approach?
- Key themes
- What are the key challenges for the future?
- Implications for the delivery of health and social care
- Conclusion
- Summary

Introduction

This last chapter brings together some of the key themes of this book, and sets out the social policy agenda for the next decade. We have demonstrated that social policy is intrinsically linked to the conceptualization and delivery of health and health care and, that it is important for health and social care professionals to have an understanding of wider social policy perspectives on factors that impact on health and social care. We have argued that an understanding of difference and divisions in society, and how these relate to inequalities and social exclusion, are central to an understanding of social policy and its relevance to professional practice.

We have also discussed the way in which the state has responded to changes in society, and earlier chapters discuss health and welfare policy developments. In particular, we identify a number of important policy trends in relation to the restructuring of welfare, to focus more on the individual, increasing diversification and fragmentation of service delivery, a focus on defining responsibilities (of the state, communities and individuals), and the changing role of health and social care professionals and the organizations they work within. This chapter draws these themes together to discuss the collective impact on the provision of health and social care in the twenty-first century; it will also highlight the growing importance and impacts of globalization, workforce issues, public health, changing patterns of health service use and delivery and new technologies. We are, however, keenly aware that we have been able only to touch on many issues, and that in particular we have had to confine much of our discussion to the UK. We are also aware that there are large unknown factors about patterns of health and illness, for example, the extent to which there is a hidden future disease burden from variant CJD, or the health effects of global warming, which have origins which are as much social (such as the isolation of older people) as natural causes (Klinenberg 2002).

Why a social policy approach?

Taking a social policy approach is valuable, since we need to be interested in the wider determinants of health problems and understand the broader social context, and in particular the role of the state. As the Acheson Inquiry (1998) and the Wanless Reports (2002, 2004) demonstrate very well, many if not most of the causes of, and preventative actions for, health problems lie outside the remit of the DoH and the NHS. The issues are often deeply political, since they concern the balance between the collective good and individual freedoms, and thus rely on persuasion and can be politically risky, since governments generally shy away from the label of the 'nanny state'. As Taylor-Gooby (2004: 77) comments, *'regulation is limited and compulsion only deployed against politically weak groups such as young unemployed people'*. This balance between collective good and individual freedom may shift over time as certain constraints on our freedom become accepted, for example, wearing seatbelts and a limit on alcohol intake when driving; it seems likely that the balance of opinion is now shifting on the freedom to smoke.

Although the Labour government has tried systematically to create 'joined-up government' (Bogdanor 2005) to address complex issues which cross-departmental boundaries, such as social exclusion, policies and interest groups will sometimes conflict. Chapter 5 refers to the growing public health problem of obesity, in which a major player is the food industry which is largely resisting the introduction of controls; another example given below, is the role of the pharmaceutical industry in driving up prescribing costs. Historically, an example of policy conflict and conflict of interest is provided by MAFF, the Ministry of Agriculture, Food and Fisheries. The Phillips Report (2000), on the BSE crisis of the mid-1990s, considered that the Ministry promoted the interests of farmers over those of consumers; it was reconfigured in 2001, and the Food Standards Agency was set up in 2000. More recently, the relaxation of the licensing laws in 2006, in which the policy lead rested with the Department of Culture, Media and Sport, led to concerns that it would lead to more binge drinking; alcohol-related problems lie behind a quarter of acute male admissions to hospital (Alcohol Concern 2002), and so there are large potential costs to the NHS, quite apart from the social costs. There is also a political dimension in that local authorities have limited control, since their decisions can be readily challenged in the courts.

At various points in the text, we also refer to sudden changes in policy, and organizations which are set up but then disappear quickly. An example is given in Chapter 7 of the regulatory bodies in health and social care; a further example in Chapter 10 is the NHSU, which had a very ambitious (although shifting) remit and a large budget, but a very short life. Health Action Zones, referred to in Chapter 5, are another example. Generally, 'Whitehall watchers' consider that since the Labour government came to power, there has been some marginalization and politicization of the Civil Service, and a greater use of 'special advisers' who do not have a Civil Service background, and that this may partially account for some of the plethora of policy initiatives, not all of them well thought through.

Taking a social policy perspective also links changes in political ideas to the practice environment. As we introduced in Chapter 1, social policies link the state and society with policy developed both as a response to changes in society, but also as a process for changing society and the type of interaction between governments and citizens. An example discussed in Chapter 8 is volunteering, which has been promoted by the government not only to provide services, but to address the problem of the perceived disengagement of individuals from society. The policy of the Labour government seeks to reconcile centre-left objectives by market-friendly means. It puts considerable emphasis on enabling people to enter (and remain in) the labour market in order to provide for their own needs, for example, by making Tax Credits the main vehicle for tackling poverty. It has four key values: the equal worth of individuals, equality of opportunities rather than of outcomes, that rights entail responsibilities and the state as an enabler rather than a provider. Unlike the previous Conservative government, an emphasis is placed on involving institutions in civil society (Rhodes 2000). These aspects can be applied to changes in health and social care systems as part of wider changes in the UK welfare state.

Family policy has been touched on only briefly in this book, but it has important effects on other areas of social policy, and social policy in turn has many effects upon the family. Dramatic shifts in family structures have taken place, which may exacerbate the demographic changes outlined below. Data from the 2001 census indicate that 7 million people (a third of all households) live on their own, compared with 2 million in 1961, and that 20 per cent of families are headed by lone parents; as discussed in Chapter 4 and elsewhere in this chapter, this is a risk factor in poverty. Ormerod and Rowthorn (1997: 16) both noted economists, argue that greater family instability is creating many millions of people without close family ties, and that *'The decline of marriage is creating an army of roving males, upon whom women cannot, and do not, expect to rely'*.

Key themes

Throughout this text, reference has been made to a number of key themes that have provided a subtext to the discussion. Some of these, such as diversity and inequality, have been discussed in detail as they are particularly relevant to the main focus of health and welfare. However, there are a number of other important themes that it is important to highlight as they set much of the context for debates about the relationship between people and the welfare state, and specifically health.

In Chapter 9, we discussed the relationship between the individual and the state as being either one of citizen or consumer. Given current changes in relation to choice that dominate current policy debates about health and social care, the way health and social care services interact with the people they serve is clearly important. While of obvious policy and practical importance, choice policies are clearly based on different concepts of society from those that were prevalent in the founding of the welfare state. Therefore, we need to explore the dominant ideas that lead to shifts in policy, such as monetarism in the Thatcher era, and the Third Way in New Labour policy-making. Although the issue cannot be explored here, the politics literature would also provide insights on the effects on policy-making of the two long periods of government by a single party since 1979, and the opportunities which our 'first past the post' electoral system create for large government majorities which are then able to force policies through (Taylor-Gooby 2004).

Another subtext to much of the discussion about the relationship between the state and society, is the issue of risk and how this is conceptualized by both professionals and the public. Clearly this provides an important backdrop to debates about public health and the role of the state in taking preventive measures to protect health. Taylor-Gooby (2004) considers that there are new risks and, therefore, new needs: balancing paid work and family commitments, being frail and lacking family support, lacking job skills or having obsolete skills, and having an inadequate or insecure pension. These risks are particularly likely to affect women, young people entering the labour market, unskilled people and older people. Perceptions of risk may also have indirect effects upon health; for example, as discussed in Chapter 5, the fear of crime, often exacerbated by tabloid reporting, can increase the risk of social exclusion in older people. A heightened sense of risk may also lead to poor policy formation, as solutions which appear superficially to be sensible may have unanticipated effects; a widely discussed example of this is the Dangerous Dogs Act (Hood et al. 2000), which was ostensibly a response to widely publicized attacks on children. Another example is the recurrent public anxiety in the UK about paedophiles, which has led to a resurgence of interest in the US 'Megan's Law', which makes information on individual sex offenders publicly available. This law has not been evaluated in the USA, probably puts children more at risk by driving paedophiles underground, and diverts attention from the far greater risk of sexual abuse in a child's own family.

Power (1999) states that we live in an 'audit society', and many commentators claim that, in society in general, there has been *'an inexorable widening of the risk net as those held accountable for risk attempt to reduce its inherent uncertainty through the use of precautionary techniques and invasive systems of information collection'* (Kemshall 1998: 294). Timmins and Cox (2001) state that the Labour government created more than a dozen new inspectorates and a rise in target-setting and top-down management. Hood et al. (2001: 64) comment on the *'tendency of regulation to develop as a set of monuments or a cemetery commemorating past disasters and tragedies'*. An example discussed in Chapter 10, is the reform of medical regulation after an increased number of children died undergoing cardiac surgery at

Bristol Royal Infirmary, and their organs were retained without parental consent; a further example in Chapter 7 is the regulation of care homes, which was brought in after the Longcare Inquiry, which led to the closure of many homes and, therefore, impacted upon the acute care system. Another example is the Green Paper *Every Child Matters* (DfES 2003), which arose from the damning Laming Inquiry into the death of Victoria Climbie, whose needs were unrecognized by many agencies and who was eventually killed by her aunt (although as the discussion of social work in Chapter 10 sadly illustrates, reports on child deaths tend to show the same recurring factors, and it is debatable whether they can be totally prevented).

A further theme, identified in the book, has been the role of lay people as producers of health and welfare. We have introduced concepts of co-production and self-care, which raise important issues about the role of service users, carers and health and social care professionals. At the heart of these discussions are the way we define expertise and how we understand knowledge is produced. There is also said to be a new relationship between medicine, society and the state (Sheaff *et al.* 2003; Salter 2004), which is likely to be a central factor in the efforts to regulate health care and to control its costs.

An important concept, that is relevant to all these areas, is the notion of power. This includes the power of governments to effect change, and of populations to resist, and the perceived erosion of medical power. As discussed below, legal challenges to clinical decision-making indicate that there have been shifts in power, however patchy, and that service users are now more aware of their capacity to effect change. An example in 2006 was a Bedfordshire woman who was unprepared to wait for a hip replacement locally, had the surgery in France, and then invoiced the PCT, which refused to pay. At the time of writing, the European Court of Justice has found against the PCT, which has appealed; the case now hinges on what is an unacceptable delay in treatment.

At the same time the concept of stewardship has become increasingly important in relation to health and health services; it can be defined as the social contract (an agreement) between the government and its people, where government processes are held in trust for the people, and founded on principles of ethics as well as efficiency (Saltman and Ferroussier-Davis 2000). The WHO has supported stewardship as a way to conceptualize the role of governments in terms of their responsibility for the health of their populations. Its very nature implies a stronger activist role by government to ensure that ethically sound and efficient policy is formulated and delivered for greatest good. In global health policy today this is a powerful idea. Many health reforms, especially in developing countries, have been driven by pure economic considerations, with little thought as to the impact they were likely to have on poor people. Thus, the introduction of semi-privatized health care, fee-for-service and the undermining of central government authority and ability to deliver health services, greatly increased the hardship experienced by the poor, and widened the inequalities between rich and poor (World Bank 2001). Stewardship implies not only that governments have the responsibility to use public funds in a responsible manner, but also to invest these in ways that address suffering among its poorest people and reduce inequality among its citizens. Stewardship, therefore, gives governments a role as custodian of the health and well-being of the population. Thus, such an approach fits with current developments in the UK, where there is an increasing move from government as provider of health and welfare services, to a role as a regulator and funder of services. However, key debates remain as to what extent government responsibility should extend to guaranteeing access to health and welfare services and, in particular, specific types of treatment where new and increasingly expensive drugs and interventions are constantly being introduced (Wanless 2002).

Overall, Timmins and Cox (2001) argue that there has been an obsession with applying private sector style productivity increases to the public sector in England. Appealing to idealism is no longer sufficient, and the public service ethos has declined. The central concept of the welfare state as being concerned with society's welfare remains, although a key criticism of the post-war welfare state has been that it was too paternalistic, and dominated by a professional view about the needs of service users (see Chapters 1 and 2). The recent shift towards a more individualistic approach, such as welfare consumerism and the development of consumer choice, appears to be an appropriate response. However, as earlier chapters have cautioned, there are important issues relating to access, equity and fragmentation that arise from such an approach. In health care, the need to address broader public health issues and changing needs within health care systems, has led to debates about the nature of the relationship between the state and society and the role of government.

Drawing on the discussion in the preceding chapters, the following sections in this chapter examine the challenges for the future and what the implications are both for those who work in the health and social care system and for the organization of health and social care services.

What are the key challenges for the future?

Diversity

One of the fundamental changes in welfare has been the increasing recognition that there are substantial differences between groups and individuals in society. The UK is increasingly becoming more diverse and old notions of social divisions structured around class are less relevant today. This is not to say that structured differences in society no longer exist, but that in analysing the delivery and impact of social policies, we need to be sensitive to a range of divisions and differences in society and the way these interact with inequalities, poverty and health. While immigration has led to a more multicultural society, this is not the only factor. Increasing nationalism in areas such as Wales and Scotland, growing numbers of older people and recognition of the rights of specific groups in society, such as homosexuals and lesbians, and the special problems of people with specific health problems and people with disabilities, have changed the way we view society and, therefore, the interaction between the state and society. In particular, it is now understood that many differences in society are socially constructed and that ageism, racism and other forms of discrimination, result from the way people conceptualize differences and how these views are often institutionalized. This is as true for the NHS and social services as it is for any institution, such as the police.

Two consequences emerge from analyses of these societal changes. The first is the fact that our understanding of equality and equity has become more sophisticated, with more attention being paid to the multiple dimensions of inequalities of health (Braham and Jones 2002). Secondly the acknowledgement of difference and diversity has been part of the impetus to shift towards more individualistic approaches to welfare, and underpins ideas of welfare consumerism. It is right that we need to treat people differently to be fair and equal, respecting difference, but ensuring that the same quality of treatment and respect is given to everyone. Culturally sensitive services, such as those needed for black or Asian carers or people with specific religious beliefs, are clearly important. Delivering these represents an enormous challenge for public welfare services. In the UK responses to such differences directly relate to policies advocating decentralization and localism, as local responsiveness is seen as key to meeting divergent needs. In England, the increasing fragmentation of services may lead to more culturally and socially responsive services, although increasing fragmentation may lead to problems of coordination and produce perverse incentives as happened in Sweden (Blomqvist 2004).

Changing demographics

The International Institute for Applied Systems Analysis (Lutz *et al.* 2001) forecasts that the world population, currently just over 6 billion, is likely to peak at about 9 billion in 2070 and then decline. As a result, there will be a very significant ageing of the population, especially in western Europe and Japan. This is a revision of previous projections by the United Nations, which assumed that the fertility rate would not fall below the average of 2.1 per woman required to sustain population numbers; the evidence is that it has already fallen below this level in much of western Europe, and is likely to do so in other parts of the world as they develop. While such a population shift may reduce some of the long-term pressure on the world's resources, Lutz *et al.* (2001) also warned of the potentially serious inter-generational political conflict ahead, as a political majority of older people insist on better services, which a smaller working population may have difficulty providing. Harding *et al.* (2006) report that over-85s are the fastest-growing demographic group, and that the birth rate (number per 1000 population) has decreased across Europe since 1960, for example, by 32 per cent in the UK. The decrease is often at least as great or greater in Catholic countries despite their avowed pronatalism; 28.5 per cent in Ireland and 56.4 per cent in Portugal. Germany is considering pronatalist policies, such as tax breaks and more nursery places in order to address this imbalance, which will have severe consequences for the provision of services and for the maintenance of financial stability when such a large proportion of the population is economically inactive.

Financial stability

Although the years since 1997 have shown considerable financial stability, the sudden financial problems in the NHS which materialised in 2005/6 show that this cannot be taken for granted. If this stability is lost, then the major proposals discussed earlier (such as the Wanless Reports and the Turner Commission on pensions) will be badly damaged, particularly since NHS-specific inflation usually runs at a higher rate than that for the economy as a whole. Under the most optimistic 'fully engaged' scenario produced by Wanless (2002) in which there is a sharp decline in smoking, obesity and other risk factors, it will cost £154 billion at 2002 prices to provide a good quality health service for Britain in 2022, more than doubling the 2002 budget and raising spending on health from 7.7 per cent of GDP to 10.6 per cent. The peak growth will be in the first five years. If people do not adopt a better lifestyle or engage more in self-care, or the NHS does not modernize and increase productivity, the bill could rise to £184 billion or 12.5 per cent of GDP, and although life expectancy will improve to a certain extent, much of that extension will be in poor health.

Barr (2001) argues that the state has an important role in managing risk and uncertainty, and in providing financial stability, which he terms *the welfare state as piggy-bank*, this will become more necessary in a world of volatile financial markets and interconnected national economies. Taylor-Gooby (2004) considers that there are challenges to industrial societies in Europe as they become post-industrial, resulting from population shifts (including changes in family patterns), changes in labour markets and economic globalization, which produce new risks. European welfare states developed from the 1950s to the 1970s in generally favourable circumstances: growing economies, stable employment largely based on manufacturing, stable family structures and governments able to manage largely through neo-Keynesian policies, in which government expenditure was a key element of economic growth. In the shift to a post-industrial society, employment is less stable and less unionized, and the reduction in male employment particularly affects unskilled people. Weak economic growth is exacerbated by the ability of multinational firms to remove capital, reinforced by the open market policy of the 1994 Maastricht Treaty, and also the impact of high volume currency speculation. (An example of the latter is the currency speculation which resulted in 'Black Wednesday', a catastrophic fall in the stock market in 1992. This resulted in great cuts in public spending; one such cut was a reduction in nursing training places, which caused staffing instability in many parts of the NHS for the rest of the decade.)

Inequalities

The extent to which financial inequalities continue to exist in the UK is
starkly illustrated by the statistic that more than half a million people earn
less than £10 per week, whereas 1.5 million earn more than £1,100 a week.
An analysis by the Institute for Fiscal Studies (2006), the leading tax think-
tank, found that the Labour government has been unable to alter greatly
the inequalities created under the Conservatives, and may be unable to do
so, in view of the priority given to health, education and overseas development which would squeeze other expenditure, such as anti-poverty
programmes. In the 1980s, the incomes of the richest 20 per cent rose
almost ten times more quickly than those of the poorest 20 per cent.
However, the picture for the poor has improved somewhat, if the very poor
and the very rich are excluded from the analysis. The government has
succeeded in cutting child poverty, although it has not been able to
achieve the target of a 25 per cent reduction by 2005 which it set itself.
Nevertheless, 700,000 children have been lifted out of poverty since 1998.
In 1997, 2.8 million pensioners were poor; this has been reduced by 1
million and pensioners are now not at any greater risk of poverty than the
rest of the population. The number of houses below the decency level has
also been reduced. It is difficult to see how these targets can be further
improved on, without greater taxation at the top levels of income (which is
unlikely).

As discussed above, the Labour government puts considerable emphasis
on the labour market as a route to social inclusion. Government policies
targeted specific groups through New Deal programmes, particularly
young people and lone parents. Progress on targets is generally slow
(Taylor-Gooby 2004); 16 per cent of households, and 44 per cent of lone
mothers are jobless (ONS 2001), and poverty is almost insoluble for those
outside the labour force. In Labour's second term, the compulsion for job
seekers was tightened and the system made more coordinated, by bringing
together the job-search component of the Department for Education and
Employment and the Department of Social Security, as the new Department for Work and Pensions. This is a good example of how the remit of a
government department may be revised as a social problem is construed in
a different way, in this case the centrality of employment for social
inclusion.

Inequalities in health are also still wide. Smoking and obesity are the
most important lifestyle determinants of future health; it is estimated that
half the difference in survival to 70 years of age, between social class 1 and
5, is due to the higher prevalence of smoking in the latter. Reflecting on
previous public health targets, Wanless (2004) considers that the smoking
one was unambitious, whereas the 1992 obesity and the 2002 physical
activity targets were 'highly aspirational'. There is a real danger of failing to
teach hard-to-reach groups, given the lack of knowledge on how to do so.
Wanless also recognizes the balance between individual choice and the
need to improve the health of the population. *The NHS Plan* (DoH 2000a)
set out a specific vision for the NHS, but was sketchy on public health,
although it did make a policy commitment to develop non-medically
qualified public health specialists. The public health role was spread very

thinly when it devolved to PCTs (and may be further disrupted with the mergers of PCTs being undertaken in 2006). Despite at least 30 years of government espousal of public health aims, both policy and the media focus largely on acute services.

Long-term conditions

As discussed in Chapter 7, tackling long-term conditions has become one of the key health care issues of the twenty-first century. Consequently, there have been a number of policy initiatives and service developments for people with long-term conditions in public health (DoH 2004a), user participation (DoH 2003d), social care, promoting user choice (DoH 2005b, 2005e), housing and financial support (Department of Work and Pensions 2005c). NSFs have established specific standards and preferred mechanisms of service delivery (DoH 1999e, 2000b, 2001e, 2005f). Some are broad, for example, the goal of 'seamless' patient-centred care which cuts across the NHS, local authorities, independent and voluntary sectors (DoH 1997, 1998b, 2004f; Welsh Assembly 2001; Scottish Executive 2003; DoH, Social Services and Public Safety Northern Ireland 2004). Others are more specific, such as the public service targets focused specifically on improved standards of service delivery to people with long-term conditions, and performance targets for chronic disease management and health promotion in the new GMS contract (DoH 2004h, DoH 2004i, 2004j).

Reducing mortality from chronic illness and maintaining health among people experiencing long-term conditions, requires engagement with lifestyle factors (Wanless 2002). There is also increasing recognition that while the pathologies of chronic disease are diverse, the needs of people with long-term conditions are broadly similar in that they have to learn to manage the disease, integrate it with their everyday life, engage in health maintenance activities, confront the progression of the disease and, in many cases, their death from the disease. For the health service to influence the overall prevalence of chronic illness and the morbidity of the population, it needs not only to develop clinically effective interventions, but also acceptable strategies to engage directly with the individual and the family. However, patient views, on the availability of support for long-term conditions, suggest that the NHS is not providing appropriate or adequate services (Coulter 2006). The emphasis on self-care, while important, will require different sorts of services to ensure that there is not simply a shift of care from formal health and social care services to the informal sector, placing increased burdens on service users, their carers, families and communities and creating further inequalities of health and welfare.

Implications for the delivery of health and social care

Although productivity in the health service has been increasing by about 2 per cent per year for the past 20 years, *Securing Our Future Health* (Wanless 2002) highlighted four key areas for further productivity gains: better use of ICT, more self-care by patients, better use of the skilled workforce and a redirection of existing NHS resources towards treatments that are cost-effective.

Better use of ICT

It is anticipated that staff will use common technologies, such as webcams and email, to communicate with patients in both health and social care; bar coding medicines should also make administration safer. 'Telecare' refers to any service which brings health and social care direct to the user, generally in their own homes, with the support of ICT. This includes fall alarms, sensors for gas and 'wander' monitors for people with dementia. 'Telehealth' is defined as the remote monitoring of vital signs, such as temperature and blood pressure. Proponents of telecare argue that it is not intended to replace human contact, but by enabling frequent monitoring and measurement, it can free up staff for better quality interventions. Wanless (2006) concludes that if telecare is to be more widely used, a much greater awareness among potential users is required, and that there are ethical issues in monitoring people with dementia, who are not able to give informed consent, but that the level of acceptability is generally high.

Self-care and management of long-term conditions

The management of long-term conditions challenges many of the assumptions that underpin the acute medical model of care, dominant in western health care delivery systems (Abel-Smith 1994; DoH 2004i). The traditional focus on acute care has led to clinical effectiveness being defined through access to medical technology, rather than through increasing the health capacity of the patient, family and community, despite evidence that health technology has only a marginal impact on health gain (Wanless 2002). In addition, the acute medical model emphasizes medical outcomes rather than those determined by patients or nursing and other health professionals, and is at odds with the need for patient-centredness in long-term conditions (Cullum *et al.* 2005; DoH 2005a). Recent key policy documents (DoH 2005c, 2005e, 2005k, 2006) emphasize the need for both services and professionals to provide integrated, efficient and enabling interventions, to help people prevent potential chronic disease or manage enduring conditions.

As discussed in Chapter 7, the majority of people with long-term conditions are able to self-care with carefully targeted professional input, and other US models currently being piloted within the UK, such as *Kaiser Permanente, Pfizer Health Solutions, Pursuing Perfection* and the *Expert Patient Programme*, have the facilitation of patient self-management as a key aim (DoH 2001d; Wilson 2001; Kennedy *et al.* 2005a, 2005b). The wide and varied roles in nursing, midwifery and health visiting, such as school nursing, practice nursing, community midwifery and smoking cessation, lend themselves to a variety of relationships, with people living with long-term conditions, ranging from health promotion to caring for those with highly complex needs. Nursing has long been recognized as having a key role to play in helping people to manage long-term conditions (Audit Commission 1999; Kratz 1978). There has not, however, been proactive engagement with the client groups' needs and, until recently, nursing in the UK has not fully realized its potential to meet the needs of chronically ill people (Gibbon 1994; Nolan and Nolan 1995, 1999; ENB 1999). The global focus on long-term conditions and consequent examples of innovative practice elsewhere, combined with a succession of national policies focusing on long-term conditions, have provided a catalyst for UK nurses to address their contribution (WHO 2002). Developing specialist nurse roles or enhancing the skills of generalist nurses to focus systematically on particular groups of patients, have been shown to be effective approaches to supporting people with long-term conditions (Colledge *et al.* 2003); the most high profile role is that of the community matron, whose remit is to work with people with complex health problems, and to stabilise and co-ordinate their care.

There are also important roles for the wider health professional team with physiotherapists, occupational therapists and other allied health professionals, playing key support roles (NHS Modernization Agency 2005). The roles of health promotion specialists, pharmacists, care workers, housing and social workers, are also key in providing adequate care and support. This shifts the focus away from narrower concepts of general practice primary care, and leads to new ways of delivering primary and community care.

Better use of the skilled workforce

According to Wanless (2002) the health care workforce might need to increase by 300,000 by 2022, including 62,000 doctors, 108,000 nurses, 45,000 therapists and scientists, and 74,000 health care assistants. The number of GPs would need to more than double, from 26,000 to more than 55,000. There would also need to be a shift of work from doctors to nurses, and from nurses to health care assistants.

There is also, as illustrated above, an increasing recognition of the important role of other health professionals in the NHS. Developments in pharmacy and the use of community pharmacies as a base for support and care, have been highlighted in recent policy documents and have an important role in the management of, and support for, people with long-term conditions (DoH 2006). The roles of a wide range of professions allied to health, such as physiotherapists, occupational therapists and counsellors, are likely to expand, raising questions about the way care is organized in the community. As discussed in Chapter 10, the skill mix is likely to shift towards more specialized roles for registrants, and the development of skilled helper grades. Recent changes to community dental contracts are placing dentistry more firmly on the agendas of local primary care organizations, and tackling the shortage of NHS dentistry is likely to lead to different approaches to the provision of dental services. Outside the NHS, the rapid growth in the numbers of CAM practitioners is leading to pressures on how they should be regulated and what kind of relationship there should be between CAM and the NHS (Thomas *et al.* 2003).

The health care service of the future will have an increasingly wide range of practitioners, and it is likely that many traditional boundaries between professions, will become increasingly blurred. In order for this to occur, however, Lahey and Currie (2005: 206) argue that regulatory and medicolegal boundaries will need to be addressed: '*institutional structures that connect the distinct disciplinary processes of each profession ... seem particularly important in a world of interprofessional practice that leads to greater interprofessional dependency. The danger otherwise is that autonomous disciplinary processes fail to make the adjustment to interprofessional practice that ... is a risk when malpractice allegations are litigated*'. Interprofessional working is seen as a remedy for the communication failures identified in major incidents, such as the Bristol Inquiry and also the case of Victoria Climbie, both referred to above. D'Amour *et al.* (2005) conclude that the concept of collaboration, which underpins interprofessional working, includes the concepts of sharing, partnership, power and interdependency, although the literature does not indicate how patients and other service users can be integrated into the team. Generally, both the research and practice in interprofessional working are still in their early stages in the UK, although they have policy support.

Cost-effective treatments

Containing costs will be crucial if future health needs are to be addressed. Wanless (2004) considers that knowledge of genetics and of individual risk factors, could have an increasing influence in creating a 'fully engaged' population, since health promotion and prevention could be more individualized. By 2016, the first results should be available from the Biobank, which began recruiting in March 2006. DNA samples, health and lifestyle information, will be collected from half a million people between 40 and 69, with the aim of looking for potential indicators of the development of disease, and whether there is a correlation between particular genotypes and the susceptibility to particular diseases. This will have great implications for the NHS and for staff; the NHS National Genetics Education and Development Centre opened in 2005 to address training needs in interpreting genotype risk profiles, ordering tests and giving advice. Advances in pharmacogenetics may lead to personalized medicines in the next 20 years, and formed the centrepiece of the 2003 genetics White Paper; this is exemplified by Herceptin, the drug appropriate for some women with breast cancer. However, Hedgecoe's (2004) study shows that there is a contrast between the expectations of the proponents of pharmacogenetics, and the scepticism and ethical reservations of clinicians. It is likely, therefore, that change will be incremental rather than revolutionary.

Containing the cost of health is likely to be problematic, since the pharmaceutical industry, or 'big pharma', is a major world player. £33 billion is spent annually on drug promotion, and there is evidence that drug companies are promoting their products through patients groups (Boseley 2006). Arguments about the entitlement to treatment are likely to increase, often using the courts; this has been seen recently in relation to the prescription of Herceptin for early stage breast cancer, when, at the time, its use had been assessed by NICE only for the later stages (Moore 2006). Although, at least in theory, the NICE evidence base can be used to justify decisions, they cannot be depoliticized, and NICE has been heavily criticized for making narrow, prescriptive decisions (Carlisle 2006). Little evidence exists to support some of the most complex decisions in health and social care, other than somewhat subjective impressions of whether the person is, or is not, responding to care. It would, for example, be difficult to use cost-benefit arguments in the recent court cases on prolonging intensive care for severely handicapped infants, or in relation to social care. SCIE, the Social Care Institute for Excellence, does not assess evidence in the same way as NICE, since its starting point is acceptability to the service user, and the availability of randomized controlled trials in social care is limited.

Organization of care

In the 2002 NHS Delivery Plan, it was announced that overseas health companies would be invited to deliver services, either in their own or NHS premises. These concepts have been more fully developed in recent policy documents on patient choice (DoH 2004a, 2006). Proposals in England for more provider plurality, and greater private and not-for-profit, involvement in health care are further developed than in the other countries of the UK, although Scotland is about to develop private finance for primary care premises and is looking at non-NHS service delivery. Wales and Northern Ireland have not developed these approaches and remain wholly NHS, although private provision has been used to tackle Welsh waiting lists. The extent of changes can be seen in the recent changes to out-of-hours services, which have involved new organizational developments across the NHS and private sectors, new types of practitioner being developed (such as the emergency care practitioner) and new partnerships being formed between out-of-hours care and ambulance services. A key consequence of these changes has been a disinvestment in out-of-hours cover via NHS Direct (Staines 2006). Although patient satisfaction with NHS Direct is generally high, it has not reduced the pressure on the NHS to the extent anticipated. NHS Direct will also need to compete with private providers to run GP out-of-hours services, illustrating how vulnerable parts of an organization can be to policy changes.

Changes in primary care contracts, the increasing use of the private sector and changes to the status of NHS trusts (such as Foundation Trusts), will introduce significant changes to the structure of UK health care services. The experience of PMS and walk-in centres has started to open the doors to new ways of thinking about the structure and delivery of general practice and the role and position of the GP. Privately-run companies have already started to run these services in England (Derbyshire, East London and the Liverpool Street Station walk-in centre) and developments in new forms of practice organization are likely to continue (Lewis *et al.* 2006). Competition and patient choice in England, will also bring pressure to bear on the numbers, range and configuration of hospital services. There will be changes to the way hospitals are organized, and the transfer of services between hospitals, developing centres of clinical excellence and building clinical partnerships across hospitals and across the primary and secondary sectors, will be more common. These moves will also be partly driven by policy, such as the changes that have been made as a result of the implementation of Cancer Plan (DoH 2000), such as clinical networks. The changes will have enormous implications for the way professionals work and also for how patients access and use services.

Conclusion

In Chapter 1, we introduced Baldock *et al.*'s (2003) categorization of social policy, as being concerned with the intentions and objectives that lie behind policies, the administrative and financial arrangements that are used to deliver policies and the outcomes of policies, particularly in terms of who gains and loses. Throughout the book, we have drawn these three strands of social policy analysis together to examine the development of health and welfare services and policy in the UK. The importance of taking this broad approach to social policy should, hopefully, be self-evident. Health and social care practitioners need an understanding of why particular services exist, the way they work and what impact they have on the users and people who come into contact with them.

In this chapter, we have attempted to convey a sense of how policy is formulated, and its relevance to health and social care professionals. We have addressed key themes which underlie health and social care, and key challenges for the future, in the context of the uncertainties created by globalization. Although it is difficult to know how health and social care will evolve, and which policies will continue to have currency, the overall move away from state provision has now existed under both Conservative and Labour administrations, and seems likely to continue, as will the difficulties of containing the costs of care, in the light of developing technologies and increasingly informed and 'querulous citizens' (Taylor-Gooby *et al.* 2003).

Summary

- Social policy analysis enables us to understand the broader social context for health care, particularly the role of the state. Although the Labour government has tried to achieve 'joined-up government', policy goals may sometimes conflict, and governments also need to balance individual freedom and the collective good.
- Key underlying themes are changes in the relationship between the individual and the state, and the growth of risk as a key factor in policy-making, leading to increasing regulation.
- Other key themes are the growing empowerment of service users, and

the need for stewardship, as the role of the state shifts from provision to commissioning services from an increasingly diverse range of providers, including private and not-for-profit organizations.

- Challenges include growing population diversity and demographic changes leading to greater demands upon services from increasingly informed consumers.
- Inequalities are likely to persist but must be addressed, not only from the perspective of social justice, but also because social inequalities create health inequalities, and a greater need for services.
- Wanless (2002) highlighted four key areas for further productivity gains: better use of ICT, more self-care by patients, better use of the skilled workforce and a redirection of existing NHS resources towards treatments that are cost-effective.

GLOSSARY

Absolute poverty: *see* poverty, absolute.

Academy school: a new type of secondary school developed by the Labour government, with some private sector sponsorship, more autonomy than other schools, and generally a focus on a particular specialism.

'Actively seeking work': in order to qualify for unemployment benefit, it is necessary to demonstrate that steps are actively being taken to find employment.

Altruism: concern for others, putting others before oneself. Some policy analysts have argued that families, and women in particular, may have to exhibit 'compulsory altruism', i.e. they are expected to put others' needs first.

Artefact explanation: a spurious correlation – an apparent relationship due to the effect on both elements of some third factor.

Attendance allowance: benefit paid to people with care needs who require assistance night and/or day. Replaced by disability living allowance for those under retirement age.

Audit Commission: an independent public body responsible for ensuring that public money is spent economically, efficiently and effectively in the areas of local government, housing, health, criminal justice and fire and rescue services.

Basic income: an income paid to all irrespective of work performed or needs experienced.

Behavioural explanation: the assumption that poverty, poor educational achievement, poor health etc., can be explained by the behaviour of the people themselves; for example, that poor health is the outcome of a freely chosen but inappropriate lifestyle.

Benefits, earnings-related: benefits which vary according to the level of previous earnings.

Benefits, flat-rate: benefits paid at a single rate for all, as opposed to 'earnings-related' benefits.

Benefits, insured: welfare benefits paid on the basis of an insurance contribution record (e.g. unemployment pay).

Benefits, means-tested: welfare benefits paid on the basis of a financial test of means; paid only to those with a low income and/or low levels of saving (e.g. income support).

Benefits, non-contributory: welfare benefits paid without requiring a record of insurance contributions or a test of means (e.g. child benefit, non-contributory invalidity benefit).

Benefits, selective: *see* benefits, means-tested.

Benefits, universal: welfare benefits paid as of right, without a financial means test (e.g. insured and non-contributory benefits).

Bevan: Aneurin Bevan was the Welsh ex-miner who, as Minister of Health, had the main role in implementing the NHS, against the suspicion and resistance of much of the medical profession.

Beveridge: Sir William Beveridge was an eminent civil servant, academic and journalist who was asked to chair a committee to coordinate social insurance during the Second World War. He greatly expanded its remit, in order to address 'the five giants' of want, ignorance, disease, squalor and idleness, and was one of the key figures in the creation of the welfare state.

Bismarck: Otto von Bismarck introduced a system of compulsory social insurance in Germany in the 1890s, which influenced both Lloyd George (see below) and Beveridge.

Bureaucracy: hierarchical management of an organization with strict vertical lines of superordination and subordination.

Care trusts: NHS trusts which combine both health and social care; they are not widespread.

Charity Organization Society: a major philanthropic society of the nineteenth century, whose aim was surveillance over charitable donations to ensure that they were properly used by their recipients.

Commercial sector: providers of welfare services as a commercial proposition, for profit.

Commissioning (also practice-based commissioning): the identification, planning and purchasing of health and social care services.

Communitarianism: the idea that individual rights need to be balanced with social responsibilities, and that individuals do not exist in isolation, but are shaped by the values and culture of the communities and societies they live in.

Community: a concept used to refer to (1) people living in a geographical location, (2) groups of people with a sense of identity and commonality, (3) a group of people linked together through social relationships, or (4) a group of people linked by a common culture.

Community care: the provision of services to enable dependent people (1) to live outside of large residential institutions, (2) to live in their own homes or (3) to live in as 'normal' an environment as possible. Variously taken to mean the location of care or the source of care – care *in* and *by* the community.

Community care grant: a grant paid out of the Social Fund to allow the purchase of basic household items to enable someone to live in the community.

Community matrons: senior nurses, generally with a district nursing background and additional training e.g. in prescribing, whose role is to coordinate the care of people living in the community with a range of complex illnesses. The role is a new one in the UK.

Competitive tendering: putting up service contracts for 'auction' to commercial and other concerns, with the intention of accepting the cheapest offer which promises to provide the service efficiently and effectively.

Complementary therapy: a range of treatments such as aromatherapy, acupuncture, homeopathy and Chinese medicine, which are increasingly used in addition to orthodox medicine. The term CAM (complementary and alternative medicine) is also used. Although championed by the Prince of Wales, it is medically contentious since the evidence base for it is not well established.

Conservatism: a set of political beliefs emphasizing social order and tradition; associated with the Conservative Party in Britain (although the type of Conservatism introduced by Prime Minister Margaret Thatcher in the 1980s was a radical move away from tradition).

Consumerism: a broad concept which is becoming influential in health care; at its heart is the ability to make an informed choice.

Co-payments: term used when both the patient or service user and the state contribute towards the cost of a service or item; for example, the prescription charge does not generally cover the cost of medication, and so both the patient and the state contribute.

Correlation: systematic co-variation, such that the value of one variable is to some extent predictable from the other. Examples include the relationship of height and weight or social class and income.

Crisis in health: the recognition from the 1970s onwards that healthcare systems in developed countries would continue to experience cost pressures.

Cycle of deprivation: *see* poverty cycle.

Decarceration: term deriving from the Latin *carcer*, a prison, used to refer to the move of patients out of large asylums.

Demography: the study of the structure of populations (e.g. the proportion of older people in a population).

Dependency: a state of reliance on the support of welfare services – can be financial, physical and/or psychological.

Dependent population: people who are not economically active. Generally used to refer to those below the age of paid employment (children) and people over the age of retirement.

Deprivation, material: being unable to afford the basic goods and services taken for granted in a given country.

Deprivation, social: being unable to participate in normal day-to-day social activities. This may be the result of material deprivation, but it could be because of, for example, old age or disability.

Deterrence: making a behaviour or course of action unattractive to someone; for example, measures used to deter people from applying for state benefits.

Direct payments: from April 1997, disabled people of working age could receive money to employ their own carers; this right was extended to older people in 2000.

Disability living allowance: non-contributory, non-means-tested benefit paid to people under the age of retirement who need constant care by day and/or night and/or have severe mobility problems. With the exception of the terminally ill, there is a qualifying period of six months.

Discrimination: to exclude someone from goods, services, employment, housing etc., because of some characteristic (e.g. gender, race) or to offer them inferior terms.

Disincentive to work: the argument that high levels of social security benefits to the unemployed will make them less likely to seek paid employment.

'Dole': colloquial term for unemployment benefit.

Domiciliary care: personal, social and domestic care provided in a person's home. Provision of domiciliary care is seen as a means of enabling people to remain in their own homes, who might otherwise have had to move into residential care.

Earnings-related benefits: *see* benefits, earnings-related.

Eligibility: generally used to mean that a person meets the criteria for receiving a welfare benefit and/or service.

Empowerment: giving people the power to make decisions for themselves. This can involve giving them money so that they can purchase services for themselves and/ or knowledge so that they can make informed choices.

Endemic: latent, always present in the population (generally used in relation to diseases).

Epidemic: a major outbreak of a condition (generally used in relation to infectious diseases, but now extended to other major problems such as obesity).

Equality: equal treatment – everyone being treated, in some sense, in the same way.

Equity: fair treatment – the treatment of like cases in the same way.

Ethnic minority: a group having a different culture from the majority of the population. In Britain, the term is most frequently used to refer to people of Afro-Caribbean or southern Asian descent.

Eugenics: the argument that the race can be improved either by encouraging the 'fit' to breed (positive eugenics) or by preventing the 'unfit' from breeding (negative eugenics).

Expert patient: a programme introduced in the 1990s originating in the USA which looks at the role of the patient in managing their own health problem. The NHS introduced the programme in the UK for people with long-term and chronic health problems and involves training patients to self-manage aspects of their health problems.

Expressed needs: the welfare needs that people themselves say they have.

Fabian Movement: a political movement and philosophy associated with one wing of the Labour Party, which believes in social reformation through gradual change; supporters of a classic welfare state with universal benefits and equity.

Family: a group of people related by kinship ties. In modern Britain, generally used to refer to the 'nuclear family' of mother, father and dependent children, as opposed to the 'extended family', comprising a wider group of relatives.

Felt needs: needs that people feel they have.

Fiscal policy: state economic policy, especially with reference to taxation.

Fiscal welfare: redistribution through the tax system (e.g. tax relief on mortgage interest).

Flat-rate benefit: *see* benefits, flat-rate.

Foundation trust: an NHS trust with greater independence from the Department of Health. Foundation Trusts have to meet a series of strict criteria to attain that status; the policy is a recent one and it remains to be seen whether it will succeed.

Friendly Society: a mutual aid organization developed for the protection of its members; usually concerned with sickness, unemployment and old age.

Fundholder: *see* GP fundholders.

Gender roles: roles taken on by men and women that are associated with one gender. Assumed to be the result either of natural (biological) differences or of social expectations (socialization).

General practitioner (GP): a medical doctor who provides a comprehensive medical service for a list of patients in the community.

Governance: a process promoted by the Labour government from 1998; it integrates quality assurance activities, clinical audit, clinical risk management, clinical effectiveness and staff and organizational development.

GP fundholders: GPs who had devolved budgets to provide and purchase medical care on behalf of their patients (a policy implemented in the 1990s by the Conservative government, and discontinued, then reinvented, by Labour through practice-based commissioning).

Green Paper: a government discussion paper.

Gross domestic product (GDP): the total income of a country.

Gross national product (GNP): the value of a country's total production.

Health Action Zones: an area based approach to tackling health inequalities introduced by the Labour Government in 1998 but phased out in the early 2000s.

Health inequalities: *see* inequalities, health.

Health selection: the argument that an individual's social class is determined at least in part by his or her health; that is, those who are healthiest are the 'fittest' and are upwardly socially mobile.

Healthcare Commission: an independent body, set up to promote and drive improvement in the quality of healthcare and public health. Its main duties in England are to assess the management, provision and quality of NHS healthcare and public health services, review the performance of each NHS trust and award an annual performance rating, regulate the independent healthcare sector through registration, annual inspection, monitoring complaints and enforcement, and carry out investigations of serious failures in the provision of healthcare.

Healthy Cities Project: policy advocated by the World Health Organization for joint strategies by health authorities and local government to improve the health of residents by both target-setting and policy initiatives.

Healthy Living Centres: community based interventions to promote health funded through the National Lottery introduced by the Labour Government in 1998.

Horizontal redistribution: redistribution between people in different social circumstances, without necessarily having regard to resources. Often used to refer to redistribution across the life course.

Hospices: the modern hospice movement originated in 1967; they provide care mainly for terminally ill patients, and are noted particularly for holistic care and for having developed pain relief.

Housing association: a not-for-profit organization which provides and manages homes for people who cannot afford to buy on the open market, which may or may not have charitable status. They increasingly view themselves as businesses.

Housing benefit: means-tested benefit for those on low income to assist with the cost of rented housing.

Housing tenure: the basis on which people occupy housing – owner occupation, rental (private), rental (council) or rental (housing association).

Ideology: a set of interrelated values and beliefs.

Income support: means-tested benefit for unemployed/non-employed people, who may also be in receipt of other income maintenance benefits such as unemployment pay or disability living allowance.

Individualism: (1) the argument that each person, individually, is able to take action independently of other people in society (i.e. individuals can take control of their own lives and make decisions for themselves), (2) the view that poverty, educational failure, etc. can be explained by the inadequacies (biological or acquired) of individuals themselves.

Individualistic policies: policies which focus on each individual separately.

Inequalities, health: the differential health experiences of groups in society. Most frequently used to refer to inequalities in health between socially and economically privileged and deprived or less privileged groups.

Inequalities, material: the differential access to goods and services (e.g. housing, health services, income, diet etc.) experienced by socially and economically privileged and deprived or less privileged groups.

Informal carer: one who cares for another, being neither employed to do so nor a member of a voluntary organization. Generally the spouse or parent, or child, of the dependent person, but may include other relatives, friends and neighbours.

Informal sector: the provision of welfare by family and friends without payment; generally assumed to be based on feelings of affection but may be based on feelings of duty/loyalty.

Insurance benefits: *see* benefits, insured.

Keynesianism: economic policies based on the ideas of John Maynard Keynes, an influential economist in the 1940s and 1950s who believed in investment by the state.

Laissez-faire: literally 'leave to do'; used to refer to economic policies that argue that the state should not intervene in the economic market.

Learning difficulty (or learning disability): slow intellectual development. The term mental handicap was used until recently, but is now not acceptable.

Less eligibility: the deterrence principle enacted in the 1832 Poor Law, that those given relief (benefits) should be treated less favourably than the poorest person not on relief.

Liberalism: the argument that individuals must be left free to make choices and that the state should make minimal intervention in society, providing only a legal framework and defence.

Life chances: the differential opportunities for economic, educational and social success. Often argued to be based on social class at birth, those with middle-class parents being said to have superior life chances to those with working-class parents.

Life course: the series of changes that take place as people go through the course of their lives; biological and social changes including, for example, childhood, adolescence, adulthood, marriage, parenting, bereavement and old age.

Life expectancy: the number of years that a person can expect to live, on average. Usually given for life expectancy at birth but can be calculated from any given age.

Lloyd George: David Lloyd George was a Liberal politician (Chancellor, and then Prime Minister) who introduced the first state pensions and unemployment insurance in the UK, in 1911.

Local authorities: a term which includes county councils and borough councils, with the responsibility for providing a range of services, such as education and some health services; their range of powers has reduced since the 1990s, as, for example, schools have gained greater autonomy.

Localism: a philosophy which emphasizes more local participation in decision making and in the provision of services.

Lone parent family: the head of the family in which there is only one parent, through death, divorce or separation. In Britain, 90 per cent of single parents are women.

Long-term care: care needed by dependent people, particularly older people.

Low pay: an income less than that paid on average in a country. There is considerable disagreement as to what counts as low pay, however.

Managed market: term used to refer to the internal markets set up by the National Health Service and Community Care Act 1990, to encourage competition between providers of health care in Britain, also referred to as quasi-markets. Also used to refer to the social market, that the same legislation required to be stimulated, in the provision of community care.

Managerialism: a related term used in the 1990s was New Public Management. The assumption that private sector practices are more effective than those in the public sector, and that the public sector should be competitive, and should regard service users as customers or consumers.

Manual workers: people who work with their hands. Often referred to as the 'working-class'.

Marketization: the process of making the delivery of state welfare services more like services delivered by the commercial sector. Can be achieved either by 'privatization' or by introducing managed markets.

Material inequalities: *see* inequalities, material.

Means test: a test of financial means (income and/or savings) to determine eligibility for benefits and/or services.

Means-tested benefits: *see* benefits, means-tested.

Mixed economy of welfare: the provision of welfare services and benefits by more than one sector – state, commercial, voluntary and informal.

Mobility allowance: an allowance formerly paid to people who could not walk or had great difficulty in walking. Claimants had to be eligible for the allowance before their 65th birthday. Now incorporated within disability living allowance for those aged under 65.

Modernization Agency: an agency set up in 2001 to disseminate new processes and practices in the NHS, in order to improve the quality of care and to meet targets such as reduced waiting times. It was merged into the NHS Institute for Innovation and Improvement in 2005.

Morbidity: ill health.

Mortality: death.

Mutual aid: the principle of joining together, with others, to provide help or support for each other in times of adversity.

National efficiency: term used at the time of the Boer War to refer to the ability of people, particularly the working-class, to undertake military service or to work in factories.

National Institute for Health and Clinical Excellence (NICE): an organization set up in 1999 to provide guidance on the clinical and cost-effectiveness of treatments and protocols. In 2005 it incorporated the Health Development Agency, which provided guidance on public health.

National service frameworks (NSFs): sets of recommendations produced by the

Department of Health for the clinical management of particular health problems, such as heart disease and diabetes; some have a wider focus, such as the NSF for older people.

New Labour: the label attached to the Labour Party since the mid 1990s, particularly associated with its 'modernization' under Tony Blair. This includes a move towards the middle ground in politics, and the development of markets in welfare provision.

New Right: the term used to refer to the ideologies espoused by the political right since the late 1970s, particularly in Britain and the USA. Generally combines a commitment to Conservative values in terms of morality and the family with Liberal (free-market) economic principles. Also referred to as Thatcherism in the UK.

NHS Direct: an English telephone advice line set up by the Labour government in 1998, staffed primarily by nurses, supported by computer algorithms. Scotland has a similar organization.

NHS trusts: agencies within the health service providing services for purchase (e.g. hospitals, community services and ambulance services).

Non-contributory benefits: *see* benefits, non-contributory.

Non-employed: those who do not have and are not seeking paid employment (e.g. students, people over the age of retirement, women with full-time domestic responsibilities).

Non-take-up: failure to claim benefits, most commonly associated with means-tested benefits.

Normalization: enabling people to live as normally as possible; empowering people to participate in society.

Occupational schemes: *see* pension, occupational.

Occupational welfare: *see* welfare, occupational.

Paid volunteering: small cash payments to volunteers, for example good neighbour schemes.

Paternalism: the principle of doing things for people's benefit, without seeking their consent.

Patient and public involvement: although there has been the opportunity for the public to have a say on the running of the local NHS since 1974 (through Community Health Councils), these were abolished in 2003 and replaced by Patient Advice and Liaison Services.

Patriarchy: literally, 'rule of the father'. Now generally used to refer to a society in which men have power over women.

Pauperism: term used under the New Poor Law to refer to the state of being dependent on relief (benefits); derives from the Latin *pauper*, meaning poor.

Payment by Results: key English NHS policy to underpin market style reforms in the NHS to work alongside patient choice so that health care providers are paid for each patient they treat.

Pension, occupational: retirement pension provided by an employer, to which the employee may or may not have contributed during his or her working life. Benefits are based on years of service.

Pension, private: a pension – usually on retirement but could be, for example, on permanent disability – arranged by an individual with an insurance company. An employer may contribute to a private pension. Benefits are based on contributions paid.

Pension, state: retirement pension paid by the state on the basis of a contribution record. Those who have not opted-out may be entitled to an additional earnings-related element.

Pension, supplementary: a means-tested pension paid to retirement pensioners on low income.

Performance indicators: targets used to assess work performance; originally associated with employment in which employees are on performance-related pay, but also used for measures of the effectiveness of a department or service.

Performance-related pay: an element of earned income dependent on achieving agreed targets.

Personal care needs: needs for help with personal care tasks such as toileting, washing and dressing.

Personal social services: the range of services, including social work, residential and domiciliary care, which are the statutory responsibility of local authority social services departments.

Perverse incentive: term used when a policy has unanticipated (and unwanted) effects.

Pharmacogenetics: the sequencing of the human genome has enabled geneticists to study whether variations in particular genes increase susceptibility to a particular disease, for example by altering the production of a cellular protein. It may then be possible to produce a monoclonal antibody to that protein. An example of this is Herceptin for HER2 positive breast cancer. Pharmacogenetics should also provide information on the differences in cellular biology which, for example, make Afro-Caribbean people more susceptible to hypertension, and which lead to differences in the response to particular drugs. This may enable more 'tailoring' of treatment in the future.

Philanthropy: (literally the love of mankind) term used to refer to charitable work where there is the expectation that the recipients of charity will change their behaviour.

Policy vacuums: gaps in policy and provision.

Poor Law: legislation passed in the sixteenth century to establish who was responsible for the maintenance of poor people, many of whom were wandering beggars.

Poor Law infirmary: hospital for the poor, in the nineteenth and early twentieth centuries.

Post-industrial society: a society in which the economy is no longer based on agriculture or industry, but on service industries such as tourism or finance; generally this entails less financial stability, and a shift from male to female employment.

Poverty: severe deprivation, usually associated with inadequate resources, especially financial. How it should be measured is disputed.

Poverty, absolute: the inability to provide for basic food and shelter; starvation.

Poverty cycle: the movement in and out of poverty (however defined) experienced across the life course by low income groups.

Poverty, feminization of: the argument that poverty is a major problem for women because of the growth of women dependent on means-tested benefits, either as heads of single-parent households or as older women.

Poverty, relative: being poor in relation to average standards of living in a society; not being able to participate in the day-to-day activities that are taken for granted by others.

Poverty, subsistence: having just sufficient resources to live at the bare minimum.

Poverty trap: a situation that arises when people's income increases and they move off welfare benefits, such that their net income does not increase or increases only marginally.

Practice-based commissioning: introduced in the English NHS in 2005 where individual GP practices or groups of practices undertake the purchasing of care for their patients.

Premature death: death occurring before the average life expectancy has been achieved.

Primary care: is not well defined, often meaning simply those health services which are delivered outside hospital (i.e. secondary or acute care). Increasingly primary care is used synonymously with general practice; this means that primary care nurses, such as district nurses (who are not employed by GPs), can be overlooked in policy formation.

Private Finance Initiative (PFI): a scheme initiated by the Conservative government in the mid 1990s and continued by Labour, by which private firms have built NHS hospitals, and are then reimbursed over a long time period. Although it has enabled a large-scale building programme, critics state that it will lead to much greater expense, and that the NHS will be locked into expensive hospital provision, some of which may not be needed in the future.

Private sector: *see* commercial sector.

Privatization: transfer to the commercial or voluntary sector of previously state-owned services.

Progressive taxation: a fiscal policy that means that, as income rises, the amount of tax paid/deducted rises.

Pronatalism: policies intended to encourage people to have children.

Provident Society: *see* Friendly Society.

Public sector: services managed and financed by the state.

Quango: an abbreviation for quasi-autonomous non-governmental organization.

Quasi-market: *see* managed market.

Redistribution: transfer of resource from some people to others, or from one life stage to another.

Registrar General's Classification: an occupational class measure that divides occupations into five category bands, roughly by income and status.

Relative poverty: *see* Poverty, relative.

Remuneration package: the sum total received from an employer, including salary plus additional rewards such as use of car, health insurance, sick pay, pension plan, workplace nursery etc.

Residential care: care in which help and support is provided in a residential setting; usually seen as 'more normal' than care in long-stay hospitals.

Residual welfare state: a welfare state that makes only minimum provision at a minimum level for those on low incomes. Eligibility for benefits is generally means-tested.

Residuum: term used in the nineteenth century to refer to the unemployed dependent on relief from the workhouse. The term 'underclass' has been used to refer to the same population in the 1980s and 1990s.

Retirement: leaving paid employment. In Britain, the retirement age is often seen as synonymous with entitlement to a state pension. Although early retirement is not uncommon, and in some occupations it has become the norm for men and women to retire at 60, this is likely to alter. The state pension age is likely to rise due to the increasing proportion of the population who are not economically active, and there are concerns about the inadequacy of many people's contributions to their pension.

Safety net: residual welfare services and/or benefits for those on low incomes or without income altogether, who would not otherwise be able to provide for themselves.

Sanitary reform: usually used to refer to the public health reforms in the nineteenth century, concerned primarily with the provision of sewers and clean water.

Selective benefits: *see* benefits, means-tested.

Selectivity: a policy of focusing resources on people in need; usually involves financial means-testing.

Semi-profession: the term used by Etzioni to characterize occupations, such as nursing, which in his view did not have the autonomy nor the knowledge base of the full professions, such as medicine.

Shadow state: term used by some theorists to refer to a system where some state functions are devolved to other organizations such as voluntary organizations; this may make accountability less clear.

Skill mix: the combination of services from different agencies and/or different grades or kinds of staff, differently trained and qualified, to best satisfy the needs of a given client or group of clients.

Social care needs: needs for help with tasks such as cooking, shopping, and transport.

Social class: the division of the population into economic groups. Most social scientists argue that there are a number of social classes in Britain which have their own interests and try to protect them. The official categorization of social class used to be that devised by the Registrar General, with six main groups or classes:

1. professional and higher managerial
2. semi-professional, lower management
3. 1 routine non-manual
   2 skilled manual
4. semi-skilled manual
5. unskilled manual.

Replaced in 2001 by the National Statistics Socio-Economic Classes (see Chapter 4).

Social control: control exercised by some people over others, either for the benefit of society generally or of a specific social group. People are controlled when they are made or induced to act in ways in which they would not otherwise choose, in order to receive benefits/ services, or when their options are restricted.

Social deprivation: *see* deprivation, social.

Social enterprise: a business with primarily social objectives whose surpluses are principally reinvested for that purpose in the business or in the community, rather than being driven by the need to maximize profit for shareholders and owners.

Social exclusion: a term which is broader than simply poverty, and which refers to how some people are excluded from full participation in society due to lack of skills, education, poverty or disability.

Social Fund: a cash-limited fund established by the Social Security Act 1986. There are two elements: community care grants and loans.

Social policy: policies designed to meet people's welfare needs. The study of social services and the welfare state.

Social problem: a problem which is seen to relate to society as a whole or specific groups within it. Can be seen as a problem for society and/or a problem that has social as opposed to individual causes. For example, crime is seen as a social problem because it creates problems for society generally; it may be seen as having social and/or individual causes.

Social security: income maintenance benefits. In Britain, the term refers to insured and means-tested benefits.

Standardized mortality ratio: the ratio of the number of deaths, observed in a population, to the number expected if the population had the same age and sex structure as the standard population, multiplied by 100. Standardization allows comparisons between groups with different age and sex distributions. Without standardization, for example, a population with a higher death rate may be assumed to be less healthy, whereas the reason may be a higher proportion of very old people in the population (as in some towns on the south coast of England).

State: the formal political institutions of a society, including both central and local government.

State retirement pension: *see* pension, state.

Statutory services: services provided or at least purchased by the public sector and prescribed by law or regulation.

Stewardship: the social contract between the government and its people, whereby government is for the greatest good of the people and public funds are used in a responsible manner.

Stigma: literally 'visible blemish'; a sense of shame, a 'spoiled identity', a loss of status. Stigmatization may led to social rejection because of actual or assumed physical and/or moral characteristics.

Strategic health authorities (SHAs): since the NHS was set up, the government has tried a variety of structures to manage it, trying to resolve the tensions between sensitivity to local need and achieving national consistency. For many years there was a structure of 14, then 8, regions, and districts; until the purchaser-provider split of the 1990s the districts managed both hospitals and community services. This structure was changed in 2001 to a single layer of SHAs, and in 2006 the number of these was reduced (in London, for example, one SHA has replaced five).

Structural dependency: dependency caused by economic position and relationship to society, rather than by people's individual characteristics or behaviour.

Subsistence poverty: *see* poverty, subsistence.

Supplementary pension: *see* pension, supplementary.

Surveillance: literally 'oversight'; the monitoring of behaviour/performance of a group or individual.

Targeting: directing services and/or benefits to those most in need; usually involves using financial means-testing and/or strict criteria of eligibility.

Teaching hospital: a hospital used for training medical students; generally they have the highest status.

Tenure: in housing policy, the right by which people occupy their house (e.g. renting from a housing association, owner-occupation).

Third Way: the political philosophy underpinning New Labour; it tries to find a balance between the welfare state and the provision of services through the market.

Two-tier provision: there was a particular concern during the mid 1990s that the patients of GPs who were GP fundholders would receive a better standard of service than others.

Underclass: a group below the class system, dependent on state benefits. Used both by those who see the group as excluded by structural factors from participating and by those who see the underclass as morally undesirable.

Unemployed: those who do not have paid employment and are actively seeking it.

Unemployment trap: the situation where people are better off on benefit than in paid employment.

Universal benefits: *see* benefits, universal.

Universality: the distribution of benefits or services to everyone – or at least everyone in a broad category.

Vertical redistribution: redistribution between people on different levels of wealth or income; usually redistribution from the wealthier to the poorer members of society.

Voluntary provision: provision made by the voluntary sector, that is, nongovernmental organizations.

Voluntary sector: independent provision which is not for profit, usually on the basis of charity or mutual aid. There is a huge variation in the size of organizations, with many tiny ones and a few very large players.

Welfare dependency: dependency on welfare, i.e. state, benefits. The New Right has argued that the provision of welfare benefits means that those on them become dependent – that is, they develop a psychological state such that they do not seek to help themselves by, for example, finding employment, but are content to remain on benefit. The welfare state is said to stifle initiative and incentives to hard work and independence and to encourage the attitude that 'the state will provide'.

Welfare, occupational: welfare provided through the workplace.

Welfare pluralism: the provision of welfare by more than one sector, and the argument that it should be so provided.

Welfare state: a state that organizes/provides welfare services – that is, services to deal with a wide range of social problems. The classic welfare state is one where the state is seen as the provider of a comprehensive range of welfare services.

White Paper: a government paper setting out the policy and actions required on a particular topic.

Workhouse: building to which poor people with no means of support were admitted; able-bodied paupers were expected to undertake repetitive, heavy work. Since many were ill or old, the workhouse inadvertently became a hospital, and many of the old buildings were then inherited by the NHS. Conditions in the workhouse are graphically described in the first part of Dickens' *Oliver Twist.*

BIBLIOGRAPHY

Abbott, P.A. (1982) Towards a social theory of mental handicap, PhD thesis, Thames Polytechnic.

Abbott, P.A. and Meerabeau, E. (1998) *The Sociology of the Caring Professions*. London: Routledge.

Abbott, P.A. and Sapsford, R.J. (1987) *Community Care for Mentally Handicapped Children: The Origins and Consequences of a Social Policy*. Milton Keynes: Open University Press.

Abbott, P.A. and Sapsford, R.J. (1990) Health visiting: Policing the family? in P.A. Abbott and C. Wallace (eds) *The Sociology of the Caring Professions*. Basingstoke: Falmer Press.

Abbott, P.A. and Wallace, C. (eds) (1990) *The Sociology of the Caring Professions*. Basingstoke: Falmer Press.

Abbott, P.A. and Wallace, C. (1992) *The Family and the New Right*. London: Pluto.

Abbott, P.A, Wallace, C. and Tyler, M. (2005) *Introduction to Sociology: Feminist Perspectives*. London: Routledge.

Abel-Smith, B. (1964) *The Hospitals 1800–1948: A Study in Social Administration in England and Wales*. London: Heinemann.

Abel-Smith, B. (1994) *An Introduction to Health: Policy, Planning and Financing*. London: Longman.

Abel-Smith, B. and Titmuss, K. (eds) (1987) *Selected Writings of Richard M. Titmuss: The Philosophy of Welfare*. London: Allen and Unwin.

Acheson, D. (chair) (1998) *Independent Inquiry into Inequalities in Health*. London: HMSO.

Acheson, D. (2000) Health inequalities impact assessment, *Bulletin of the WHO*, 78(1): 75–6.

Ackers, H.L. (1994) Citizenship, dependency and gender in comparative social policy analysis, paper presented to a conference on Employment, Work and Society, Canterbury, September.

Akid, M. (2002) Underfunding is jeopardizing lives, *Nursing Times*, 98(6): 8.

Alcohol Concern (2002) *Your Very Good Health? A report demonstrating the impact of alcohol related problems on the NHS*. London: Alcohol Concern.

Aldridge, J. and Becker, S. (1993) *Children Who Care*. Loughborough: Loughborough University in association with Nottingham Association of Voluntary Services.

Allsop, J. and Mulcahy, J. (1996) *Regulating Medical Work: Formal and Informal Controls*. Buckingham: Open University Press.

Andersen, R.M. *et al.* (1983) Exploring dimentions of access to medical care, *Health Services Research*, 18(1): 49–74.

Anderson, W., Florin, D., Gillam, S. and Mountford, L. (2002) *Every Voice Counts: Primary Care Organizations and Public Involvement*. London: King's Fund.

Annandale, E. and Hunt, K. (2000) *Gender Inequalities in Health*. Buckingham: Open University Press.

Anthias, F. (1998) Rethinking social divisions: Some notes towards a theoretical framework, *The Sociological Review*, 46: 505–35.

Appleby, J. (2005) *Independent Review of Health and Social Care Services in Northern Ireland Report to the Northern Ireland Office*. Belfast: Northern Ireland Office.

Arber, S. (1990) Opening the 'black box': Inequalities in women's health, in P. Abbott and G. Payne (eds) *New Directions in the Sociology of Health*. Basingstoke: Falmer.

Arber, S. and Ginn, J. (1991) *Gender and Later Life: A Sociological Analysis of Resources and Constraints*. London: Sage.

Arksey, H. (2002) Rationed care: Assessing the support needs of informal carers in English social services authorities, *Journal of Social Policy*, 31: 81–101.

Armstrong, D. (1984) *The Political Anatomy of the Body: Medical Knowledge in Britain in the Twentieth Century*. Cambridge: Cambridge University Press.

Arnstein, S. (1969) A ladder of participation, *Journal of the American Planning Association*, 35(4): 216–24.

Ascher, K. (1987) *The Politics of Privatization: Contracting-out Public Services*. London: Macmillan.

Ashton, H. (1991) Psychotropic drug prescribing for women, *British Journal of Psychiatry*, 158 (suppl. 10): 30–5.

Ashton, J. (1992) *Healthy Cities*. Buckingham: Open University Press.

Ashton, J. and Seymour, H. (1988) *The New Public Health*. Buckingham: Open University Press.

Askham, J. and Chisholm, A. (2006) *Patient-Centred Medical Professionalism: Towards an Agenda for Research and Action*. Oxford: Picker Institute Europe.

Askham, J., Henshaw, L. and Tarpey, M. (1995) *Social and Health Authority Services for Elderly People from Black and Minority Ethnic Communities*. London: HMSO.

Atkin, K. and Rollings, J. (1992) Informal care in Asian and Afro/Caribbean communities: A literature review, *British Journal of Social Work*, 22: 405–18.

Audit Commission (1986) *Making a Reality of Community Care*. London: HMSO.

Audit Commission (1996) *What the Doctor Ordered: A Study of GP Fundholders in England and Wales*. London: Audit Commission.

Audit Commission (1998) *A Fruitful Partnership: Effective Partnership Working*. London: Audit Commission.

Audit Commission. (1999) *First assessment: a review of district nursing services in England and Wales* London: Audit Commission for Local Authorities and the National Health Service in England and Wales.

Audit Commission (2000) *Forgot me not: mental health services for older people*. London, Audit Commission.

Audit Commission (2004) *Transforming Health and Social Care in Wales*. Cardiff: Audit Commission in Wales.

Babb, P., Butcher, H., Church, J. and Zealey, L. (2006) *Social Trends*. London: Office for National Statistics, www.statistics.gov.uk.

Baggott, R. (2000) *Public Health: Policy and Politics*. Basingstoke: Macmillan.

Baggott, R. (2002) Regulatory politics, health professionals, and the public interest, in J. Allsop and M. Sake (eds) *Regulating the Health Professions*. London: Sage.

Baggott, R. (2004) *Health and Health Care in Britain*. Basingstoke: Palgrave Macmillan.

Baggott, R., Allsop, J. and Jones, K. (2005) *Speaking Truth for Patients and Carers: Health Consumer Groups and the Policy Process*. Basingstoke: Palgrave Macmillan.

Bailey, C. and Pain, R. (2001) Geographies of infant feeding and access to primary health care, *Health and Social Care in the Community*, 9(5): 309–17.

Bainbridge, I. and Ricketts, A. (2003) *Improving older people's services: an overview of performance*. London, Social Services Inspectorate.

Balchin, P. and Rhoden, M. (2002) *Housing Policy*, 4th edn. London: Routledge.

Balcombe, J., Strange, N. and Tate, G. (1993) *Wish You Were Here: How UK and Japanese-owned Organizations Manage Attendance*. London: The Industrial Society.

Baldock, J. (2003) On being a welfare consumer in a consumer society, *Social Policy and Society*, 2: 65–71

Baldock, J. and Ungerson, C. (1991) What d'ya want if you don' want money? A feminist critique of paid volunteering, in M. Maclean and D. Groves (eds) *Women's Issues in Social Policy*. London: Routledge.

Baldock, J., Manning, N. and Vickerstaff, S. (eds) (2003) *Social Policy*. Oxford: Oxford University Press.

Balloch, S. and Taylor, M. (2001) *Partnership Working: Policy and Practice*. Bristol: Policy Press.

Baly, M. (1995) *Nursing and Social Change*, 3rd edn. London: Routledge.

Bambra, C. (2004) The worlds of welfare: Illusory and gender blind? *Social Policy and Society*, 3: 201–11.

Banks, O. (1981) *Faces of Feminism*. Oxford: Martin Robertson.

Barclay Committee (1982) *Social Workers: Their Roles and Tasks*. London: National Institute for Social Work, Bedford Square Press.

Barker, D.J.P. (1998) *Mothers, Babies and Health in Later Life*. London Churchill Livingstone.

Barnes, M., Harrison, S., Mort, M. and Shardlow, P. (1999) *Unequal Parties: User Groups and Community Care*. Bristol: Policy Press.

Barr, N. (2001) *The Welfare State as Piggy Bank: Information, Risk, Uncertainty and the Role of the State*. Oxford: Oxford University Press.

Barton, R. (1959) *Institutional Neurosis*. London: Wright.

Bauld, L., Chesterman, J., Davies, B. and Judde, K. (2000) *Caring for Older People: An Assessment of Community Care in the 1990s*. Ashgate: Aldershot.

Baxter, K., Bachmann, M. and Bevan, G. (2000) Primary care groups: Trade-offs in managing budgets and risk, *Public Money Management*, 20: 53–62.

Bayley, M. (1973) *Mental Handicap and Community Care*. London: Routledge and Kegan Paul.

Becher, T. (1994) Freedom and accountability in professional curricula, in T. Becks (ed.) *Governments and Professional Education*. Buckingham: Open University Press.

Beck, U. (1992) *Risk Society*. Newbury Park, CA: Sage.

Becker, H.S. (1970) *Sociological Work*. Chicago, IL: Aldine.

Bell, D. and Bowse, A. (2006) *Financial Care Models in Scotland and the UK*. York: Joseph Rowntree Foundation.

Ben-Shlomo, Y. and Davey-Smith, G. (1991) Deprivation in infancy or adult life: Which is more important for mortality risk? *Lancet*, 337: 530–4.

Benzeval, M., Judge, K. and Solomon, M. (1992) *The Health Status of London: A Comparative Perspective*. Initiative Working Paper No. 1. London: King's Fund.

Berridge, V. and Blume, S. (eds) (2005) *Poor Health*. London: Frank Cass.

Berthoud, R. (1998) *The Incomes of Ethnic Minorities*, Institute for Social Research Report. London: Institute for Social Research.

Beveridge, W. (1948) *Voluntary Action*. London: Allen and Unwin.

Bines, W. (1994) *The Health of Single Homeless People*. Housing Research Findings No. 128. York: Joseph Rowntree Foundation.

Blane, D., Brunner, E. and Wilkinson, R. (eds) (1996) *Health and Social Organization: Toward a Health Policy for the Twenty-First Century*. London: Routledge.

Blaxter, M. (1990) *Health and Lifestyle*. London: Routledge.

Blomqvist, P. (2004) The choice revolution: Privatization of Swedish welfare services in the 1990s, *Social Policy and Administration*, 38(2): 139–55.

Blythman, J. (2004) *Shopped: The Shocking Power of British Supermarkets*. London: Fourth Estate.

Boaden, R. Dusheiko, M., Gravelle, H., Parker, S. Pichard, S., Roland, M. *et al.* (2005) *Evercare Evaluation Interim Report: Implications for Supporting People with Long-term Conditions*. Manchester: University of Manchester National Primary Care Research and Development Centre.

Bochel, C. and Bochel, H. (2004) *The UK Social Policy Process*. Basingstoke: Palgrave Macmillan.

Bogdanor, V. (ed.) (2005) *Joined-Up Government*. Oxford: Oxford University Press.

Bond, M., Irving, L. and Cooper, C. (2001) *Public Involvement in Decision-Making in Primary Care Groups*. Sheffield: University of Sheffield School of Health and Related Research.

Boseley, S. (2006) Greater use of cholesterol drug urged to fight heart disease, *Guardian*, 22 May: 8.

Bowlby, J. (1954) *Maternal Deprivation*. Harmondsworth: Penguin.

Bradley, S.J. (2003) Pride or Prejudice – issues in the history of children's nurse education, *Nurse Education Today*, 23(5): 362–7.

Braham, P. and Jones, L. (eds) (2002) *Social Differences and Social Divisions*. Oxford: Blackwell.

Braye, S. and Preston-Shoot, M. (2002) Social work and the law, in R. Adams, L. Dominelli and M. Payne (eds) *Social Work Themes, Issues and Critical Debates*, 2nd edn. Basingstoke: Palgrave.

Brewer, M., Goodman, A., Shaw, J. and Sibieta, A. (2005) *Poverty and Inequality in Britain: 2006*. London: Institute for Fiscal Studies.

Brindle, D. (1998) Media blood sport, *Guardian Society*, 2 December.

British Medical Association (1987) *Deprivation and Ill Health*. London: BMA.

British Social Attitudes (2005) British Social Attitudes: the 22nd Report London: Sage

Brock, C. and Griffiths, A. (2003) Twentieth Century Mortality Trends in England and Wales In *Health Statistics Quarterly*, no 18 London: ONS. Pp 5–17.

Brookes, M. and Copps, J. (2004) *A Surer Funding Framework for Improved Public Services*, www.acevo.org.uk.

Buchan, J. and Calman, L. (2004a) *Skill-mix and policy change in the health workforce: nurses in advanced roles*. OECD, Organisation for economic co-operation and development, Paris.

Buchan, J. and Calman, L. (2004b) *The global shortage of registered nurses: an overview of issues and actions*. Geneva, International Council of Nurses.

Buchan, J. and Seccombe, I. (2004) *Fragile future? A review of the UK nursing labour market in 2003*. London, Royal College of Nursing.

Buckle, J. (1984) *Mental Handicap Costs More*. London: Disablement Income Group Charitable Trust.

Budd, S. and Mills, S. (2000) *Professional Organization of Complementary and Alternative Medicine in the United Kingdom 2000*. Exeter: University of Exeter.

Bulmer, M. (1987) *The Social Basis of Community Care*. London: Allen and Unwin.

Bunce, C. (2001) The care homes catastrophe. *Nursing Times*, 2 August, 97, 31, p.22.

Burgner, T. (1998) *Independent Longcare Enquiry*. Buckinghamshire County Council.

Burke, S., Meyrick, J. and Speller, V. (2001) *Public Health Skills Audit 2001 – Research Report*. London: Health Development Agency.

Burnett, A. and Peel, M. (2001) What brings asylum seekers to the United Kingdom? *British Medical Journal*, 322: 485–8.

Burstow, P. (2002) Charities left to foot care home bills in Laing and Buisson *Community Care Market News*. February, 18, 9, p.189.

Cabinet Office (2002) *Private Action, Public Benefit*. London: Cabinet Office.

Cahill, M. (1994) *The New Social Policy*. Oxford: Blackwell.

Campling, J. (1988) Social policy digest. *Journal of Social Policy*, 17: 85–109.

Campbell, C. and Aggleton, P. (1999) Young people's sexual health: A framework for policy debate, *Canadian Journal of Human Sexuality*, 8(4): 249–63.

Carlisle, D. (2006) A furore too far: The widespread disquiet undermining NICE, *Health Service Journal*, 22 June: 14–5.

Carmichael and Charles (2003) The opportunity costs of informal care: Does gender matter? *Journal of Health Economics* 22, 781–803.

Carpenter, M. (1977) The new manageralism and professionalism in nursing, in M. Stacey *et al.* (eds) *Health Care and the Division of Labour*. London: Croom Helm.

Carr-Hill, R. and Jenkins-Clarke, S., (2003) Focus: Workforce and Workload: Are nursing resources used effectively? *Nursing, Times, Research*, 8, 238–48.

Carter, J. (2003) *Ethnicity, Exclusion and the Workplace*. London: Sage.

Cartwright, A. and Anderson, R. (1983) *General Practice Revisited: A Second Study of Patients and Their Doctors*. London: Tavistock.

Carvel, 2001,

Carvel, J. (2002) Concern as women outnumber men in medical schools, *Guardian*, 4 July: 11.

Carvel, J. (2005a) Nurses to get far-reaching prescribing powers, *Guardian*, 10 November: 4.

Carvel, J. (2005b) ER style doctors' aides for NHS, *Guardian*, 5 November: 4.

Caton Hughes, H. (2005) *More than Good Intentions: Opportunity and Diversity in Hospital and Community Volunteering*. London: National Association of Hospital and Community Friends.

CCETSW (1991) *Rules and Requirements for the Diploma in Social Work*, 2nd edn. London: CCETSW.

Central Statistical Office (1995) *Social Trends 95*. London: HMSO.

Challis D, Hughes J. Frail old people at the margins of care: some recent research finding. *Br J Psychiatry* 2002; 180: 126–30

Challis, D. *et al.* (2001) Intensive care-management at home: An alternative to institutional care? *Age and Ageing*, 30(5): 409–13.

Chandola, T., Bartley, M., Wiggins, R. and Schofield, P. (2003) Social inequalities in health by individual and household measures of social position in a cohort of healthy people, *Journal of Epidemiology and Community Health*, 57: 56–62.

Church of England Working Party (1985) *Faith in the City*. London: Church House.

Clarence, E. and Painter, C. (1998) Public services under New Labour: collaborative discourses and local networking, *Public Policy and Administration*, 13(3): 8–37.

Clark, D. (1999) Cradled to the grave? Terminal care in the United Kingdom, 1948–67, *Mortality*, 4(3): 225–47.

Clark, H., Dyer, S. and Horwood, J. (1998) *That bit of help*. Bristol: Policy Press.

Clarke, J. (2004) Dissolving the public realm? The logics and limits of neo-liberalism, *Journal of Social Policy*, 33: 27–48.

Clarke, J., Cochrane, A. and McLaughlin, E. (eds) (1994) *Managing Social Policy*. London: Sage.

Clarke et al 1998

Clarke, J., Smith, N. and Vidler, E. (2005) Consumerism and the reform of public services: Inequalities and instabilities, in M. Powell, L. Bauld and K. Clarke (eds) *Social Policy Review 17*. Bristol: Policy Press/Social Policy Association.

Clarke-Jones, J. (2006) Doctors and nurses, *Public*, April: 36–7.

Coburn, D. (2000) Income Inequality, social cohesion and the health status of populations: The role of neo-liberalism, *Social Science and Medicine*, 51: 135–46.

COI (Central Office for Information) (1948)

Challis, D. and, Hughes, J. Frail old people at the margins of care: some recent research findings. *Br J Psychiatry* 2002; 180: 126–30.

Coker, N. (ed.) (2001) *Racism in Medicine: An Agenda for Change*. London: King's Fund.

Coldman, A. and Duffy, A. (2000) Inspection culture needs revamp. *Community Care*, 13–19 January, p.19.

Cole, I. and Furbey, R. (1994) *The Eclipse of Council Housing*. London: Routledge.

Cole, A. (2006) How to find 'frequent fliers'. *Health Service Journal*, 4 May, pp.20–22.

Colledge, M., Eve, R., Mares, P. and Robinson, M. (2003) *Implementing the National Service Framework for Coronary Heart Disease at Primary Care Trust and General Practice Level. A Study of Barriers and Opportunities*. London: The Centre for Innovation in Primary Care/Nuffield Institute of Health.

Comas-Herrera, A. *et al.* (2006) *Thirty-five Years On: Future Demand for Long-term Care in England*. Research Summary 35, March. Canterbury: University of Kent, Personal Social Services Research Unit.

Commission on Social Justice (1994) *The Justice Gap*. London: Institute for Public Policy Research.

Cooper, H. (2002) Investigating socio-economic explanations for gender and ethnic inequalities in health, *Social Science and Medicine*, 54: 693–706.

Cooper, L., Coote, A., Davies, A. and Jackson, C. (1995) *Voices Off: Tackling the Democratic Deficit in Health*. London: Institute for Public Policy Research.

Corben, S. and Rosen, R. (2005) *Self-Management for Long-Term Conditions. Patients' Perspectives on the Way Ahead*. London: King's Fund.

Cornwell, J. (1984) *Hard-Earned Lives: Accounts of Health and Illness from East London*. London: Tavistock.

Coulter, A. (1997) Partnerships with patients: the pros and cons of shared clinical decision-making. *Journal of Health Services Research and Policy*. 1997 Apr;2(2): 112–21.

Coulter, A. (2006) *Engaging Patients in Their Healthcare*. Oxford: Picker Institute Europe.

Coulter, A. and Florin, D. (2001) Partnership in the primary care consultation, in S. Gillam and F. Brooks (eds) *New Beginnings: Towards Patient and Public Involvement in Primary Health Care*. London: King's Fund.

Counsel and Care (1992) *From Home to a Home*. London: Counsel and Care.

Cox, D. (1991) Health service management: A sociological view – Griffiths and the non-negotiated order of the hospital, in J. Gabe, M. Calnan and M. Bury (eds) *Sociology of the Health Service*. London: Routledge.

Cree, V. (2002) The changing nature of social work, in R. Adams, L. Dominelli and M. Payne (eds) *Social Work Themes, Issues and Critical Debates*, 2nd edn. Basingstoke: Palgrave.

Cullum, N., Spilsbury, K. and Richardson, G. (2005) Nurse led care, *British Medical Journal*, 330(7493): 682–3.

Curtis, P. 2006 'Frequent flyers' costing NHS £2.3bn a year. *Guardian*, 13 February. p.6.

Curtis and Jones (1998) Is there a place for geography in the analysis of health inequality? *Sociology of Health and Illness*, 20(5): 645–72.

Dahlberg, L. (2005) Interaction between voluntary and statutory social service provision in Sweden: A matter of welfare pluralism, substitution or complementarity? *Social Policy and Administration*, 39(7): 740–63.

Dalley, G. (1988) *Ideologies of Caring*. London: Macmillan.

D'Amour, D., Ferrada-Videla, M., Rodriguez, L.S.M. and Beaulieu, M. (2005) The conceptual basis for interprofessional collaboration: Core concepts and theoretical frameworks, *Journal of Inter-Professional Care*, Supplement 1, 116–31.

Davey-Smith, G., Blane, D. and Bartley, M. (1994) Explanations for socio-economic differentials in mortality: Evidence from Britain and elsewhere, *European Journal of Public Health*, 4: 131–44.

Davey-Smith G. *et al.* (1997) Lifetime socio-economic differentials in mortality: Prospective observational study, *British Medical Journal*, 314: 547–52.

Davis, A. (1993) Community care, in P. Spurgeon (ed.) *The New Face of the NHS*. London: Longman.

Davies, C. (1995) *Gender and the Professional Predicament in Nursing*. Buckingham: Open University Press.

Davies, C. (2002) What about the girl next door? Gender and the politics of professional self-regulation, in G. Bendelow, M. Carpenter, C. Vautier and S. Williams (eds) *Gender Health and Healing*. London: Routledge.

Davies, C. and Beach, A. (2000) *Integrating professional Self-regulation: A History of the United Kingdom Central Council for Nursing, Midwifery and Health Visiting*. London: Routledge.

Davies, H. and Joshi, H. (1998) Gender and income Inequality in the UK 1968–90: The Feminization of Earnings or of Poverty? *Journal of the Royal Statistical Society. Series A (Statistics in Society)*, 161(1): 33–61.

Davies, H.T.O. and Harrison, S. (2003) Trends in doctor-manager relationships, *British Medical Journal*, 326: 646–9.

Davies, M.M. and Bath, P.A. (2001) The maternity information concerns of Somali women in the United Kingdom, *Journal of Advanced Nursing*, 36: 237.

Davies, S. (1987) Towards the remoralization of society, in M. Loney *et al.* (eds) *The State or the Market*. London: Sage.

Deacon, A. (2002) *Perspectives on Welfare*. Buckingham: Open University Press.

Deakin (2001) *In Search of Civil Society*. Basingstoke: Palgrave.

Dean, M. (2005) It is time to consider the future for hospices and how they are financed, *Guardian*, 20 July: 5.

Dearden, C. and Becker, S. (2004) *Young Carers in the UK*. London: Carers UK/The Children's Society.

Derbyshire Welfare Rights Service (1983) *Annual Report* Derby: DWRS

DETR/DSS (2000) *Quality and Choice: A Decent Home for All*. London: The Stationery Office.

DfES (Department for Education and Science) (2003) *Every Child Matters*. London: DfES.

DHSS (1979) *Report of the Committee of Enquiry into Mental Handicap Nursing and Care*: The Jay Report, Cmnd 4768. London: HMSO.

DHSS (Department of Health and Social Security) (1981) *Growing Older*. Cmnd 8173. London: HMSO.

DHSS (Department of Health and Social Security) (1983) *Report of the Social Security Advisory Committee*. London: HMSO.

DHSS (Department of Health and Social Security) (1986) *Primary Health Care: An Agenda for Discussion*. London: DHSS.

DHSS (Department of Health and Social Security) (1987) *Promoting Better Health: The Government's Programme for Improving Primary Health Care*. Cmnd. 249. London: HMSO.

DHSS (Department of Health and Social Security) (1988) *Griffiths Report on Community Care*. London: DHSS.

Dixon, J. *et al.* (1994) Distribution of NHS funds between fundholding and non-fundholding practises, *British Medical Journal*, 309: 30–4.

Dixon, J. *et al.* (2004) Can the NHS learn from US managed care organizations? *British Medical Journal*, 328: 223–5.

DoH (Department of Health) (1989a) *Working for Patients*. Cm 555. London: HMSO.

DoH (Department of Health) (1989b) *Caring for People*. London: HMSO.

DoH (Department of Health) (1993) *Changing Childbirth*. London: The Stationery Office.

DoH (Department of Health) (1995) *The Health of the Nation: Variations in Health. What can the Department of Health and the NHS do?* London: HMSO.

DoH (Department of Health) (1996) *Patient Partnership*. London: DoH.

DoH (Department of Health) (1997) *The New NHS*. London: HMSO.

DoH (Department of Health) (1998a) *Independent Inquiry into Inequalities in Health Report* (Chaired by Sir Donald Acheson). London: The Stationery Office.

DoH (Department of Health) (1998b) *Getting it Right Together: Compact Relations Between the Government and the Voluntary Sector in England*. Cm 4100. London: The Stationery Office.

DoH (Department of Health) (1998c) *Priorities and Planning Guidance 1998–2000*. London: DoH.

DoH (Department of Health) (1998d) *Signposts for Success in Commissioning and Providing Health Services for People with Learning Disabilities*. London: DoH.

DoH (Department of Health) (1999a) *Saving Lives: Our Healthier Nation*. London: The Stationery Office.

DoH (Department of Health) (1999b) *Making a Difference: Strengthening the Nursing, Midwifery and Health Visiting Contribution to Health and Healthcare*. London: The Stationery Office.

DoH (Department of Health) (1999c) *Fit for the Future?* London: DoH.

DoH (Department of Health) (1999d) *Caring for Carers: A National Strategy for Carers*. London: DoH.

DoH (Department of Health) (1999e) *National Service Framework for Mental Health*. London: DoH.

DoH (Department of Health) (1999f) Complaints Against Nursing Homes. London: DoH.

DoH (Department of Health) (2000a) *The NHS Plan: A Plan for Investment, A Plan for Reform*. Cm 4818 London: The Stationery Office.

DoH (Department of Health) (2000b) *National Service Framework for Coronary Heart Disease*. London: DoH.

DoH (Department of Health) (2001a) *Shifting the Balance of Power*. London: DoH.

DoH (2001b) *Health Inequalities Consultation*. London: DoH.

DoH (Department of Health) (2001c) *The Report of the Chief Medical Officer's Project to Strengthen the Public Health Function*. London: HMSO.

DoH (Department of Health) (2001d) *The Expert Patient: A New Approach to Chronic Disease Management for the 21st Century*. London: DoH.

DoH (Department of Health) (2001e) *The National Service Framework for Older People*. Standard 5. London: DoH.

DoH (Department of Health) (2001f) *Valuing people: A New Strategy for Learning Disability for the 21st Century*. London: DoH.

DoH (Department of Health) (2001g) *Working Together, Learning Together: A Framework for Lifelong Learning for the NHS*. London: DoH.

DoH (Department of Health) (2002a) *Shifting the Balance of Power: Next Steps*. London: DoH.

DoH (Department of Health) (2002b) *Tackling Health Inequalities: Cost-Cutting Review*. London: DoH.

DoH (Department of Health) (2003a) *Building on the Best: Choice, Responsiveness and Equity in the NHS*. London: DoH.

DoH (Department of Health) (2003b) *Chief Executive's Report to the NHS*. London: DoH.

DoH (Department of Health) (2003c) *Advanced Primary Nurse Competencies*. London: Modernization Agency.

DoH (Department of Health) (2003d) *Making Partnership Work for Patients, Carers and Service Users*. London: DoH.

DoH (Department of Health) (2003e) *NHS Foundation Trusts – A Guide to Developing Governance Arrangements*. London: DoH.

DoH (Department of Health) (2004a) *Choosing Health: Making Healthy Choices Easier*. Cm 6374. London: The Stationery Office.

DoH (Department of Health) (2004b) *Health and Personal Social Services Statistics for England*. London: DoH.

DoH (Department of Health) (2004c) *Improving Chronic Disease Management*. London: DoH.

DoH (Department of Health) (2004d) *Research evidence on the usefulness of self-care support networks for care of people with minor ailments, acute illness and long-term conditions and those taking initiatives to stay healthy*. London: DoH.

DoH (Department of Health) (2004e) *Regulation of Health Care Staff in England and Wales*. London: DoH.

DoH (Department of Health) (2004f) *The NHS Improvement Plan*. London: DoH.

DoH (Department of Health) (2004g) *Community Matrons Chief Nursing Officer Newsletter*, July: 2.

DoH (Department of Health) (2004h) *Quality and Outcomes Framework*. London: DoH.

DoH (Department of Health) (2004i) *National Standards, Local Action: Health & Social Care Standards and Planning Framework*. London: DoH.

DoH (Department of Health) (2004j) *Distillation of Chronic Disease Management Programmes in the UK*. London: Matrix Research and Consultancy/Modernization Agency.

DoH (Department of Health) (2005a) *Self Care – A Real Choice*. London: DoH.

DoH (Department of Health) (2005b) *Commissioning a Patient-Led NHS*. London: DoH.

DoH (Department of Health) (2005c) *Supporting People with Long-Term Conditions: An NHS and Social Care Model to Support Local Innovation and Integration*. London: DoH.

DoH (Department of Health) (2005d) *Tackling Health Inequalities: Status Report on the Programme for Action*. London: DoH.

DoH (Department of Health) (2005e) *Independence, Well-being and Choice: Our Vision for the Future of Social Care for Adults in England*. London: DoH.

DoH (Department of Health) (2005f) *National Service Framework for Long-term Conditions*. London: DoH.

DoH (Department of Health) (2005g) *Self Care Support: A compendium of Practical Examples Across the Whole System of Health and Social Care*. London: DoH.

DoH (Department of Health) (2005h) *Public Attitudes to Self Care: Baseline Survey*. London: DoH.

DoH (Department of Health) (2005i) *Self Care Support: Baseline Study of Activity and Development in Self Care Support in PCTs and Local Areas*. London: DoH.

DoH (Department of Health) (2005j) *Chief Nursing Officer's Review of Mental Health Nursing: Consultation Document*. London: DoH.

DoH (Department of Health) (2005k) *Supporting People with Long-Term Conditions: Liberating the Talents of Nurses Who Care for People With Long-Term Conditions*. London: DoH.

DoH (Department of Health) (2006) *Our Health, Our Care, Our Say*. London: DoH.

Department of Health, Social Services and Public Safety Northern Ireland (2004) *Caring for People Beyond Tomorrow*. Belfast: PCDU.

DSS (Department of Social Security) (1989) *Children Come First*, vols 1 and 2. London: HMSO.

DSS (Department of Social Security) (1991) *Social Security Statistics 1990*. London: HMSO.

DSS (Department of Social Security) (1998) *A New Contract for Welfare: The Gateway to Work*. Cm 401. London: DSS.

Department of Trade and Industry (2002)

DWP (Department of Work and Pensions) (2003) *Opportunity for All*. Cm 5956. London: DWP.

DWP (Department of Work and Pensions) (2005a) *Income Related Benefits Estimates of Take-Up in 2002/2003*. London: DWP.

DWP (Department of Work and Pensions) (2005b) *Age and Opportunity*. London: DWP.

DWP (Department of Work and Pensions) (2006) *Green Paper 'A new deal for welfare: empowering people to work*. London: DWP.

DWP (Department of Work and Pensions) (2006a) *New Deal for Welfare*. London: DWP.

DWP (Department of Work and Pensions) (2006b) *Security in Retirement: Towards a New Pensions System*. London: DWP.

Dingwall, R. (1977) *The Social Organization of Health Visitor Training*. London: Croom Helm.

Dixon, J. (2001) Another healthcare funding review: More of the same, *British Medical Journal*, 322(7282): 312–13.

Dolowitz, D.P. *et al.* (1999) *Policy Transfer and British Social Policy*. Buckingham: Open University Press.

Dominelli, L. (1997) *Sociology for Social Work*. London: Macmillan.

Donzelot, J. (1980) *The Policing of Families*. London: Hutchinson.

Douglas, J.W.B. (1964) *The Home and the School*. London: McGibbon and Kee.

Dowding (1992): Choice: Its Increase and Its Value *British Journal of Political Science*, Vol.22(3), 301–314.

Dowler, E., Turner, S. and Dobson, B. (2001) *Poverty Bites: Food, Health and Poor Families*. London: CPAG.

Doyal, L. (1995) *What Makes Women Sick: Gender and Political Economy*. London: Macmillan.

Duncan, C., Jones, K. and Moon, G. (1993) Do places matter? A multi-level analysis of variations in health-related behaviour in Britain, *Social Science and Medicine*, 37: 725–33.

Eachus, J. *et al.* (1996) Deprivation and cause specific morbidity: Evidence from the Somerset and Avon survey of health, *British Medical Journal*, 312: 287–92.

Elford, J., Whinchup, P. and Shaper, A.G. (1991) Early life experience and cardiovascular disease – longitudinal and case-control studies, *International Journal of Epidemiology*, 20: 833–44.

Ellins, J. and Coulter, A. (2005) *How Engaged are People in their Health Care? Findings of a National Telephone Survey*. London: The Health Foundation.

Elwyn, G., Edwards, A. Kinnersley, P. and Grol R. (2000) Shared decision-making: the neglected second half of the consultation, *British Journal of General Practice*, 49: 477–82.

English National Board for Nursing. Midwifery and Health Visiting. (1997) *New directions in rehabilitation: exploring the nursing contribution*. London: English National Board for Nursing, Midwifery and Health Visiting.

Enhoven, A.V. (1985) *Reflections on the Management of the National Health Service*. Occasional Paper No. 5. London: Nuffield Private Hospital Trust.

Entwistle, V.A. *et al.* (2006) Which surgical decisions should patients participate in? Reflections on women's recollections of discussions about different types of hysterectomy, *Social Science and Medicine*, 62: 499–509.

Epstein, S. (1996) *Impure Science: AIDS, Activism and the Politics of Knowledge*. Berkeley, CA: University of California Press.

Equal Opportunities Commission (1984) *Carers and Services: A Comparison of Men and Women Caring for Dependent Elderly People*. Manchester: EOC.

Ernst, E. and White, A. (2000) The BBC survey of complementary medicine use in the UK, *Complementary Therapies in Medicine*, 8: 32–6.

Esping-Anderson, G. (1990) *The Three Worlds of Welfare Capitalism*. Cambridge: Polity Press.

Etzioni, A. (1969) *The Semi-Professions and their Organization*. New York, NY: Free Press.

Eurostat (1990) *Poverty in Figures*. Luxembourg: European Community Statistical Office.

Evers, A. (1993) The welfare mix approach: Understanding the pluralism of welfare systems, in A. Evers and I. Svetlik (eds) *Balancing Pluralism: New Welfare Mixes in Care for the Elderly*. Aldershot: Avebury.

Exworthy, M. and Halford, S. (1999) *Professionals and the New Managerialism in the Public Sector*. Buckingham: Open University Press.

Exworthy, M. and Peckham, S. (1998) The contribution of coterminosity to joint purchasing in health and social care, *Health and Place*, 4(3): 233–43.

Exworthy, M. and Peckham, S. (2006) Access, choice and travel: Implications for health policy, *Social Policy and Administration*, 40(3): 267–87.

Fallowfield L.J. *et al.* (1990) Psychological outcomes of different treatment policies in women with early breast cancer outside a clinical trial, *British Medical Journal*, 6752: 575–80.

Farrell, C. (2004) *Patient and Public Involvement in Health: The Evidence for Policy Implementation.* London: DoH.

Fearn, R. (1987) Rural health care: A British success or a tale of unmet need? *Social Science and Medicine*, 40: 309–14.

Fielding, N., Reeve, C. and Simey, M.C. (1991) *Active Citizens, New Voices and Values.* London: Bedford Square Press.

Finch, J. (1990) The politics of community care in Britain, in C. Ungerson (ed.) *Gender and Caring: Work and Welfare in Britain and Scandinavia.* Hemel Hempstead: Harvester Wheatsheaf.

Finch, J. and Groves, D. (1983) *A Labour Of Love: Women, Work and Caring.* London: Routledge and Kegan Paul.

Fisher, B. and Gilbert, D. (2001) Patient involvement and clinical effectiveness, in S. Gillam and F. Brooks (eds) *New Beginnings: Towards Patient and Public Involvement in Primary Health Care.* London: King's Fund.

Flood, S. (2005) A brief history of the NHSU, *Health Service Journal Supplement*, 24 February: 3–7.

Flood, S. (2006) University challenge, *Health Service Journal Supplement*, 23 February: 3–7.

Flynn, N. (1996) A mixed blessing? How the contract culture works, in C. Hanvey and T. Philpot (eds) *Sweet Charity – the role and workings of voluntary organizations.* London: Routledge.

Flynn, N. and Hurley, D. (1993) *The Market for Care.* London: LSE.

Fogelman, K., Fox, H. and Power, C. (1987) *Class and Tenure Mobility: Do They Explain the Social Inequalities in Health Among Young Adults in Britain?* National Child Development Study Working Paper No. 21. London: City University Social Statistics Research Unit.

Follett, B. and Paulson-Ellis, M. (2001) *A Review of Appraisal, Disciplinary and Reporting Arrangements for Senior NHS and University Staff with Academic and Clinical Duties.* London: DfES.

Fotaki, M. *et al.* (2005) *Patient Choice and the Organisation and Delivery of Health Services: Scoping Review.* Manchester: University of Manchester.

Foucault, M. (1963) *The Birth of the Clinic.* London: Tavistock.

Foucault, M. (1975) *Discipline and Punish: The Birth of the Prison.* New York, NY: Pantheon Books.

Fox, A.J. and Goldblatt, P.O. (1982) *Longitudinal Study 1971–1975: England and Wales.* London: UK Office of Census and Population Surveys.

Franklin, A.W. (1964) Children's hospitals, in F. Poynter (ed.) *The Evolution of Hospitals in Britain.* London: Pitman Medical.

Freidson, E. (1971) *Profession of Medicine.* New York, NY: Dodd Mead.

Friedman, M. and Friedman, R. (1980) *Free to Choose.* Harmondsworth: Penguin.

Frankel, S. *et al.* (1996) Birthweight, body-mass index in middle-age and incident coronary heart disease, *Lancet*, 346, 1478–80.

Fyfe, N.R. and Milligan, C. (2003) Space, citizenship, and voluntarism: Critical reflections on the voluntary welfare sector in Glasgow, *Environment and Planning*, 35: 2069–86.

Fry, J. and Hodder, J.P. (1994) *Primary Healthcare in an International Context.* London: Nuffield Provincial Hospitals Trust.

Gakidou, E.E., Murray, C.J. and Frenk, J. (2000) Defining and measuring health inequality: An approach based on the distribution of health expectancy, *Bull World Health Organ*, 78(1): 42–54.

Garside, P. (1999) Evidence based mergers, *British Medical Journal*, 318, 345–6.

George, V. and Wilding, P. (1994) *Welfare and Ideology*. Hemel Hempstead: Harvester.

George, V. and Wilding, P. (1999) *British Society and Social Welfare: Towards a Sustainable Society*. London: St Martin's Press.

Gibbon, B. Stroke nursing care and management in the community: a survey of district nurses' perceived contribution in one health district in England. *Journal of Advanced Nursing* 20(3): 469–76.

Giddens, A. (1998) Risk society: The context of British politics, in J. Franklin (ed.) *The Politics of Risk Society*, pp. 23–34. Cambridge: Polity Press.

Gilbert, D. *et al.* (2001) *Signposts: A Practical Guide to Patient and Public Involvement in Wales*. Cardiff: OPM/NAW.

Gillam, S. and Pencheon, D. (1998) Managing demand in general practice, *British Medical Journal*, 316: 1895–8.

Ginsberg, N. (1992) *Divisions of Welfare*. London: Sage.

Gladstone, D. (1995) Introduction: Change, continuity and welfare, in D. Gladstone (ed.) *British Social Welfare: Past, Present and Future*. London: UCL Press.

Gladstone, F. (1979) *Voluntary Action in a Changing World*. London: Bedford Square Press.

Glendinning, C. (1983) *Unshared Care: Parents and their Disabled Children*. London: Routledge and Kegan Paul.

Glendinning, C. and Millar, J. (eds) (1992) *Women and Poverty in Britain in the 1990s*. Hemel Hempstead: Harvester Wheatsheaf.

Glendinning, C., Powell, M. and Rummery, K. (2002) *Partnerships, New Labour and the Governance of Welfare*. Bristol: Policy Press.

Glennerster, H., Matsaganis, M. and Owens, P. (1994) *Implementing Fundholding: Wild Card or Winning Hand?* Buckingham: Open University Press.

Goffman, E. (1961) *Asylums*. New York, NY: Doubleday.

Goldblatt, P.C. (1990) Mortality and alternative social classification, in P.C. Goldblatt (ed.) *Longitudinal Study: Mortality and Social Organization 1971–1981*. OPCS Series L No. 6. London: HMSO.

Gott, C. and Johnston, K. (2002) *The Migrant Population in the UK: Fiscal Effects*. RDS Occasional Paper No 77. London: Home Office.

Gould, M. (2006) HIV/AIDS centre closure threat, *Health Services Journal*, 6 April: 13.

Graham, H. (1984) *Women, Health and the Family*. Brighton: Wheatsheaf.

Graham, H. (1993a) *Hardship and Health in Women's Lives*. London: Harvester Wheatsheaf.

Graham, H. (1993b) Feminist perspectives on caring, in J. Bornat, C. Pereira, D. Pilgrim and F. Williams (eds) *Community Care: A Reader*. London: Macmillan.

Graham, L. *et al* (1998) Penetration of complementary therapies into NHS trust and private hospital practice, *Complementary Therapies in Nursing and Midwifery*. 4(6): 160–5.

Green, D.G. (1993) *Reinventing Civil Society: The Rediscovery of Welfare Without Politics*. London: Institute of Economic Affairs Health and Welfare Unit.

Greener, I. (2004): The three moments of New Labour's health policy discourse *Policy & Politics*, 32(3), 303–316.

Greener, I. (2005) The role of the patient in health care reform: Customer, consumer or creator? in S. Dawson and C. Sausmann (eds) *Future Health Organizations and System*. Basingstoke: Palgrave.

Greer, S. (2004) *Four Way Bet: How Devolution has led to Four Different Models for the NHS*. London: The Constitution Unit, UCL.

Greer, S. (2005) *Territorial Politics and Health Policy: UK Health Policy in Comparative Perspective*. Manchester: Manchester University Press.

Griffiths, R. (1983) *Report of the NHS Management Enquiry*. London: DHSS.

Griffiths, R. (1988) *Community Care: Agenda for Action*. London: HMSO.

Groves, D. (1991) Women and financial provision in old age, in M. Maclean and D. Groves (eds) *Women's Issues in Social Policy*. London: Routledge.

Guardian (2004) National number crunch, 11 February.

Guest D. *et al.* (2004) *An Evaluation of the Impact of Nurse, Midwife and Health Visitor Consultants*. London: King's College.

Gutch, R. (1992) *Contracting: Lessons from the USA*. London: National Council for Voluntary Organizations.

Gwatkin, D. (2000) Health inequalities and the health of the poor: What do we know? What can we do? *Bulletin of the WHO*: 78(1): 3–18.

Gwyn and Elwyn (1999) When is a shared decision not (quite) a shared decision? Negotiating preferences in a general practice encounter, *Social Science and Medicine*, 49(4): 437–47.

Hadley, R. and Hatch, S. (1981) *Social Welfare and the Future of the State: Centralized Social Services and Participating Alternatives*. London: Allen and Unwin.

Haffinden, S. (2006) The voluntary sector is taking direct hits from the NHS cash crisis, *Guardian*, 19 April.

Ham, C. (2004) *Health Policy in Britian*. Basingstoke: Macmillan.

Hancock, M., Calnan, M. and Manley, G. (1999) Private or NHS General Dental Service care in the United Kingdom? A study of public perceptions and experiences, *Journal of Public Health Medicine*, 21(4): 415–20.

Hantrais, L. (1995) *Social Policy in Europe*. London: Routledge.

Hargadon, J. and Staniforth, M. (2000) *A Health Service of All the Talents: Developing the NHS Workforce*. London: Department of Health.

Harrison, S., Milewa, T. and Dowswell, G. (2002a) *Patient and Public Involvement in NHS Primary Care: Final Report of a Department of Health Research Study*. Manchester: University of Manchester Department of Applied Social Science.

Harrison, S., Milewa, T. and Dowswell, G. (2002b) Public and user involvement in the National Health Service, *Health and Social Care in the Community*, 10(2): 1–4.

Hart, A. (2001) *Addressing Inequalities in Health: New Directions in Midwifery Education and Practice*. London: English National Board for Nursing, Midwifery and Health Visiting.

Hassell, K., Rogers, A. and Noyce, P. (2000) Community pharmacy as a primary health and self-care resource: A framework for understanding pharmacy utilization, *Health and Social Care in the Community*, 8(1): 40–9.

Hazell, R. and Jervis, P. (1998) *Devolution and Health*. Nuffield Trust Series 3. London: University College London and the Nuffield Trust.

Healthcare Commission (2005) *State of Healthcare 2005*. London: Healthcare Commission.

Hedgecoe, A. (2004) *The Politics of Personalized Medicine: Pharmacogenetics in the Clinic*. Cambridge: Cambridge University Press.

Hedley, R. and Davis Smith, J. (1992) *Volunteering and Society: Principles and Practice*. London: Bedford Square Press.

Heenan, D. and Birrell, D. (2006) The integration of health and social care: The lessons from Northern Ireland, *Social Policy and Administration*, 40(1): 47–66.

Heginbotham, C. (1990) *Return to Community: The Voluntary Ethic and Community Care*. London: Bedford Square Press.

Henkel, M. (1994) Social work: An incorrigibly marginal profession? in T. Becher (ed.) *Governments and Professional Education*. Buckingham: Open University Press.

Henwood, M. (1998) *Ignored and Invisible? Carers Experience of the NHS*. London: Carers National Association.

Henwood, M. (2002) No grey areas, *Health Service Journal*, 12 December: 24–7.

Heptinstall T. *et al.* (2004) Asylum seekers: A health professional perspective. *Nursing Standard* 18(25): 44–53.

Heron, E. and Dwyer, P. (1999) Doing the right thing: Labour's attempt to forge a new welfare deal between the individual and the state, *Social Policy and Administration*, 33(1): 91–104.

Hetherington, P. (2003) Working wonders, *Guardian Society*, 21 May: 8.

Higgins, J. (1988) *The Business of Medicine*. London: Macmillan.

Hills, J. (1993) *The Future of Welfare: A Guide to the Debate*. York: Joseph Rowntree Foundation.

Hills, J. (1994) *Inquiry into Income and Wealth, Vol. 12: A Survey of the Evidence*. London: Joseph Rowntree Foundation, Income and Wealth Inquiry Group.

Himmelweit, S. (2002) Making visible the hidden economy: The case for gender-impact analysis of economic policy, *Feminist Economics*, 8(1): 49–70.

Hirschmann, A.O. (1970) *Exit, Voice and Loyalty: Responses to Decline in Firms, Organizations and States*. London: Harvard University Press.

Hirst, J. (1999) High and dry, *Community Care*, 25 November-1 December, 20–1.

Hirst, M. (1999) *The Risk of Informal Care: An Incidence Study*. Working Paper 1680. York: Social Policy Research Unit, University of York.

Hirst, M. (2001) Trends in informal care in Great Britain during the 1990s, *Health and Social Care in the Community*, 9(6): 348–57.

Hood, C., Baldwin, R. and Rothstein, H. (2000) Assessing the Dangerous Dogs Act: when does a regulatory law fail? *Public Law*, summer: 282–305.

Hood, C., Rothstein, H. and Baldwin, R. (2001) *The Government of Risk: Understanding Risk Regimes*. Oxford: Oxford University Press.

Howarth, C., Kenway, P., Palmer, G. and Miorelli, R. (1999) *Monitoring Poverty and Social Exclusion 1999*. York: Joseph Rowntree Foundation.

House of Commons (1993) *Hansard*, Col. 1010, 27 July and *Hansard*, 18 October. London: HMSO.

House of Commons (2003) *Inequalities in Access to Maternity Services*, Eighth Report of Session 2002–3, Hc 696. London: TSO.

House of Commons Health Committee (2004a) *Obesity: Third Report of Session 2003–4*. London: The Stationery Office.

House of Commons Health Committee (2004b) *Palliative Care: Fourth Report of Session 2003–4*. London: The Stationery Office.

House of Commons Health Select Committee (1999) *Regulation of Private and Other Independent Healthcare*, Fifth Report, 1998/9 session. London: The Stationery Office.

House of Lords Select Committee on Science and Technology (2000) *Complementary and Alternative Medicine*. London: The Stationery Office.

Housing Corporation (2005) *Building Homes, Transforming Lives: Annual Report and Accounts 2004/5*. London: The Stationery Office

Hugman, R. (1991) *Power and the Professions*. Basingstoke: Macmillan.

Hugman, R. (1998) Social work and de-professionalization, in P. Abbott and E. Meerabeau (eds) *The Sociology of the Caring Professions*. London: UCL Press.

Humphrey, A. and Bromley, C. (2006) *Home Sweet Home in British Social Attitudes: The 22nd Report*. London: National Centre for Social Research.

Humphreys, N.A. (1885) Preface *Vital Statistics: A Memorial Volume of Selections from the Reports and Writings of William Farr*. London: The Sanitary Institute of Great Britain.

Humphris, D. and Macleod Clark, J. (2002) *Shaping a Vision for a 'New Generation' Workforce*. Southampton: University of Southampton.

Hunter, D.J. (1980) *Coping with Uncertainty: Policy and Politics in the National Health Service*. Chichester: Research Studies Press/Wiley.

Hunter, D. (1994) From tribalism to opportunism: The management challenge to medical dominance, in J. Gabe, D. Kelleher and G. Williams (eds) *Challenging Medicine*. London: Routledge.

Hunter, D. (1998a) The NHS: Looking to the future, *British Journal of Health Care Management*, 4(5): 226–8.

Hunter, D. (1998b) A disunited kingdom? *Health Management*, October: 10–12.

Hunter, D., McKeganey, N. and McPherson, I. (1988) *Care of the Elderly: Policy and Practice*. Aberdeen: Aberdeen University Press.

Hutt R, Rosen, B. and McCauley, J. (2004) *Case-managing long-term conditions: what impact does it have in the treatment of older people?* London, King's Fund.

Illsley, R. (1986) Occupational class, selection and the production of inequalities in health, *Quarterly Journal of Social Affairs*, 2: 151–65.

Institute for Fiscal Studies (2006) *Poverty and Inequality in Britain*. London: Institute for Fiscal Studies.

Institute of Economic Affairs (1995) *Dismantling The Welfare State: Tough Love or the Good Samaritan*. London: IEA Health and Welfare Unit.

Irvine, D. (2003) *A Doctor's Tale: Professionalism and Public Trust*. Oxford: Radcliffe Medical Press.

Iversen, T. (1997) The effect of a private sector on the waiting time in a national health service *Journal of Health Economics* 16(4), 381–396.

James, N. (1992) Care = organization + physical labour + emotional labour, *Sociology of Health and Illness*, 14: 488–509.

Jay Report (1979) *Report of the Committee of Enquiry into Mental Handicap Nursing and Care*. London: HMSO, Cmnd 4768.

Jervis, P. and Plowden, W. (eds) (2000) *Devolution and Health: First Annual Report*. London: The Constitution Unit, UCL.

Jervis, P. and Plowden, W. (2003) *The Impact of Political Devolution on the UK's Health Services*. London: Nuffield Trust.

JM Consulting (1998) *The Regulation of Nurses, Midwives and Health Visitors*. Bristol: JM Consulting Ltd.

JM Consulting (1999) *Review of the Delivery of the Diploma in Social Work*. London: DoH.

Johnson, N. (1990) Problems for the mixed economy of welfare, in A. Ware and R.E. Goodin (eds) *Needs and Welfare*. London: Sage.

Joint NHS Privatization Unit (1990) *The Privatization Experience*. London: JNPU.

Jones, A. (1992) An investigation into the factors affecting the diet of low-income groups, BSc dissertation, University of Northumbria.

Jones, H. (1994) *Health and Society in Twentieth-Century Britain*. Harlow: Longman.

Jones, K. (1991) *The Making of Social Policy in Britain 1930–1990*. London: Athlone Press.

Jones, P.G. and Cameron, D. (1984) Social class: An embarrassment to epidemiology? *Community Medicine*, 6: 37–46.

Jordan, B. (1984) *An Invitation to Social Work*. Oxford: Martin Robertson.

Joseph Rowntree Foundation (2002) *Calculating a Fair Price for Care?* York: JRF.

Jowell, R. *et al.* (eds) (1995) *British Social Attitudes: The 11th Report*. Aldershot: Dartmouth.

Kaplan, G.A. *et al.* (1996) Inequality in income and mortality in the United States: Analysis of mortality and potential pathways, *British Medical Journal*, 312: 999–1003.

Katbamna, S. *et al.* (2004) Do they look after their own? Informal support for South Asian carers, *Health and Social Care in the Community*, 12(5): 398–406

Kawachi, I. and Berkman, L.F. (2002) *Neighbourhoods and Health*. Oxford: Oxford University Press.

Kawachi, I., Kennedy, B.P., Lockner, K. and Prothrow-Smith, D. (1997) Social capital, income inequality and mortality, *American Journal of Public Health*, 50: 245–251.

Kemp, P.A. (2005) Social security and welfare reform under New Labour, in M. Powell *et al.* (eds) *Social Policy Review 17: Analysis and Debate in Social Policy, 2005*. Bristol: Policy Press/Social Policy Association.

Kemshall, H. (1998) *Risk in Probation Practice*. Aldershot, Ashgate.

Kendall, J. (2000) The mainstreaming of the third sector into public policy in England in the late 1990s: Why and wherefores, *Policy and Politics*, 28: 541–62.

Kendall, J. and Knapp, M. (1995) A loose and baggy monster: Boundaries, definitions and typologies, in J. Davis Smith, C. Rochester and R. Hedley (eds) *An Introduction to the Voluntary Sector*. London: Routledge.

Kennedy, A., Rogers, A. and Gately, C. (2005a) Assessing the introduction of the expert patients programme into the NHS: A realistic evaluation of recruitment to a lay-led self-care initiative, *Primary Health Care Research and Development*, 6(2): 137–48.

Kennedy, A., Rogers, A. and Gately, C. (2005b) From patients to providers: Prospects for self-care skills trainers in the National Health Service, *Health and Social Care*, 13(5): 431–40.

Kennedy, B.P., Kawachi, I. and Prothrow-Smith, D. (1996) Income distribution and mortality: Cross-sectional ecological study of the Robin Hood Index in the United States, *British Medical Journal*, 312: 1004–7.

Kerr, D. (2005) *A National Framework for Service Change in the NHS in Scotland*. Edinburgh: Scottish Executive.

King, R.D., Raynes, N.V. and Tizzard, J. (1971) *Patterns of Residential Care*. London: Routledge and Kegan Paul.

King's Fund (2001) *Future Imperfect*. London: King's Fund.

Kingston, P. (2004) Duty of Care. Education Guardian, 13 July p.14.

Kirk, S. and Glendinning, C. (1998) Trends in community care and patient participation: Implications for the roles of informal carers and community nurses in the UK, *Journal of Advanced Nursing*, 28 (2): 370–81.

Klein, R. (2001) *The New Politics of the NHS*. London: Longman.

Klein, R. (2002) The state and the profession: The politics of the double bed, *British Medical Journal*, 301: 701–2.

Klein, R. (2005) Transforming the NHS, in M. Powell *et al.* (eds) *Social Policy Review 17*. Bristol: Policy Press, Social Policy Association.

Klein, R. and Lewis, J. (1976) *The Politics of Consumer Representation: A Study of Community Health Councils*. London: Centre for Studies in Social Policy.

Klinenberg, E. (2002) *Heat Wave: a social autopsy of disaster in Chicago*. Chicago, IL: University of Chicago Press.

Kratz, C.R. (1978) *Care of the long-term sick in the community: particularly patients with stroke* Edinburgh: Churchill Livingstone.

Kuh, D. and Ben-Shlomo, Y. (eds) (1997) *A Life Course Approach to Chronic Disease Epidemiology: Tracing the Origins of Ill Health from Early to Adult Life*. Oxford: Oxford Medical Publications.

Lahey, W. and Currie, R. (2005) Regulatory and medico-legal barriers to interprofessional practice, *Journal of Interprofessional Care*, 19(1): 197–223.

Laing, R.D. (1964) *Sanity, madness and the family*. London, Tavistock.

Laing and Buisson (1993) *Laing's Review of Private Healthcare 1993*. London: Laing and Buisson.

Laing and Buisson (2000) Concerns over care home closures mount. *Community Care Market News*. October, 7(6): 1.

Laing and Buisson (2001) *Care of Elderly People Market Survey 2001*.

Land, H. (1991) Time to care, in M. Maclean and D. Groves (eds) *Women's Issues in Social Policy*. London: Routledge.

Le Grand, J., Mays, N. and Mulligan, J.A. (eds) (1998) *Learning from the NHS Internal Market: A Review of the Evidence*. London: King's Fund.

Levin, P. (1997) *Making Social Policy*. Buckingham: Open University Press.

Levitas, R. (1998) *The Inclusive Society*. Basingstoke: Macmillan.

Levitas, R. (2006) The concept and measurement of social exclusion, in C.

Pantazis *et al.* (eds) *Poverty and Social Exclusion in Britain*. Bristol: Policy Press.

Lewis, J. (1980) *The Politics of Motherhood*. London: Croom Helm.

Lewis, J. (1992) Gender and the development of welfare regimes, *European Journal of Social Policy*, 2: 159–74.

Lewis, J. (2001) Older People and the Health-Social Care Boundary in the UK: Half a Century of Hidden Policy Conflict *Social Policy and Administration* 35 343–359.

Lewis, J. (2002) Gender and welfare state change, *European Societies*, 4(4): 331–57.

Lewis, G. (2003) "Difference" and social policy in Ellison, N. and Pierson, C. *Developments in British Social Policy* 2 Basingstoke: Palgrave MacMillan pp90–106.

Lewis, J. and Surender, R. (eds) (2004) *Welfare State Change: Towards a Third Way?* Oxford: Oxford University Press.

Lewis, J., Bernstock, P. and Bovell, V. (1995) The community care changes: Unresolved tensions in policy and issues in implementation, *Journal of Social Policy*, 24: 73–94.

Lewis, R., Hunt, P. and Carson, D. (2006) *Social Enterprise and Community-based Care: Is There a Future for Mutually-Owned Organizations in Community and Primary Care?* London: King's Funds.

Little, P. Everitt, M., Williamson, I., Warner, G., Moore, M., Gould, C., Ferrier, K. and Payne S. (2001) Preferences of patients for patient centred approach to consultation in primary care: Observational study, *British Medical Journal*, 322: 468–72.

Lister, R. (1997) *Citizenship: Feminist Perspectives*. Basingstoke: Macmillan.

Lister, R. (2003) *Citizenship: feminist perspectives*. New York: New York University Press.

Lock, C.S. (1906) *Introduction to Annual Charities Register and Digest*, 15th edn. London: Longman.

Lomax, E.M.R. (1996) *Small and Special: The Development of Hospitals for Children in Victorian Britain*. London: Wellcome Institute for the History of Medicine.

Lorig, K. *et al.* (1996) *Outcome Measures for Health Education and Other Health Care Interventions*. London: Sage.

Loudon, I., Horder, J., Webster C. (1998), *General Practice under the National Health Service 1948–1997* Oxford: Clarendon Press.

Lowe, R. (1993) *The Welfare State in Britain Since 1945*. London: Macmillan.

Lowe, S. and Hudson, J. (2004) *Understanding the Policy Process: Analysing Welfare Policy and Practice* Bristol: Policy Press.

Lupton, C., Peckham, S. and Taylor, P. (1998) *Managing Public Involvement in Health Care Purchasing*. Buckingham: Open University Press.

Lutz, W., Sanderson, W. and Scherbov, S. (2001) The end of world population growth, *Nature*, 2 August: 543–5.

Lyle, J. (1958) The effects of an institutional environment upon the verbal development of imbecile children I: Verbal intelligence, *Journal of Mental Deficiency*, 3: 122–8.

Lyle, J. (1959a) The effects of an institutional environment upon the verbal development of imbecile children II: Speech and language, *Journal of Mental Deficiency*, 4: 1–13.

Lyle, J. (1959b) The effects of an institutional environment upon the verbal development of imbecile children III: The Brooklands Residential Family Unit, *Journal of Mental Deficiency*, 4: 14–22.

Lynch, J.W. *et al.* (1998) Income inequality and mortality in metropolitan areas of the United States. *American Journal of Public Health*, 88(7): 1074–80.

Macdonald, J. (1992) *Primary Health Care*. London: Earthscan.

MacGregor, G. (1990) Privatization on parade, *Health Service Journal*, 3 May: 670–71.

Mack, J. and Lansley, S. (1985) *Poor Britain*. London: Allen and Unwin.

Mahony, C. (2005) Give and take, *Health Service Journal*, 3 February: 36.

Malpass, P. and Murie, A. (1994) *Housing Policy and Practice*, 4th edn. London: Macmillan.

Malpass, P. and Murie A. (1999) *Housing policy and practice*. 5th edn. Basingstoke: Macmillan.

Margellos, H., Silva, A. and Whitman, S. (2004) Comparison of Health Status Indicators in Chicago: Are Black–White Disparities Worsening? *American Journal of Public Health*. 94(1): 116–121.

Marmot, M. *et al.* (1984) Inequalities in death: Specific explanations of a general pattern, *Lancet*, 1: 1003–6.

Marmot, M. *et al.* (1991) Health inequalities among British civil servants: The Whitehall II Study, *Lancet*, 337: 1367–93.

Marmot, M. *et al.* (1997) Social inequalities in health: Next questions and converging evidence, *Social Science and Medicine*, 44(6): 901–10.

Marsh, A., Gordon, D., Pantazis, C. and Heslop, P. (2000) *Home Sweet Home: The Impact of Poor Housing on Health*. Bristol: The Policy Press.

Marshall, T. (1975) *Social Policy in the Twentieth Century*, 4th edn. London: Hutchinson.

Marshall, T. (1981) *The Right to Welfare and Other Essays*. London: Heinemann.

Martin, S. and Boaz, A. (2000) Public participation and citizen-centred local government, *Public Money and Management*, 20(2): 47–53.

Mason, C. and Clarke, J. (2001) *A Nursing Vision of Public Health*. Belfast and Dublin: Department of Health, Social Services and Public Safety/ Department of Health Care.

Masterson, A. (2000) Cross-boundary working: A macro-political analysis of the impact on professional roles, *Journal of Clinical Nursing*, 11: 331–9.

May, M. and Brunsden, E. (1994) Workplace care in the mixed economy of welfare, in R. Page and J. Baldock (eds) *Social Policy Review 6*. Canterbury: Social Policy Association.

Mays, N. and Bevan, G. (1987) *Resource Allocation in the Health Service*. Occasional Papers in Social Administration No. 81. London: Bedford Square Press.

Mays, N. *et al.* (eds) (2001) *The Purchasing of Health Care by Primary Care Organizations*. Buckingham: Open University Press.

McKeown, T. (1976) *The Role of Medicine: Dream, Mirage or Nemesis?* London: Nuffield Hospitals Trust.

McKinlay, J.B. (1995) *Bringing the Social System Back in: An Essay on the Epidemiological Imagination*. Boston, MA: New England Research Institute.

Means, R. and Smith, R. (1998) *Community Care: Policy and Practice*. Basingstoke: Macmillan.

Means R., Smith, R. and Morbey, H. (2002) *From Community Care to Market Care?* Bristol: Policy Press.

Meerabeau, E. (2001) Back to the bedpans: The debates over preregistration nursing education in England, *Journal of Advanced Nursing*, 34(4): 427–35.

Meerabeau, E. (2004) Be good, sweet maid, and let who can be clever: A counter reformation in English nursing education? *International Journal of Nursing Studies*, 41: 285–92.

Meerabeau, E. and Antoncino, J. (2002) *The views of residential care home owners on the implementation of the Care Standards Act*. BSA Medical Sociology Conference, York, September.

Merrison Report (1975) *Report of the Committee of Inquiry into the Regulation of the Medical Profession*. Cmnd 6018. London: The Stationery Office.

Milburn, A. (2000) A healthier nation and healthier economy: The contribution of a modern NHS. LSE Health Annual Lecture, 8 March.

Miles, A. (1991) *Women Health and Medicine*. Buckingham: Open University Press.

Miles, I. (1986) The emergence of sick children's nursing, part 2, *Nurse Education Today*, 6: 133–8.

Milewa, T., Harrison, S., Ahmad, W. and Tovey, P. (2002) Citizens' participation in primary health care planning: Innovative citizenship practice in empirical perspective, *Critical Public Health*, 12(1): 39–53.

Milewa, T., Valentine, J. and Calnan, M. (1998) Managerialism and active citizenship in Britain's reformed health service: Power and community in an era of decentralization, *Social Science and Medicine*, 47(4): 507–17.

Milligan, C. (1998) Pathways of dependence: The impact of health and social care restructuring – the voluntary experience, *Social Science and Medicine*, 46(6): 743–53.

Milligan, C. (2000) 'Breaking out of the asylum': Developments in the geography of mental ill health – the influence of the informal sector, *Health and Place*, 6: 189–200.

Ministry of Health (1944) *A National Health Service*. Cmd 6502. London: HMSO.

Mohan, J. (1995) *A National Health Service?* Basingstoke: Macmillan.

Montgomery, J. (1998) Professional regulation: A gendered phenomen? in S. Sheldon and M. Thomson (eds) *Feminist Perspectives on Health Care Law*. London: Cavendish.

Moon, G. and Lupton, D. (1995) Within acceptable limits: Health care provider perspectives on community health councils in the reformed British NHS, *Policy and Politics*, 23(4): 335–46.

Moon, G. and North, N. (2000) *Policy and Pace: General Medical Practice in the UK*. Basingstoke: Macmillan.

Moore, A. (2006) Prescription for conflict, *Health Service Journal*, 1 June: 29–30.

Moran, M. (2002) *Understanding the Regulatory State*, http://journals.cambridge.org/action/displayAbstract, 32: 391–413.

Morris, J. (1993) *Independent Lives: Community Care and Disabled People*. Basingstoke: Macmillan.

Morris, L. (1994) *Dangerous Classes: The Underclass and Social Citizenship*. London: Routledge.

Moser, K.A., Fox, A.J. and Jones, D.R. (1986) Unemployment and mortality in the OPCS Longitudinal Study, in R.G. Wilkinson (ed.) *Class and Health*. London: Tavistock.

Moynihan, R. and Henry, D. (2005) *Selling Sickness: How the World's Biggest Pharmaceutical Companies are Turning Us All Into Patients*. New York, NY: Nation Books.

Mulholland, H. (2002) A few home truths, *Nursing Times*, 98(40): 11.

Munro, J.F., Nicholl, J.P., O'Cathain, A. and Knowles, E. (2000) Impact of NHS Direct on demand for immediate care: Observational study, *British Medical Journal*, 321: 150–3.

Muntaner, C. and Lynch, J. (1999) Income inequality, social cohesion and class relations: A critique of Wilkinson's neo-Durkheimian research program, *International Journal of Health Services*, 29(1): 59–81.

Murie, A. (1993) Restructuring housing markets and housing access, in R. Page and J. Baldock (eds) *Social Policy Review 5*. Canterbury: Social Policy Association.

Murie, A. and Forrest, R. (1980) *Housing Market Processes and the Inner City*. Report to the SSRC Inner Cities Working Party.

Murphy, B. *et al.* (1997) Women with multiple roles: The emotional impact of caring for ageing parents, *Ageing and Society*, 17: 277–91.

Murray, C.J., Gakidou, E.E. and Frenk, J. (1999) Health inequalities and social group differences: What should we measure? *Bull World Health Organ*, 77(7): 537–43.

National Audit Office (2005) *Dealing with the Complexity of the Benefits System*. London: National Audit Office.

National Consumer Council (1999) *Self-regulation of Professionals in Health Care: Consumer issues*. London: National Consumer Council.

National Council for Civil Liberties (1951) *Fifty Thousand Outside the Law*. London: NCCL.

Navarro, V. (2002) A critique of social capital, *International Journal of Health Services*, 32(3): 423–32.

Nazroo, J.Y. (1997) *The Health of Britain's Ethnic Minorities: Findings from a National Survey*. London: Policy Studies Institute.

NCC (National Consumer Council) (2004) *Making Public Services Personal: A New Compact for Public Services*. London: NCC.

Netten, A., Darton, R. and Williams, J. (2003) Nursing home closures: effects on capacity and reasons for closure. *Age and Ageing*, 32, 3, 332-337.

Nettleton, S. (1998) Losing homes through mortgage possession: A 'new' public health issue, *Critical Public Health*, 8(1): 47–58.

Newman, G. (1906) *Infant Mortality: A Social Problem*. London: Methuen.

Newman, J. and Vidler, E. (2006) Discriminating customers, responsible patients, empowered users: Consumerism and the modernization of health care, *Journal of Social Policy*, 35(2): 193–210.

Newsome, P.R.H. (2003) Current issues in dental practice management part 1: The importance of shared values, *Primary Dental Care*, 37–9.

NHS Executive (1996) *Patient Partnership: Building a Collaborative Strategy*. Leeds: DoH.

NHS Modernization Agency (2005) *Long-Term Conditions Workforce Design Manual*, www.natpact.nhs.uk.

NHS Scotland (2000) *Our National Health: A Plan for Action, a Plan for Change*. Edinburgh: NHS Scotland.

NHS Scotland (2001) *Patient Focus and Public Involvement*. Edinburgh: SEHD

NHS Scotland (2005) *National Framework for Service Change in the NHS Scotland: Self care, Carers, Volunteering and the Voluntary Sector: Towards a more Collaborative Approach*. Edinburgh: NHS Scotland.

NHS Wales (2001) www.wales.nhs.uk/publications/nhssstrategydoc.pdf. Cardiff: National Assembly for Wales.

NHS Wales (2005) *Designed for Life*. Cardiff: Wales Assembly Government.

NHS CRD (Centre for Reviews and Dissemination) (1995) *Review of the Research on the Effectiveness of Health Service Interventions to Reduce Variations in Health*. York: University of York.

NHSE/IHSM/NHS Confederation (1998) *In the Public Interest: Developing a Strategy for Public Participation in the NHS*. London: DoH.

NS (National Statistics) (2006). Downloaded from http://www.statistics.gov.uk/cci/nugget.asp?id=12, on 8/09/2006.

NS (National Statistics) (2004). Downloaded from http://www.statistics.gov.uk/CCI/nugget.asp?ID=918&Pos=6&ColRank=2&Rank=1000 on 10/10/06.

Nolan, M. and Nolan, J. (1995) Responding to the challenge of chronic illness. *British Journal of Nursing* 4(3): 145–7.

Nolan, M. and Nolan, J. (1999) Rehabilitation, chronic illness and disability: the missing elements in nurse education. *Journal of Advanced Nursing* 29(4): 958–66.

Nolan, P. (1995) Mental health nursing – origins and development, in M. Baly (ed.) *Nursing and Social Change*, 3rd edn. London: Routledge.

O'Connor, A.M., Légaré, F. and Stacey, D. (2003) Risk communication in practice: The contribution of decision aids, *British Medical Journal*, 327: 736–40.

ODPM (Office of the Deputy Prime Minister (2005) *Sustainable Communities: People, Places and Prosperity*. London: ODPM.

Office of Health Economics (2000) *Compendium of Health Statistics*, 12th edn. London: OHE.

O'Hara, M. (2006) Pain but no gain, *Guardian*, 10 May: 3.

Oliver, M. and Barnes, C. (1998) *Disabled People and Social Policy from Exclusion to Inclusion*. Harlow: Longman.

Ong, B.N. (1993) *The Practice of Health Services Research*. London: Chapman and Hall.

Ong, P. and Banks, B. (2003) *Complementary and Alternative Medicine: The Consumer Perspective*. London: Foundation for Integrated Health.

ONS (2001) *Birth Statistics 2001 Series FM1 No 31 Conceptions Supplement* London: ONS.

ONS (2002) *Infant Mortality Rates by District*, www.statistics.gov.uk.

ONS (2006) *Labour Market Statistics*, www.statistics.gov.uk.

Opinion Leader Research (2006) *Your Health, Your Care, Your Say*. London: DoH.

Oppenheim, C. (1990) *Poverty: The Facts*. London: Child Poverty Action Group.

Ormerod, P. and Rowthorn, R. (1997) Why family ties bind the nation, *Times Higher*, 29 August: 16.

Ottewill, R. and Magirr, P. (1999) Changes in ownership of community pharmacies: Policy implications, *Public Money and Management*, 19(2): 39–44.

Ottewill, R. and Wall, A. (1992) *The Growth and Development of the Community Health Services*. Sunderland: Business Education Publishers Ltd.

Owen, D (1965) *English Philanthropy 1660–1960*. Oxford: Oxford University Press.

Painter, C. and Clarence, W.E. (2001) UK Local Action Zones and changing urban governance, *Urban Studies*, 38(8): 1215–32.

Palmer, G., Carr, J. and Kenway, P. (2005) *Monitoring Poverty and Social Exclusion 2005*. York: Joseph Rowntree Foundation/New Policy Institute.

Pantazis, C., Gordon, D. and Levitas, R. (2006) *Poverty and Social Exclusion in Britain*. Bristol: Policy Press.

Parker, G. (1999) Impact of the NHS and Community Care Act (1990) on Informal Carers. In *With respect to old age*, Research volume 3.

Parsons, T. (1951) Social structure and dynamic process: The case of modern medical practice, in *The Social System*, pp. 428–79. New York, NY: The Free Press.

Pascall, G. (1996) *Social Policy: A New Feminist Analysis*. London: Tavistock.

Patel, N. (1999) Black and minority ethnic elderly: perspectives on long-term care. *Royal Commission of Long-Term Care – Research* Volume 1.

Payne, F. and Jessopp, L. (2001) NHS Direct: Review of activity data for the first year of operation at one site, *Journal of Public Health Medicine*, 23(2): 155–8.

Peckham, S. (2004) Community orientated approaches to health: Reconciling individual and community needs, in J. Kai and C. Drinkwater (eds) *Primary Care in Urban and Disadvantaged Communities*. Abingdon: Radcliffe Medical Press.

Peckham, S. and Exworthy, M. (2003) *Primary Care in The UK: Policy, Organization and Management*. Basingstoke: Palgrave.

Peckham, S., Exworthy, M., Greener, I. and Powell, M. (2005) Decentralizing health services: More accountability or just more central control? *Public Money and Management*, 25(4): 221–8.

Pendleton, D. *et al.* (1984) *The Consultation: An Approach to Learning and Teaching*. Oxford: Oxford University Press.

Pensions Commission (2005) *A new pension settlement for the twenty-first century*. (Chair: Lord Turner) London, The Stationery Office.

Peterson, A.R. and Lupton, D. (1996) *The New Public Health: Health and Self in the Age of Risk*. London: Sage.

Pettigrew, A., Ferlie, E. and Mackie, L. (1992) *Shaping Strategic Change*. London: Sage.

Phillips Report (2000) *The Inquiry into BSE and Variant CJD in the United Kingdom*. London: The Stationery Office.

Phillipson, C. and Scharf, T. (2004) *The Impact of Government Policy on Social Exclusion Among Older People*. London: ODPM.

Philpott, J. (1994) Unemployment, inequality and inefficiency: The incidence and cost of unemployment, in A. Glynn and D. Milliband (eds) *Paying for Ill Health*. London: Rivers Drain Press.

Philpot, T. (2005) Speak out, *Health Service Journal*, 13 October: 2.

Piachaud, D. (1979) *The Cost of a Child*. London: Child Poverty Action Group.

Pickard, L. (2002) The decline of intensive intergenerational care of older people in Great Britain, 1985–1995. *Population Trends 110* pp31–41.

Pickard, S., Shaw, S. and Glendinning, C. (2000) Health care professionals' support for older carers, *Ageing and Society*, 20: 725–44.

Pickard, S., Jacobs, S. and Kirk, S. (2003) Challenging professional roles: Lay carers' involvement in health care in the community, *Social Policy and Administration*, 37(1): 82–96.

Pollock, A. (2005) *NHS plc: The Privatization of Our Health Care*. London: Virgo.

Pollock, A.M. and Whitty, I.M. (1990) Crisis in our hospital kitchens: Ancillary staffing during an outbreak of food poisoning in a long stay hospital, *British Medical Journal*, 300: 383–5.

Popay, J. and Jones, G. (1990) Patterns of wealth and illness among lone parents, *Journal of Social Policy*, 19: 499–534.

Poulton, B. *et al.* (2000) *The contribution of Nurses, Midwives, and Health Visitors to the Public Health Agenda*. Belfast: DHSSPS.

Powell, M.A. (1997) *Evaluating the NHS*. Buckingham: Open University Press.

Powell, M. (1998) *New Labour, New Welfare State*. Bristol: Policy Press.

Powell, M. (1999) *New Labour New Welfare State: The 'Third Way' in British Social Policy* Bristol: Policy Press.

Powell, M.A. (2000) New Labour and the third way in the British welfare state: A new and distinctive approach? *Critical Social Policy*, 20(1): 39–60.

Powell, M. and Barrientos (2004) Welfare regimes and the welfare mix, *European Journal of Political Research*, 43: 83–105.

Powell, M. and Exworthy, M. (2000) Variations on a theme: New Labour, health inequalities and policy failure, in A. Hann (ed.) *Analysing Health Policy*. Aldershot: Ashgate.

Powell, M. and Exworthy, M. (2001) Joined-up solutions to address health inequalities: Analysing policy, process and resource streams, *Public Money and Management*, 21(1): 21–6.

Powell, M. and Hewitt, M. (1998) The end of the welfare state? *Social Policy and Administration*, 32(1): 1–13.

Powell, M., Bauld, L. and Clarke, K. (2005) *Social Policy Review 17: Analysis and Debate in Social Policy, 2005*. Bristol: Policy Press/Social Policy Association.

Power, M. (1999) *The audit society: rituals of verification*. Oxford University Press.

Pratchett, L. (2004) Local autonomy, local democracy and the 'New Localism', *Political Studies*, 52: 358–75.

Putnam, R.D. (2000) *Bowling Alone: The Collapse and Revival of American Community*. New York, NY: Simon and Schuster.

Ralph, A. (1997) Unpalatable truths, *Times Higher*, 3 October: 20.

Reading, P. (1994) *Community Care and the Voluntary Sector*. Birmingham: Ventura Press.

Redding, M. (1979) *Universality and Selectivity: Strategies in Social Policy*. London: National Economic and Social Council.

Rhodes, M. (2000) Social democracy and the Third Way in British welfare, *West European Politics*, 23(2): 178–9.

Rodger, J.J. (2003) Social solidarity, welfare and post-emotionalism, *Journal of Social Policy*. 32(3): 403–21.

Rogers A, Hassell, K. and Nicholas, G. (2000) *Demanding Patients*. Buckingham: Open University Press.

Rose, G. and Marmot, M. (1981) Social class and coronary heart disease, *British Heart Journal*, 45: 141–56.

Rose, N. (1985) *The Psychology Complex: Psychology, Politics and Society in England, 1869–1939*. London: Routledge & Kegan Paul.

Rose, N. (1989) Individualizing psychology, in J. Shotter and K.J. Gergen (eds) *Texts of Identity*. London: Sage.

Rosenthal, M. (1995) *The Incompetent Doctor: Behind Closed Doors*. Buckingham: Open University Press.

Rowntree, B.S. (1901) *Poverty: A Study in Town Life*. London: Macmillan.

Rowntree, B.S. (1941) *Poverty and Progress*. Harlow: Longman.

Royal Commission (1958) *Report of the Royal Commission on the Law Relating to Mental Illness and Mental Deficiency*. London: HMSO.

Royal National Institute for the Blind (1991) *Blind and Partially Sighted Adults in the UK*. London: RNIB.

Royston, G. *et al.* (1992) Modelling the use of health services by populations of small areas to inform the allocation of central resources to larger regions, *Socio-Economic Planning Sciences*, 26: 169–90.

Rummery, K. and Coleman, A. (2003) Primary health and social care services in the UK: Progress towards partnership? *Social Science and Medicine*, 56(8): 1773–82.

Ryan, C. (2000) Dodgy docs force nurse crackdown, *Nursing Times*, 96: 12–13.

6 P (1997) The new politics of welfare contracting, in 6 P and J. Kendall (eds) *The Contract Culture in Public Services: Studies from Britain, Europe and the USA*. Aldershot: Arena.

Salter, B. (2004) *The New Politics of Medicine*. Basingstoke, Macmillan.

Saltman, R. and Von Otter, C. (1992) *Planned Markets in Health Care*. Buckingham: Open University Press.

Saltman, R. and Ferroussier-Davis (2000) The concept of stewardship in health policy, *Bulletin of the World Health Organization*, 78(6): 732–9.

Saraceno, C. (1987) Division of family labour and gender identity, in A. Showstack Sassoon (ed.) *Women and the State*. London: Hutchinson.

Savage, W. (1986) *A Savage Enquiry*. London: Virago.

Scharf, T. *et al.* (2002) *Growing Older in Socially Deprived Areas: Social Exclusion in Later Life*. London: Help the Aged.

Schulz, R. and Beach, S. (1999) Caregiving as a risk factor for mortality: Caregiver Health Effects Study, *Journal of the American Medical Association*, 282: 2215–19.

Scottish Executive (2001) *Nursing for Health – A Review of the Contribution of Nurses, Midwives and Health Visitors to Improving the Public Health*. Edinburgh: The Stationery Office.

Scottish Executive (2003) *Partnership For Care: Scotland's Health White Paper*. Edinburgh: Scottish Executive.

Scull, A. (1977) *Decarceration: Community Treatment and the Deviant*. London: Prentice-Hall.

Secretary of State for Northern Ireland (1998) *Fit for the Future: A Consultation Document on the Government's Proposals for the Future of Health and Personal Social Services in Northern Ireland*. Belfast: The Stationery Office.

Secretary of State for Scotland (1997) *Designed to Care: Renewing the National Health Service in Scotland*. Cmd. 3811. Edinburgh: The Stationery Office.

Secretary of State for Wales (1997) *A Voice for Wales*. Cmd. 3718. Cardiff: The Stationery Office.

Secretary of State for Wales (1998) *NHS Wales: Putting Patients First*. Cmd. 3841. Cardiff: The Stationery Office.

Seebohm Committee (1968) *Report of the Committee on Local Authority and Allied Personal Social Services*. Cmnd 3703. London: HMSO.

Seidler, E. (1990) An historical survey of Children's hospitals, in L. Granshaw and R. Porter (eds) *The Hospital in History*. London: Routledge.

Sen, A. (1999) *Development as Freedom*. Oxford: Oxford University Press.

Sen, A. (2001) Economic progress and health, in D. Leon and G. Walt (eds) *Poverty, Inequality and Health*. Oxford: Oxford University Press.

Sharma, U. (1994) The equation of responsibility: Complementary practitioners and their patients, in S. Budd and U. Sharma (eds) *The Healing Bond*. London: Routledge.

Shaw, I. and Aldridge, A. (2003) Consumerism, Health and Social Order *Social Policy and Society* 2(1), 35–43.

Shaw, M. *et al.* (1999) *The Widening Gap. Health Inequalities and Policy in Britain*. Bristol: Policy Press.

Sheaff, R. *et al.* (2003) A subtle governance: 'soft' medical leadership in English primary care. *Social Health and Illness*, 25(5): 408–28.

Shi, L., Starfield, B., Politzer, R. and Regan, J. (2002) Primary care, self-rated health and reductions in social disparities in health, *Health Services Research*, 37: 529–50.

Shipman Inquiry (2002–5) First, second, third, fourth and fifth report. London: The Stationery Office.

Siahpush, M. (1999) A critical review of the sociology of alternative medicine: Research on users, practitioners and the orthodoxy. *Health*, 4(2): 159–78.

Sigerist, H. (1943) *Civilization and Disease*. Chicago, IL: Chicago University Press.

Silverman, D. (1987) *Communication and Medical Practice: Social Relations in the Clinic*. London: Sage.

Sim, F., Walters, R. and Schiller, G. (2003) *A Diversity of Talents: Public Health People in London*. Cardiff: UK Public Health Association Annual Conference.

Simon, C. and Kendrick, T. (2001) Informal carers – the role of general practitioners and district nurses, *British Journal of General Practice*, 51: 655–7.

Skellington, R. and Morris, P. (1992) *Race in Britain Today*. London: Sage.

Smith, J. *et al.* (2004) *A Review of the Effectiveness of Primary Care-Led Commissioning and its Place in the NHS*. London: The Health Foundation.

Social Exclusion Unit (1999) *Teenage Pregnancy*. Cm 4342. London: TSO.

Social Exclusion Unit (2004a) *Mental Health and Social Exclusion*. London: TSO.

Social Exclusion Unit (2004b) *Breaking the Cycle: Taking Stock of Progress and Priorities for the Future*. London: ODPM.

Social Services Inspectorate (1987) *From Home Help to Home Care*. London: HMSO.

Social Trends (2006) www.statistics.gov.uk.

Spicker, P. (1993) *Poverty and Social Security*. London: Routledge.

Spicker, P. (1995) *Social Policy: Themes and Approaches*. Hemel Hempstead: Harvester Wheatsheaf.

Stacey, M. (1992) *Regulating British Medicine: the GMC*. Chichester: Wiley.

Staines, R. (2006) What now for NHS Direct? *Nursing Times*, 11 April: 11.

Starfield, B. (1998) *Balancing Health Needs, Services, and Technology* London: Oxford University Press.

Stein, C. and Moritz, I. (1999) *A Life Course Perspective of Maintaining Independence in Older Age*. Geneva: WHO.

Stern, R., Stilwell, B. and Heuston, J. (1989) *From the Margins to the Mainstream: Collaboration in Planning Services with Single Homeless People*. London: West Lambeth Health Authority.

Stewart, J., Ruston, A. and Clayton, J. (2006) Housing as a health determinant: Is there consensus that public health partnerships are a way forward? *Journal of Environmental Health Research*.

Stewart, M. *et al.* (1995) *Patient-Centred Medicine Transforming the Clinical Method*. Thousand Oaks, CA: Sage.

Strong, P. (1979) Sociological imperialism and the profession of medicine, *Social Science and Medicine*, 13A: 199–215.

Stronks, K. *et al.* (1997) The interrelationship between income, health and employment status, *International Journal of Epidemiology*, 26(3): 592–600.

Sutherland, H., Sefton, T. and Piachaud, D. (2003) *Poverty in Britain: The Impact of Government Policy Since 1997*. York: Joseph Rowntree Foundation.

Taske, N. *et al.* (2005) *Housing and Public Health: A Review of Reviews of Interventions for Improving Health*. London: NICE.

Taylor, M. (1991) *New Times, New Challenges: Voluntary Organizations Facing 1990*. London: NCVO.

Taylor, M. (2003) *Public Policy in the Community*. Basingstoke: Palgrave Macmillan.

Taylor, M. and Langan, J. (1996) Map of the new country – what is the voluntary sector? in C. Hanvey and T. Philpot (eds) *Sweet Charity – the Role and Workings of Voluntary Organizations*. London: Routledge.

Taylor, M., Hogget, P. and Langan, J. (1994) Independent organizations in community care, in S.K.E. Saxon-Harold and J. Kendall (eds) *Researching the Voluntary Sector*, 2nd edn. London: Charities Aid Foundation.

Taylor, P., Peckham, S. and Turton, P. (1998) *A Public Health Model of Primary Care: From Concept to Reality*. Birmingham: Public Health Alliance.

Taylor-Gooby, P. (1994) What citizens want from the state, in R. Jowell, L. Brook and L. Dowds (eds) *International Social Attitudes: The 10th BSA Report*. Aldershot: Dartmouth.

Taylor-Gooby, P. (1995) Welfare outside the state, in R. Jowell *et al.* (eds) *British Social Attitudes: the 11th Report*. Aldershot: Dartmouth.

Taylor-Gooby, P. (ed.) (2004), *New Risks, New Welfare*. Oxford: Oxford University Press.

Taylor-Gooby, P., Hastie, C. and Bromley, C. (2003) Querulous citizens: Welfare knowledge and the limits to welfare reform, *Social Policy and Administration*, 37(1): 1–20.

Tew, M. (1990) *Safer Childbirth? A Critical History of Maternity Care*. London: Chapman and Hall.

Thomas, K.J. and Fitter, M. (1997) Evaluating complementary therapies for use in the NHS: Part 2 – Alternative research strategies, *Complementary Therapies in Medicine*, 5: 94–8.

Thomas, K.J., Nicholl, J.P. and Fall, M. (2001) Access to complementary medicine via general practice, *British Journal of General Practice*, 51: 25–30.

Thomas, K.J., Coleman, P. and Nicholl, J.P. (2003) Trends in access to complementary or alternative medicines via primary care in England: 1995–2001 results from a follow-up national survey, *Family Practice*, 20(5): 575–7.

Thompson, N. (2002) *Building the Future: Social Work with Children, Young People and Their Families*. Lyme Regis: Russell House Publishing.

Timmins, N. (1988) NHS regional trust internal market plans, *Independent*, 14 March.

Timmins, N. (1995) *The Five Giants*. Harmondsworth: Penguin.

Timmins, N. and Cox, B. (2001) A public realm, *Prospect*, July: 20.

Titmuss, R. (1955) The social division of welfare, in *Essays on the Welfare State*. London: Allen and Unwin.

Titmuss, R. (1963) *Income Distribution and Social Change*. London: Allen and Unwin.

Titmuss, R. (1968) *Commitment to Welfare*. London: Allen and Unwin.

Titmuss, R. (1987) *The Philosophy of Welfare: Selected Writings of Richard M. Titmuss*. London: Allen and Unwin.

Tizard, J. (1964) *Community Services for the Mentally Handicapped*. Oxford: Oxford University Press.

Toop L. (1998) Primary care: Core values: Patient centred primary care, *British Medical Journal*, 316: 1882–3.

Townsend, P. (1962) *The Last Refuge*. London: Routledge and Kegan Paul.

Townsend, P. (1979) *Poverty in the UK*. Harmondsworth: Penguin.

Townsend, P. (1993) *The International Analysis of Poverty*. New York, NY: Harvester Wheatsheaf.

Townsend, P., Whitehead, M. and Davidson, N. (eds) (1992) *Inequalities in Health: The Black Report and the Health Divide* (new edn). Harmondsworth: Penguin.

Toynbee, P. and Walker, A. (2001) *Did Things Get Better? An Audit of Labour's Successes and Failures*. London: Penguin.

Transport and General Workers' Union (1994) *In Place of Fear: The Future of the Welfare State*. London: TGWU.

Tudor-Hart, J. (1971) The inverse care law, *Lancet*, 27 February: 1405–12.

Tudor-Hart, J. (1988) *A New Kind of Doctor*. London: Merlin Press.

Turton, P., Peckham, S. and Taylor, P. (2000) Integrating primary care and public health, in J. Lindsay and P. Craig (eds) *Nursing for Public Health: Population-Based Care*. Edinburgh: Churchill Livingstone.

Twigg, J. and Atkin, K. (1995) Carers and services: Factors mediating service provision, *Journal of Social Policy*, 24: 5–30.

Ungerson, C. (1995) Gender, cash and informal care: European perspectives and dilemmas, *Journal of Social Policy*, 24: 31–52.

Wadsworth (1997)

Wagner Report (1988) *Residential Care: A Positive Choice*. London: HMSO.

Waine, B. (1992) The voluntary sector – the Thatcher years, in N. Manning and R. Page (eds) *Social Policy Review 4*. Canterbury: Social Policy Association.

Wales Assembly Government (2005) *Designed for Life: Creating World Class Health and Social Care for Wales in the 21st Century*. Cardiff: Wales Assembly Government.

Walker, A. (1982) The meaning and social domain of community care, in A. Walker (ed.) *Community Care: The Family, the State and Social Policy*. Oxford: Blackwell/Martin Robertson.

Walker, A. (1983) Care for elderly people: A conflict between women and the state, in J. Finch and D. Groves (eds) *A Labour of Love: Women, Work and Caring*. Boston, MA: Routledge and Kegan Paul.

Walker, R. (1995) *Families, Poverty and Work*. Briefings, 6, Spring 1 and 3. Loughborough: Centre for Research in Social Policy.

Walker, E. and Dewar, B.J. (2001) How do we facilitate carers' involvement in decision-making? *Journal of Advanced Nursing*, 34, 329–37.

Walshe, K. (2003) *Regulating Health Care: A Prescription for Improvement?* Buckingham: Open University Press.

Wanless, D. (2002) *Securing our Future Health: Taking a Long-Term View*. London: HM Treasury.

Wanless, D. (2003) *The Review of Health and Social Care in Wales*. Cardiff: Wales Assembly Government.

Wanless, D. (2002). (2002) *Securing our Future Health: Taking a Long-Term View*. London: HM Treasury.

Wanless, D. (2004) *Securing good health for the whole population*. Final Report. The Stationary Office.

Wanless, D. (2006) Kings fund review of social care

Ware, A. (1990) Meeting needs through voluntary action: Does market society corrode altruism? in A. Ware and R.E. Goodin (eds) *Needs and Welfare*. London: Sage.

Ware, A. and Goodin, R.E. (1990) *Needs and Welfare*. London: Sage.

Watson, P. *et al.* (1996) *The Mid-level Practitioner: A Review of the Literature of Nurse Practitioner and Physician Assistant Programmes*. Discussion paper No. 96/02. Sheffield: Trent Institute for Health Services Research.

Webster, C. (1988) *The Health Services Since the War*, vol. 1. London: HMSO.

Webster, C. (1993) *Caring for Health: History and Diversity*. Buckingham: Open University Press.

Webster, C. (1996) *The Health Services Since the War*, vol. 2. London: HMSO.

Webster, C. (2002) *The National Health Service: A Political History*, 2nd edn. Oxford: Oxford University Press.

Weekes J. *et al.* (1996) Community and contracts: Tensions and dilemmas in the voluntary sector responses to HIV and AIDs, *Policy Studies*, 17(2): 107–22.

Weich, S., Jenkins, S.P. and Lewis, G., 2002. Self reported health and income inequality. *J Epidemiol Community Health* 56, 436–441.

Weish *et al.* (2005)

Welsh Assembly (2001) *Improving Health in Wales*. Cardiff: NHS Wales.

West, P., Illsley, R. and Felman, H. (1984) The family, the welfare state and community care: Political rhetoric and public attitudes, *Journal of Social Policy*, 13: 417–46.

Wheeler, B., Shaw, M., Mitchell, R. and Dorling, D. (2005) *Life in Britain: Using Millennial Census Data to Understand Poverty, Inequality and Place*. Bristol: Policy Press.

White, A. *et al.* (1993) *Health Survey for England 1991*. London: HMSO.

Whitehead, C. (1993) Private finance for housing associations, in D. Maclennan and K. Gibb (eds) *Housing Finance and Subsidies in Britain*. Aldershot: Avebury.

Whitehead, M. (1987) *The Health Divide: Inequalities in Health in the 1980s*. London: Health Education Council.

Whitehead, M. (1994) Is it fair? Evaluating the equity implications of the NHS reforms, in R. Robinson and J. LeGrand (eds) *Evaluation the NHS Reforms*. London: King's Fund Institute.

Whitehead, M. (1995) Tackling inequalities: A review of policy initiatives, in J. Benzeval *et al.* (eds) *Tackling Inequalities in Health. An Agenda for Action*. London: King's Fund.

Whitfield, L. (1998) Assembling ideas, *Health Service Journal*, 108(5630): 14–5.

Wild, S. and McKeigue, P. (1997) Cross sectional analysis of mortality by country of birth in England and Wales, 1970–92, *British Medical Journal*, 314(7082): 705–10.

Wilding, P. (1982) *Professional Power and Social Welfare*. London: Routledge and Kegan Paul.

Wilding, P. (1992) The public sector in the 1980s, in N. Manning and R. Page (eds) *Social Policy Review 4*. Canterbury: Social Policy Association.

Wilkin, D. (1979) *Caring for the Mentally Handicapped Child*. Beckenham: Croom Helm.

Wilkinson, R.G. (1996) *Unhealthy Societies: The Afflictions of Inequalities*. London: Routledge.

Wilkinson, R.G. (1997) Health inequalities: Relative or absolute material standards? *British Medical Journal*, 314: 591–5.

Wilkinson, R.G. (2005) *The Impact of Inequality: How to Make Sick Societies Healthier*. London: Routledge.

Williams, R. (1989) *Social Policy: A Critical Introduction*. Cambridge: Polity Press.

Williamson, C. (1992) *Whose Standards?* Buckingham: Open University Press.

Wilson, P.M. (2001) A policy analysis of the Expert Patient in the United Kingdom: Self-care as an expression of pastoral power? *Health and Social Care in the Community*, 9(3): 134–42.

Wilson, P.M. (2002) The expert patient: Issues and implications for community nurses, *British Journal of Community Nursing*, 7(10): 514–9.

Wilson, T., Buck, D. and Ham, C. (2005) Rising to the challenge: Will the NHS support people with long-term conditions? *British Medical Journal*, 330: 657–61.

Wing, J.R. and Brown, G.W. (1971) *Institutionalism and Schizophrenia*. Cambridge: Cambridge University Press.

Wistow, G., Knapp, M., Hardy, B. and Allen, C. (1994) *Social Care in a Mixed Economy*. Buckingham: Open University Press.

Wittenberg, R. *et al.* (2001) Demand for long-term care for older people in England to 2031, *Health Statistics Quarterly*, 12, winter: 5–17.

Witz, A. (1992) *Professions and Patriarchy*. London: Routledge.

Wolch, J.R. (1989) The shadow state: Transformations in the voluntary sector, in J.R. Wolch and M. Dear (eds) *The Power of Geography: How Territory Shapes Social Life*. Boston, MA: Unwin Hyman.

Wood, B. (2000) *Patient Power? Patients Associations in Britain and America*. Buckingham: Open University Press.

Wood Report (1947) *The Working Party on the Recruitment and Training of Nurses*. London: HMSO.

World Bank (2001) *Attacking Poverty: World Development Report 2000/2001*. Oxford: Oxford University Press.

World Health Organization (1985) *Targets for Health for All: Targets in Support of the European Regional Strategy for Health for All by the year 2000*. Copenhagen: WHO European Regional Office.

World Health Organization (1998) *World Health Day: Safe Motherhood. Pregnancy is Special: Lets make it safe*. Geneva: WHO.

World Health Organization (2002) *Innovative Care for Chronic Conditions*. Geneva: WHO.

World Health Organization (2004) *Global Strategy on Diet, Physical Activity and Health*. Geneva: WHO.

World Health Organization (2005) *World Health Statistics*. Geneva: WHO.

World Health Organization (2006) *World Health Report*, www.who.int/publications.

World Health Organization/UNICEF (1978) *Alma Ata Declaration*. Geneva: WHO.

Yee, L. and Blunden, R. (1995) *General Practice and Carers: Scope for Change?* London: King's Fund Centre.

Younghusband, E. (1978) *Social Work in Britain 1950–1975: A Follow-Up Study*, vol 2. London: Allen and Unwin.

Zakus, J.D.L. and Lysack, C.L. (1998) Revisiting community participation, *Health Policy and Planning*, 13: 1–12.

Zollman, C. and Vickers, A. (1999) ABC of complementary medicine: Complementary medicine in conventional practice, *British Medical Journal*, 319: 901–4.

INDEX